HYPERACTIVE CHILDREN

The Social Ecology of Identification and Treatment

Edited by

Carol K. Whalen
Program in Social Ecology
University of California, Irvine
Irvine, California

Barbara Henker
Department of Psychology
University of California, Los Angeles
Los Angeles, California

1980

AP

ACADEMIC PRESS
A Subsidiary of Harcourt Brace Jovanovich, Publishers
New York London Toronto Sydney San Francisco

ACADEMIC PRESS, INC.
111 Fifth Avenue, New York, New York 10003

United Kingdom Edition published by
ACADEMIC PRESS, INC. (LONDON) LTD.
24/28 Oval Road, London NW1 7DX

Library of Congress Cataloging in Publication Data
Main entry under title:

Hyperactive children.

Bibliography: p.
1. Hyperactive children. I. Whalen, Carol K. II. Henker, Barbara A. [DNLM: 1. Hyperkinesis--In infancy and childhood. 2. Socioenvironmental therapy--In infancy and childhood. WS350.8.H9 H998]
RJ506.H9H963 618.92'8589 80-324
ISBN 0-12-745950-2

PRINTED IN THE UNITED STATES OF AMERICA

80 81 82 83 9 8 7 6 5 4 3 2 1

To Fran and Ed and Mabel and Herb

Contents

4

Childhood Hyperkinesis: Relationships between Symptomatology and Home Environment 105

CARL E. PATERNITE AND JAN LONEY

III

PATTERNS OF IDENTIFICATION AND TREATMENT: EPIDEMIOLOGICAL STUDIES

5

The Identification and Labeling of Hyperactivity in Children: An Interactive Model 145

JONATHAN SANDOVAL, NADINE M. LAMBERT, AND DANA SASSONE

List of Contributors

Numbers in parentheses indicate the pages on which the authors' contributions begin.

HOWARD ABIKOFF (221), Department of Psychiatry, Long Island Jewish–Hillside Medical Center, Glen Oaks, New York 11004

CATHERINE J. BARKETT (259), State Department of Education, Sacramento, California 95814

JAMES J. BOSCO (173), Center for Educational Research, College of Education, Western Michigan University, Kalamazoo, Michigan 49008

BONNIE W. CAMP (191), Department of Pediatrics and Psychiatry, University of Colorado Health Sciences Center, Denver, Colorado 80262

VIRGINIA I. DOUGLAS (283), Department of Psychology, McGill University, Montreal, PQ Canada H3A 1B1

RACHEL GITTELMAN (221), New York State Psychiatric Institute, New York, New York 10032

BARBARA HENKER (3, 321), Department of Psychology, University of California, Los Angeles, Los Angeles, California 90024

SIDNEY KATZ (221), Downstate Medical Center, Brooklyn, New York 11203

BARBARA K. KEOGH (259), Department of Education, University of California, Los Angeles, Los Angeles, California 90024

DONALD F. KLEIN (221), New York State Psychiatric Institute, New York, New York 10032

NADINE M. LAMBERT (145), School of Education, University of California, Berkeley, Berkeley, California 94720

JAN LONEY (105), Department of Psychiatry, University of Iowa, Iowa City, Iowa 52242

JEFFREY MATTES (221), Department of Psychiatry, Long Island Jewish–Hillside Medical Center, Glen Oaks, New York 11004

CARL E. PATERNITE* (105), Alta California Regional Center, Sacramento, California 95821

EDITH POLLACK (221), Department of Psychiatry, Long Island Jewish–Hillside Medical Center, Glen Oaks, New York 11004

STEPHEN W. PORGES (75), Department of Psychology, University of Illinois, Champaign, Illinois 61820

JUDITH L. RAPOPORT (247), Unit on Childhood Mental Illness, National Institute of Mental Health, Bethesda, Maryland 20014

STANLEY S. ROBIN (173), Center for Sociological Research, Department of Sociology, Western Michigan University, Kalamazoo, Michigan 49008

DONALD K. ROUTH (55), Department of Psychology, University of Iowa, Iowa City, Iowa 52242

JONATHAN SANDOVAL (145), Department of Education, University of California, Davis, Davis, California 95616

DANA SASSONE (145), School of Education, University of California, Berkeley, Berkeley, California 94720

KAREN M. SMITH (75), Department of Psychology, University of Illinois, Champaign, Illinois 61820

CAROL K. WHALEN (3, 321), Program in Social Ecology, University of California, Irvine, Irvine, California 92717

*Present Address: Department of Psychology, Miami University, Oxford, Ohio 45056

Preface

On occasion, each of us has been (and has been perceived as) inattentive, impulsive, overly energetic, disconcerting, or intractable. The hyperactive child is one who is seen—by parents, teachers, physicians, or all three—as having too many of these characteristics far too much of the time. Although there is no universal definition and there are no firm criteria for defining hyperactivity, there is good consensus about its "essence." Hyperactive children are youngsters in trouble at home, at school, and in the community. They are not mastering developmental hurdles with the expected speed or ease, and they require special assistance. Hyperactivity is considered as a problem for one or two children in almost every elementary school classroom in this country.[1]

[1]Diverse diagnostic labels are used in the vast literature on hyperactivity. The terms *hyperkinesis* and *hyperactivity* are used more-or-less interchangeably, and *Minimal Brain Dysfunction* (MBD) is often a third alternative. Many diagnosticians are beginning to use the term *Attention Deficit Disorder* (ADD), as recommended in the current draft of the American Psychiatric Association's Diagnostic and Statistical Manual (DSM III). In this volume we have attempted neither to distinguish among these terms nor to restrict all contributors to a common terminology. In general, children undergoing serious environmental stress (e.g., a death in the family) and those diagnosed as mentally retarded, psychotic, emotionally disturbed, or physically handicapped are excluded from this diagnostic category, even though these children, too, may engage in "hyperactive" behaviors.

It should also be noted that male nouns and pronouns are used often in this volume to refer to hyperactive children. These are not instances of "sexist" language; instead, they are accurate reflections of sex ratios. Prevalence studies typically identify four or more hyperactive boys for every hyperactive girl (see Chapters 1, 5, and 6), and many studies of hyperactivity restrict their target samples to male youngsters (see Chapter 12).

This volume can be described as a sampler of current approaches, especially social ecological approaches, to the identification and treatment of hyperactive children. The contributions survey diverse conceptual frameworks, levels of analysis, topical questions, and empirical strategies. They represent each of the major disciplines currently involved in the study of hyperactivity: education, medicine, psychology, and sociology. Some of the chapters focus on defining hyperactivity, whereas others are more concerned with intervention approaches. A common theme uniting all of the chapters is a two-pronged emphasis on children and environments, based on the proposition that hyperactivity can neither be studied nor treated independently of social and institutional contexts.

Invitations to prepare chapters went to leaders of outstanding research groups, those who are currently producing and analyzing primary data on the topic of hyperactivity. The authors were selected to provide a wide array of research orientations, and they were asked to present their most recent work and to discuss its implications. Although some chapters draw extensively on work recently released in scientific journals, none has been published elsewhere.

SOCIAL CONTEXTS: EMPIRICAL AND POLITICAL ARENAS

This book is being published at a time when the public and professionals alike are deluged with well-intentioned but poorly substantiated treatises on hyperactivity and its supposed causes and cures. From some parts of the spectrum come the assertions that hyperactivity is best understood as a purely physiological problem, perhaps a compensatory reaction to underarousal in the central nervous system, or perhaps a specific dietary allergy. From other quarters come the claims that hyperactivity is largely in the eye of the beholder and that the children are the victims of slipshod labeling practices. This latter category includes articles impugning the motives of child specialists and predicting increased use and calamitous consequences of psychostimulant therapies.

Often, these dramatic accusations and warnings find a receptive audience—perhaps because they offer easy explanations, perhaps because they are cloaked in the attractive language of individual freedom, and certainly because there is so very little empirical information on which to evaluate these plausible claims. Whatever the reasons, the topics of hyperactivity and child psychopharmacology have become targets both for sociopolitical commentators in the professional journals and for the popular press. What is unfortunate about this trend is that the growing body of empirical literature, along with the vast needs for research in the area, are often ignored.

Another unfortunate effect of this campaign against the labeling and treatment of "deviance" is that the many kernels of truth in these tirades, for example, the influence of social and attributional contexts on labeling and treatment processes, the important roles played by those who apply the labels, and the actual (rather than imagined) dangers of drug therapies, are often obscured by the polemics.

We feel strongly that these popular attacks are not only endangering children's rights to optimal treatments, but also are impeding research on child behavior problems and intervention strategies. In this climate of controversy, there is a clear need for a responsible and authoritative survey of what we know about contextual variables in the identification and treatment processes—the bidirectional transactions between children and their environments. The present volume is an attempt to fill this need.

ABOUT THIS BOOK

The first part focuses primarily on psychostimulant therapies. Chapter 1 reviews the research literature and presents a conceptual model of the multifaceted phenomenon known as hyperactivity. Emphasis is placed on the often unrecognized and difficult-to-study emanative effects or sociocognitive sequelae of pharmacotherapy. Drug treatment may influence not only a child's physiology and overt behavior, but also his cognitive structures and social environments; medication has many messages. The discussion proceeds from more microcosmic to more macrocosmic levels of analysis as the influences of pharmacotherapies on professional policies and on society's institutions are considered. At each level of analysis, a set of research questions highlights the many unresolved and intriguing issues within these widening perspectives.

Part II presents three diverse research strategies for defining hyperactivity-in-context. Routh (Chapter 2) chronicles the elusive search for an MBD syndrome and summarizes the evolution of his own research on motoric activity level. He presents a playroom assessment procedure and describes how his data have suggested and even demanded a progressive shift in emphasis from the individual child to the child–environment unit.

Current research is underscoring the seminal role of attentional processes in the academic and interpersonal difficulties experienced by hyperactive youngsters. In Chapter 3, Porges and Smith describe a combined psychophysiological–behavioral methodology for studying sustained attention in children. They are finding pathophysiological processes in *some* hyperactive youngsters and medication-related changes in specific physiological indicators that parallel behavioral improvements. Both these chapters note the continuity between normal and atypical behavior patterns and the need to study hyperactivity within a developmental framework.

While Chapters 2 and 3 each focus on a specific behavioral domain, Chapter 4 presents a multivariate approach in which Paternite and Loney have widened the net of target dimensions and research instruments. This comprehensive examination of cross-sectional and longitudinal correlates of problem behaviors yields intriguing relationships between referral and follow-up behaviors as well as between child behaviors and components of the home environment. The findings also demonstrate the potency of aggression as a predictor of long-term adaptation and the need to distinguish between hyperactive and aggressive patterns during the assessment process.

Despite the diversity of methodologies and findings, all three of these chapters illustrate the variegated characteristics subsumed under the hyperactivity rubric and the value of delineating homogeneous subgroups of hyperactive children. The assessment procedures developed by these investigators have direct clinical implications, not only for diagnosing and classifying, but also for predicting and monitoring treatment outcomes.

Part III shifts to an epidemiological level to address questions about the prevalence of hyperactivity, psychostimulant treatment, and nonpharmacologic intervention modes. Chapters 5 and 6 illuminate the multiple definitions of hyperactivity and the differential—though interdependent—roles played by parents, teachers, and physicians. Chapter 5, by Sandoval, Lambert, and Sassone, discusses the natural histories or "careers" of hyperactive children and delineates the timing and sequencing of various components of the identification and treatment processes. Bosco and Robin (Chapter 6) report data on the relationships between the diagnosis and treatment of hyperactivity and various demographic indicators such as socioeconomic level and family size. These data provide answers to important questions about how hyperactivity and pharmacotherapy are distributed within the population, answers that have sociopolitical as well as clinical implications. These two epidemiological studies also raise important questions about how some children escape or delay the labeling process, even though teacher ratings place them at the same level of "deviance" or "troublesomeness" as youngsters formally diagnosed hyperactive.

Nonpharmacologic treatment is the focus of Part IV. Two comprehensive intervention programs are described which were conducted in natural environments and evaluated using multimodal assessment instruments. Camp (Chapter 7) details the development of a cognitive–behavioral program for teaching problem-solving skills. Her findings underscore the potential value of adopting a sequential or developmental approach to treatment rather than considering various intervention programs either as competitors or as undifferentiated ingredients in a heterogeneous "package." Gittelman, Abikoff, Pollack, Klein, Katz, and Mattes (Chapter 8) report the results of a major comparative study of methylphenidate and behavior modification. Parent training, contingency management, and individual contracts in both home and school settings are key components of the behavioral intervention program. Inevitably, the findings raise penetrating questions about the relative cost-effectiveness of medication and nonpharmacologic approaches. Both these chapters present informative discussions of research strategies and underscore the intricate and oft-times puzzling interrelationships among various behavioral domains and assessment sources.

Part V centers on the match between specific child characteristics and particular intervention strategies. A pervasive theme here is that drug treatment is often effective but rarely sufficient. Rapoport (Chapter 9) emphasizes the importance of social and cognitive factors in the medical management of children taking psychostimulants. She notes, for example, how a family's preexisting attributions can either enhance or impede treatment, and how medication-related improvements may generate either functional or dysfunctional attitudes in children, teachers, and families. Combining research data and clinical impressions, Rapoport generates a set of recommendations designed to enable physicians to harness these sociocognitive subtleties in ways that will optimize treatment effects.

Keogh and Barkett (Chapter 10) take a very different approach to the "problem of the match," focusing on variables directly relevant to school success and failure. Behavioral, psychological, and educational domains of functioning are distinguished, and the differential effects of various treatment modalities are reviewed. Indications that a particular treatment approach may simultaneously have beneficial effects on social behavior and deleterious effects on academic performance underscore the need to articulate outcome goals and treatment components. Better delineation of child characteristics and classroom environments is also discussed in the context of ongoing research on the early identification of educationally high risk children.

In Chapter 11, Douglas performs a task analysis that dissects the behavioral capacities and deficiencies of hyperactive children. Malfunctions in attentional, inhibitory, and arousal mechanisms are pinpointed as the fundamental components that lead to pervasive academic and interpersonal difficulties in these youngsters. Emphasis is placed on tailoring treatment approaches to these problem areas as well as to the emanative effects of such problems on a hyperactive child's attitudes and motivation. A comprehensive cognitive training model is presented and richly amplified with clinical illustrations and guidelines. One component that distinguishes

Douglas's approach is a focus on metacognition and on teaching hyperactive children to understand, monitor, and modify their own particular problem-solving deficits.

The final section (Chapter 12) presents a brief status report of what is and is not known about identifying and treating hyperactivity. It includes some findings from social ecological studies of hyperactivity that were completed after this volume was launched, as well as some brief, frankly editorial summations. The role of recent legislative and judicial mandates and of sociopolitical currents is accented in a tentative glimpse into the future.

Acknowledgments

Several people deserve special thanks for their multifaceted contributions to this volume. Our thinking has been enriched by many lively interchanges with students and colleagues including Steve Alkus, Barry Collins, Sharon Dotemoto, Steve Hinshaw, and Bob Sprague—in addition to the contributors to this volume. We are especially grateful for the variegated talents of Doris Finck, who has participated from the inception of this project through its completion. Competent assistance was provided by Vivian Atkin, Bonnie Barron, Carla Calwell, Michael Martin, Dura Michl, and Valerie Williams. Preparation of the entire volume was aided by NIDA Grant DA 01070, and several studies reported in Chapter 12 received support from NIMH Grant MH 29475. The Program in Social Ecology of the University of California, Irvine, and the Department of Psychology of the University of California, Los Angeles, further facilitated our work.

We appreciate the encouragement of the many friends and colleagues who began to substitute the salutation "When's the book coming out?" for the more typical "How are you?" Also, we would each like to thank our very special friends who have been so patient during the evolution of this volume. Finally, the research reported in this book would not have been possible without the enthusiastic collaboration of numerous hyperactive children, as well as their families, physicians, and teachers.

I

A MULTIDIMENSIONAL OVERVIEW

1

The Social Ecology of Psychostimulant Treatment: A Model for Conceptual and Empirical Analysis[1]

CAROL K. WHALEN
BARBARA HENKER

INTRODUCTION AND OVERVIEW: CONCENTRIC CIRCLES OF INFLUENCE

Our current understanding of drug treatments for hyperactive children calls to mind the image of a huge, colorful, *n*-dimensional jigsaw puzzle. Many competent people are trying to solve the puzzle, and some of the sections are now fitting together quite well. The energetic search to complete the picture continues. We are having considerable difficulty, however, matching the new pieces to the old, and it now appears that many of the new pieces may in fact belong to entirely different puzzles. Instead of working on the original puzzle, we seem to have started several new ones, quite inadvertently, and each remains incomplete.

This puzzle metaphor aptly characterizes the current state of affairs in the area of hyperactivity and psychostimulant treatment. The more we learn about psychostimulant effects, the more questions are raised about the children who are given these medications. The more we study children labeled hyperactive, the more we need to know about the people and institutions with whom these children interact. The focus of the present chapter is a social case study, not of a group of persons, but of a class of drugs, the psychostimulants. The particular focus is on methylphenidate hydrochloride and dextroamphetamine sulfate, better known by their trade names, Ritalin

[1]The preparation of this chapter was supported, in part, by NIDA Grant DA-01070.

HYPERACTIVE CHILDREN
The Social Ecology of Identification and Treatment

ISBN 0-12-745950-2

and Dexedrine. As is the fashion with contemporary case studies, the approach is a multifaceted one that considers diverse sets of empirical data. A social ecological perspective will be introduced that provides a set of wide angle lenses for viewing the impact of intervention upon the drug taker, the drug giver, and the community at large.

Typically, 5–12% of school-aged boys may be considered hyperactive (Jones, Loney, Weissenburger, & Fleischmann, 1975; Miller, Palkes, & Stewart, 1973; Sprague, Cohen, & Eichlseder, 1977). The problem is identified much less frequently in girls than in boys. Miller *et al.* reported an incidence of only 1 in 100 girls, and other studies report ratios ranging from 3 or 4 boys to every girl (Safer & Allen, 1976) to 9 boys for every girl (Werry, 1968a). There are also some tentative indications that the antecedents and concomitants of hyperactivity in girls may differ from those in boys (e.g., Battle & Lacey, 1972; Prinz & Loney, 1974). We do not yet know what is "wrong" with these children. We do not even know that there really is such a syndrome as "hyperactivity" (or "minimal brain dysfunction"). There may be several related syndromes, or there may be none (Langhorne, Loney, Paternite, & Bechtoldt, 1976; Paternite & Loney, Chapter 4 of this volume; Routh & Roberts, 1972; Werry, 1968b). Despite these gaps in our knowledge, the weight of the evidence from well-controlled studies of drug effectiveness is now producing a verdict: A large proportion (typically 60–90%) of children who are labeled hyperactive and given psychostimulants show dramatic improvements in school, peer, and family settings. The drugs have been credited with helping the child sustain attention on academic tasks, modulate motor activity in accord with shifting situational demands, and interact more competently in social encounters (Conners, 1972a; Millichap, 1973; Sykes, Douglas, Weiss, & Minde, 1971).

We are relatively certain that behavior changes but uncertain about the mechanisms of change. Many investigators assert that stimulants have a "paradoxical" effect on preadolescent hyperactive children, serving to slow them down rather than to speed them up (Montagu & Swarbrick, 1975; Renshaw, 1975; Wender, 1971). Others insist that the effects are neither paradoxical nor unique to the young (Barkley, 1977b; Grinspoon & Singer, 1973; Sroufe & Stewart, 1973). Some maintain that children with neurological dysfunction are most likely to respond well to stimulants (Millichap, 1975b; Satterfield, Cantwell, & Satterfield, 1974); others suggest that the neurologically "normal" respond best to stimulants (Schain & Reynard, 1975) or that these drugs may facilitate learning and performance in all children (Rapoport, Buchsbaum, Zahn, Weingartner, Ludlow, & Mikkelsen, 1978). (For a comprehensive review of studies attempting to predict stimulant treatment response, see Barkley, 1976.)

Such disagreements among scientists coexist with lay proclamations that we have instituted chemical warfare against the young and are drugging our school children into submission, binding them in straitjackets and suppressing their natural responses to intolerable situations (Brown & Bing, 1976; Schrag & Divoky, 1975). Moreover, recent empirical studies provide ample reason to challenge the optimistic conclusions drawn from earlier work. There is no conclusive evidence of improvement on standardized tests of achievement and considerable reason to doubt that such improvements occur with any consistency or durability (e.g., Riddle & Rapoport, 1976; Rie, Rie, Stewart, & Ambuel, 1976a, 1976b; Weiss, Kruger, Danielson, & Elman, 1975). Recent studies of unintended but apparent side effects and intended but unapparent long-term improvement suggest the urgent need to expand our conceptual and empirical vistas in the study of hyperactivity and psychostimulant treatment.

Medication effects are, of course, multifarious and interdependent. As a first attempt at categorizing these effects, it may be useful to visualize a set of four ever-widening concentric circles surrounding the individual child (see Figure 1.1 and Table 1.1).[2] The innermost circle encompasses direct, intended psychopharmacological outcomes such as sustained attention or regulation of motoric behavior. This circle also includes direct but unintended side effects, physiological as well as psychological, short-term as well as long-term. Examples include anorexia, sleep disturbances, dysphoria, and cardiovascular changes.

The three outer concentric circles embrace what the authors have previously referred to as emanative effects, or the cognitive and social sequels of medication treatment programs (Whalen & Henker, 1976). Though elusive, these effects merit careful examination. The three circles may be distinguished by the pervasiveness of their spheres of influence. Circle 2 involves the effects of the medication on the causal attributions that the child and his significant others generate to explain the behaviors they observe and expect. What is the message of the medication, and how does this message influence a child's self-perceived competence, a parent's expectations, a teacher's structuring of learning opportunities? Circle 3 includes the effects of medication treatment programs on child health and education practices. How

[2]This formulation bears some resemblance to a model independently explicated by Bronfenbrenner (1977). Both formulations include four concentric levels of analysis, but the two differ markedly in focus and intent. Bronfenbrenner is concerned with the whole process of development and places his emphasis on the impact of diverse social settings and institutions on the growing child. The present model centers on a set of identification and treatment processes and emphasizes their impacts, first on the child, and then on ever-widening social structures. Bidirectional influences are integral to both formulations.

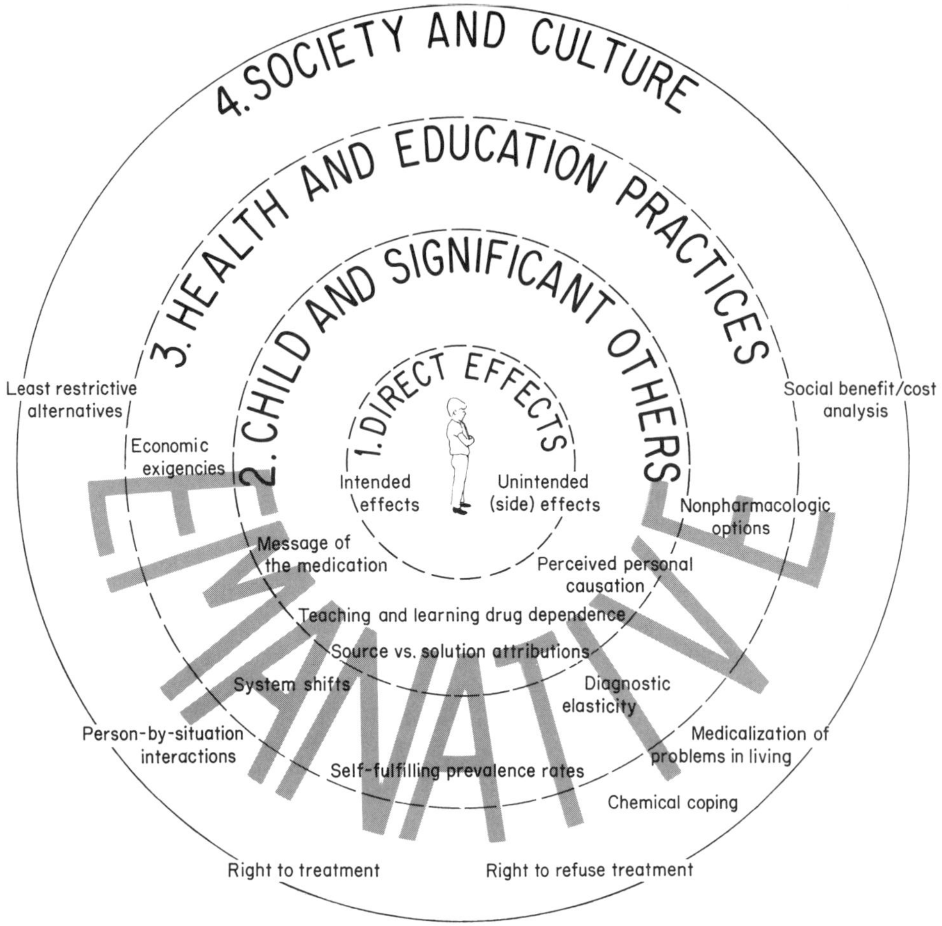

FIGURE 1.1. The direct and emanative effects of psychostimulant treatment: concentric circles of influence.

TABLE 1.1
Direct and Emanative Effects of Psychostimulant Treatment

1. Direct effects
   - Intended
     - Sustained attention
     - Behavioral modulation
     - Interpersonal competence
   - Unintended (side effects)
     - Cardiovascular functions
     - Anorexia
     - Insomnia
     - Growth retardation rates
2. Child and significant others
   - Message of the medication
   - Perceived personal causation
   - Source versus solution attributions
   - Teaching and learning drug dependence
3. Health and education practices
   - Diagnostic elasticity
   - Self-fulfilling prevalence rates
   - System shifts
   - Nonpharmacologic options
   - Economic exigencies
4. Society and culture
   - Right to treatment–right to refuse treatment
   - Medicalization of problems in living
   - Chemical coping
   - Person-by-situation interactions
   - Social benefit–cost analysis
   - Least restrictive alternatives

does the availability of an apparently effective and easily administered treatment influence diagnostic practices, educational strategies, long-term plans for prevention and intervention? The fourth circle broadens the net still further, focusing on communities, institutions, and the very fabric of society. The major questions here concern the impact of psychostimulant treatment programs on the medicalization of deviant behavior, the use of chemical solutions to problems in living, and the long-term balance of social benefits, costs, and risks.

Roughly speaking, as one moves from the inner to the outer circles, one moves along two related gradients: The first concerns the level of analysis, and the second concerns empirical access and rigor. The inner circle, focusing on the individual target child, involves molecular (microcosmic) levels of analysis. Circle 2 includes effects not only on target children, but also on families, teachers, and peers, which in turn exert relatively direct effects on the children themselves. Circles 3 and 4, the most molar or macrocosmic levels of analysis, include institutional, subcultural, and societal effects that are more widespread and enduring than those operating in the two inner circles.

The journey from the inner to the outer circle takes us not only from more micro- to more macrolevels of analysis, but also from phenomena that lend themselves readily to objective and quantitative assessments to those that require more qualitative methodologies and more speculative inferential processes. In scientific terms, the phenomena in Circles 3 and 4 and even Circle 2 are less observable and less researchable than those in the inner circle. It is easier to obtain reliable and valid measures of academic performance than of causal attributions, of a child's task attention than of a profession's gatekeeping practices, of a child's social responses than of a society's propensity to adopt chemical solutions to problems in living. As we move into the outer circles, the data become richer and also more subtle. In addition, as systematic quantitative observations become more distant or difficult to obtain, personal perceptions, attitudes, and social philosophies exert increasing influence.

Thus it is not surprising that direct drug effects such as changes in motoric regulation and social appropriateness have received the bulk of the research attention and the most careful empirical scrutiny to date. Very little is known about the broader impact of psychostimulant treatment on cognitive textures, professional practices, and social systems. There is no reason to assume, however, a strong positive relationship between researchability and potential significance; these two variables may, in fact, be inversely related. Those phenomena that have most effectively eluded empirical examination may be precisely those that have the greatest impact on society. Data from diverse sources indicate the need to take a more balanced empirical stance, one that includes studies of unintended but potentially consequential emanative effects.

The following discussion will consider, in turn, each of the four circles delineated above. The intended effects component of Circle 1 will be summarized briefly rather than examined in detail. Unintended side effects will be considered in greater detail, and then the focus will shift to an examination of emanative effects (Circles 2, 3, and 4) and a delineation of fruitful avenues for empirical investigation.

CIRCLE ONE: DIRECT AND SIDE EFFECTS OF PSYCHOSTIMULANTS AND OTHER PHARMACOLOGIC AGENTS

Short-Term, Intended Outcomes of Psychostimulants

If one could describe a "modal" hyperactive child, one would be careful to point out that in both the intellectual and the motoric realms the problems appear to be qualitative rather than quantitative. Investigators have not found consistent deficits in intellectual capacity, nor have they found consistent excesses in motoric activity (Douglas, 1972; Werry, 1978a). Rather, hyperactive children behave differently from their peers when required to regulate their activities according to externally imposed demands over an extended period of time. Their basic difficulties with attention deployment and response inhibition pervade diverse behavioral domains and cause these youngsters to be tagged as deviant in social as well as in academic settings. They are often viewed as inattentive, impulsive, erratic, and generally out of tune with the social environment (Campbell, 1976; Douglas, 1976b; Keogh, 1971; Keogh & Margolis, 1976; Ross & Ross, 1976).

The psychostimulant-induced gains seen most frequently in hyperactive children are quite predictable from the preceding profile. Psychostimulants do not necessarily decrease total activity level and may even increase locomotion (Millichap & Boldrey, 1967; Routh, 1975); nor do these drugs consistently increase intelligence or achievement test scores (Campbell, 1976; Keogh & Barkett, Chapter 10 of this volume; Knights, 1974; Rapoport, Quinn, Bradbard, Riddle, & Brooks, 1974; Werry & Sprague, 1974). Rather, they appear to influence goal-directed performance on selected measures of attention or vigilance, choice reaction time, cognitive style, and concept learning (Aman, 1978; Baxley & LeBlanc, 1976; Conners, 1976; Douglas, 1976a; Porges & Smith, Chapter 3 of this volume; Sprague & Sleator, 1973; Sroufe, 1975). These findings are apparent in placebo-controlled, double-blind studies and cannot be discounted as expectancy or other bias effects.[3] Comprehensive reviews of these outcomes are readily available, and the interested reader is referred to Barkley (1977b), Conners (1972a), Douglas (1972), Rosenthal and Allen (1978), Sroufe (1975), and Whalen and Henker (1976).

The most common paradigm for studying psychostimulant effects in children involves collecting relatively global assessments (e.g., teacher ratings) from the natural environment after the child has been on medication for several weeks or months. Some investigators are currently taking a more microscopic look at drug-related changes by administering acute doses of psychostimulants and assessing, in the laboratory, specific time–response relationships. For example, Swanson, Kinsbourne, Roberts, and Zucker (1978) measured methylphenidate-related changes on a paired-associate learning task, .5 hr, 2 hr, 3 hr, and 4 hr after drug administration. Their findings confirmed clinical consensus: The peak effect on cognitive behavior is seen between 1 and 2 hr after administration, and the effects last for about 4 hr. The authors concluded that the *behavioral* half-life of methylphenidate is about 3 hr (and emphasized the fact that we do not yet know to what extent behavioral and chemical half-lives are correlated). These findings underscore the need—when comparing drug-related changes on such diverse measures as cognitive performance, teacher ratings, and behavior observations—either to conduct detailed time–response analyses or to hold time-since-medication constant.

The Swanson *et al.* cognitive performance measure also allowed these investigators to distinguish between adverse and favorable drug responders.

[3] It is important to note that physicians, parents, and teachers have shown impressive "hit rates" when asked to guess whether children were given active medication or placebo on any particular day (e.g., Werry & Sprague, 1974). Moreover, recent research suggesting that "identical matching placebos" may be nonidentical and nonmatching (Blumenthal, Burke, & Shapiro, 1974) leads us to wonder how often the children themselves can distinguish between active drugs and placebos. Sprague and Sleator (1977) and Swanson, Kinsbourne, Roberts, and Zucker (1977) describe a process of inserting methylphenidate and placebo tablets into identical gelatin capsules in order to disguise a slight taste difference. In other published research, however, placebo procedures are rarely detailed, and thus it is difficult to determine how the placebos were created and whether they were in fact identical to the active drug in color, taste, texture, and so on. Also, the fact that physicians and parents may detect placebo–drug differences on the basis of side effects raises the question of how often children can make similar discriminations. Future studies need to address issues concerning the validity of placebo-controlled, double-blind procedures in psychopharmacological research with children. Recent data from our own research program are encouraging, indicating that similar ratings of child behaviors are obtained from staff who know that a medication study is in progress and from those who are entirely unaware of the research focus (Henker, Whalen, & Collins, 1979).

Children whose error reduction rates on methylphenidate were at least 25% compared to baseline and 10% greater than those obtained following placebo were classified as favorable responders. If a drug-related impairment greater than 10% was found, the child was classified as an adverse responder. (Since drug dosage was increased until either facilitation or impairment was obtained, there were, by definition, no "nonresponders.") Using these criteria, 70% of the sample were classified as favorable responders, and the average decrease in errors for this group was 50% following methylphenidate and 8.9% following placebo. In contrast, adverse responders showed an average 26% *increase* in errors following methylphenidate and a 26% *decrease* following placebo. This relatively straightforward procedure for distinguishing between favorable and adverse drug responders may prove invaluable in delineating homogeneous subgroups of hyperactive children, identifying optimal drug dosages for each child, and predicting treatment outcomes. Before such "diagnostic trials" can be recommended, however, replications are necessary, and the relationships between acute, transient drug effects and long-term changes must be assessed.

Drug-attributed improvements in social–adaptive behavior have also been documented quite extensively. Behavior rating scales are the most frequently used assessment procedures, and teacher ratings are considered the most reliable and valid indicators of psychostimulant effects (Rapoport *et al.*, 1974; Sleator & von Neumann, 1974). Despite repeated reports that hyperactive children have marked interpersonal difficulties and that psychostimulants improve social functioning, little information is available about the *actual* interpersonal behaviors that characterize youngsters labeled hyperactive, and attempts to relate rating scales to direct behavioral observations have been disappointing (e.g., Blunden, Spring, & Greenberg, 1974). Thus we know that hyperactive children do not get along with other people, but we do not know precisely what they do. Sprague, Barnes, and Werry's (1970) findings, based on direct behavior observations, indicated that methylphenidate increased the frequency of child-initiated positive interactions. In a study of mothers working with their hyperactive children on a cooperative tracking task, Humphries, Kinsbourne, and Swanson (1978) found that both the children and their mothers gave each other more praise and less criticism when the children were medicated than when they had taken placebos. Moreover, when children were medicated, the mothers were less directive and the children more directive than they were in the placebo condition. In another study of mother–child interaction by Barkley and Cunningham (1979), mothers were rated as less directive and more attentive when their children were on methylphenidate than when they were on placebo. Campbell (1976) has also reported that hyperactive children and their mothers show different verbal interaction patterns when the children are on methylphenidate rather than on placebo.

One of the most intriguing findings in the literature is that psychostimulants lead to improved scholastic achievement as rated by parents and teachers, but not necessarily to improved scholastic achievement as indexed by objective test results (Rie *et al.*, 1976a). Positive expectancies about the efficacy of psychostimulant treatment probably contribute to improved ratings, but to attribute these disparate data totally to placebo effects is to oversimplify and obscure a promising avenue for further study. Hyperactive children interact differently with other people when they take psychostimulants than when they do not, and these behavioral differences may influence—quite directly—adult perceptions of the child's competence.

It is also quite likely that the medication has potent effects on ongoing behaviors, without leading to enduring improvements. Rie and Rie (1977) have documented a short-lived enhancement in academic performance during methlyphenidate treatment. Compared to their performance levels without drugs, the children showed methylphenidate-related improvement on a story recall posttest administered 2 hr following the learning experience. When another posttest was administered 2 days later, however, there was no drug-related superiority. Immediate gains in test performance can, of course, create a positive halo in teachers, leading to continued perceptions of academic improvement regardless of the child's actual performance. More studies along the lines of those described should illuminate this alluring enigma by delineating not only the conditions under which hyperactive children *are perceived as* more or less competent or appropriate, but also the conditions under which hyperactive children *engage in* specific academic and interpersonal behaviors.

Side Effects and Dosage Considerations

As Werry (1978a) observes, "It is seldom possible to produce a therapeutic effect with psychotropic drugs without simultaneously producing some unwanted effects [p. 71]." Decreased appetite and sleep disturbances are the two immediate side effects most frequently reported in children taking psychostimulants. These symptoms are usually viewed by physicians as mild and short-lived. Other side effects include headaches, stomachaches, skin rash, sadness, social withdrawal, lethargy, irritability, and decreased emotional responsivity (Cohen & Douglas, 1972; DiMascio, Soltys, & Shader, 1970; Eisenberg, 1972; Greenberg, Deem, & McMahon, 1972; Katz, Saraf, Gittelman-Klein, & Klein, 1975; Loney & Ordoña, 1975; Lucas & Weiss, 1971; Millichap, 1975a; Weiss, Minde, Douglas, Werry, & Sykes, 1971;

Winsberg, Bialer, Kupietz, & Tobias, 1972). It has been suggested that methylphenidate may produce fewer side effects than dextroamphetamine (Cantwell, 1977; Conners, 1972b).

Bizarre, psychoticlike symptoms have also been reported in children given psychostimulants (e.g., Lucas & Weiss, 1971; Weiss *et al.*, 1971). These isolated case reports are reminiscent of recent research indicating that intravenous doses of psychostimulants activate preexisting psychotic symptoms in schizophrenic adults—findings that have led to the experimental use of psychostimulants during psychiatric interviews as "symptom-provocative" agents in order to facilitate differential diagnosis and treatment planning (Janowsky & Davis, 1976; Leichner, Janowsky, & Reid, 1976). The similarities and differences between acute, intravenous use of psychostimulants with schizophrenic adults and chronic, oral ingestion by hyperactive children remain to be explored.

Most side effects respond quite rapidly to dosage decrease. The usual practice is to begin a medication program with a minimal dosage (2.5–5 mg of dextroamphetamine or 5–10 mg of methylphenidate) and to increase the amount gradually until side effects are reported or a standard level has been reached, usually 10–40 mg per day for dextroamphetamine, 15–60 mg for methylphenidate. For those who compute dosage in terms of milligrams (mg) of drug per kilogram (kg) of body weight, Cantwell and Carlson (1978) report that the usual single dose range is .15–.50 for dextroamphetamine and .3–1.0 for methylphenidate. When side effects appear, the dosage is decreased (often temporarily) until the problem is ameliorated (Greenberg & Lourie, 1972; O'Malley & Eisenberg, 1973; Safer & Allen, 1976).

Prescribing a second drug to counteract the side effects of psychostimulants is also common practice (Winsberg, Yepes, & Bialer, 1976). For example, depressive episodes or separation anxiety induced by psychostimulants may be treated with imipramine, insomnia or appetite loss with thioridazine (Cantwell, 1975b; Katz *et al.*, 1975; Millichap, 1975b; Renshaw, 1975). This trend toward polypharmacy has important implications in itself, particularly since at the same time we are witnessing a rapid increase in multiple drug usage in the nonmedical or illicit realm (e.g., Ray & Wilson, 1975). No systematic information on the use of multiple psychotropic medications with children is available. The need for such information is underscored by recent findings from a survey of physicians treating adult psychiatric patients: "As the patients' symptoms persisted, combinations of drugs used in treatment became more unique and diverse. After one year of ineffective chemotherapy, combinations of three and up to six potent neuroleptics were prescribed [Sheppard, Beyel, Fracchia, & Merlis, 1974, p. 188]."

There are also empirical indications that psychostimulants significantly increase heart rate and elevate blood pressure in some children and that these drugs may decrease oxygen expenditure during exercise, possibly through vasoconstriction (Aman & Werry, 1975; Cohen, Douglas, & Morgenstern, 1971; Knights & Hinton, 1969; Rapoport *et al.,* 1974). Aman and Werry (1975) point out that the drug-induced changes in cardiorespiratory function are in fact quite small, but they also note that the dosage of methylphenidate used in their study (.3 mg/kg) was lower than those used typically in clinical practice. There are evidently marked individual differences in cardiorespiratory functions, as illustrated by a recent report of heart-rate changes that ranged from an increase of 40 beats per minute to a decrease of 17 beats per minute in children treated with methylphenidate. The average change in this group of 27 hyperactive children was an increase of 8.1 beats per minute (Ballard, Boileau, Sleator, Massey, & Sprague, 1976). The main concern is not with the immediate cardiovascular changes, but rather with the unknown, long-term consequences of artificially elevated heart rate and blood pressure.

Recent studies by Safer and his colleagues (Safer & Allen, 1973; Safer, Allen, & Barr, 1972) have raised grave concerns about the common view, succinctly expressed by Arnold (1973a), that psychostimulant side effects in children are more annoying than dangerous. Their major finding was significant growth retardation in children taking stimulants for an average duration of 3 years. Lags in expected growth rates for both height and weight were apparent. The effects were more pronounced for dextroamphetamine than for methylphenidate; in fact, no suppressant effects were found in children whose daily dose of methylphenidate did not exceed 20 mg.

Stimulant medication is often discontinued during school vacations (Arnold, 1973a; Katz *et al.,* 1975; O'Malley & Eisenberg, 1973), and these "drug holidays" allow comparisons of on-drug and off-drug growth rates. Apparently, a substantial amount of accelerated or rebound growth occurs after medication is discontinued. Safer, Allen, and Barr (1975) have documented summer weight and height rebounds 15–68% above age-expected increments, the degree of rebound being proportional to the degree of growth suppression while on medication. Summer rebound growth, however, is not sufficient to bring the children up to normative levels, and we still do not know how much compensatory growth occurs after medication is discontinued permanently.

These dramatic results require independent replication in different laboratories. Weight and height data published since the Safer *et al.* 1972 report are inconsistent (Beck, Langford, Mackay, & Sum, 1975; Gross, 1976; Quinn & Rapoport, 1975; Rie *et al.,* 1976a, 1976b; Sachar, 1977;

Weiss *et al.*, 1975). Apparently, suppression of weight gain is a more robust finding than suppression of height, but differences in dosage levels and assessment procedures used in the various studies make it difficult to draw firm conclusions from the diverse results. Sprague (1977) has challenged the methodology used by Safer and his colleagues, asserting that there is no evidence of growth suppression when procedures are standardized (e.g., McNutt, Ballard, Boileau, Sprague, & von Neumann, 1976; McNutt, Boileau, & Cohen, 1977).

In a comprehensive review of the growth rate literature, Roche, Lipman, Overall, and Hung (in press) concluded that, despite the defects of individual studies, the combined results indicate that stimulants produce a moderate suppression of weight gain and perhaps a minor slowing of height gain as well. Growth suppression is apparently related to dosage levels and may also be related to the presence or absence of drug holidays during the summer months. The effect appears to be temporary, occurring only during the first few years of treatment. There is no evidence that adult weight or height is affected by stimulant treatment during childhood. These conclusions are based on averaged group data. It is still possible that more serious growth retardation could occur in a small number of individual children, and thus careful monitoring of growth rates is indicated. It is important to note that these conclusions apply only to the prepubertal period; there is no information about the effects of stimulants on growth rates during pubescence. Such information is critically needed in view of the increasing trend to continue or even to begin psychostimulant treatment during adolescence.

The probability of most side effects, including growth retardation, increases as dosage is increased. This pattern underscores the importance of examining specific dose–response relationships. Although dose–response curves are a standard component of drug research paradigms with infrahuman animals, few dosage comparisons have been made with children. Existing data suggest that we may indeed be overmedicating children with psychostimulants. In one study, Werry and Sprague (1974) compared placebo and four levels of methylphenidate: .1, .3, .5, and 1.0 mg/kg body weight. The results from a variety of measures indicated a "fairly flat" dose–response curve. Using the placebo effect as the criterion, these authors found that their moderate dose (.3 mg/kg) was as consistently superior as the higher dosages (.5 and 1.0mg/kg). Moreover, the low dose (.1 mg/kg) was nearly as effective as the other three, indicating that for some children this minimal amount may suffice. Subsequent studies by Sprague and his colleagues have confirmed that the "zone of peak enhancement" of cognitive performance centers on .3 mg/kg of methylphenidate (Sprague & Sleator, 1976).

In a review of seven studies of 337 hyperactive children taking methylphenidate, Millichap (1973) reported that the dosage ranged from 5 to 200 mg daily (and from .2 to 2.3 mg/kg body weight). The 2.0 mg/kg cited in the literature as an average optimum dose (White, 1976) and recommended by one of the most widely read pharmacotherapy sources, Goodman and Gilman (1975), is six times greater than the dose found effective for most children by Werry and Sprague (1974) and twice as great as the maximum amount needed for any child in another study (Sleator & von Neumann, 1974). The latter authors also found that the usual practice of giving a second noontime dose may be unnecessary in most cases; only one of the children who improved on methylphenidate required this second dose. Similarly, Safer and Allen (1973) found that single daily doses were as effective in most cases as multiple doses. These findings, however, contradict reports by other clinical researchers that at least two doses are needed by most children (e.g., Katz *et al.,* 1975). The reasons for these discrepancies are unclear at the present time, although they may be related to differences in dose levels and in procedures for determining acceptable dosage limits for single administrations of methylphenidate.

Another discrepancy is apparent when comparing two studies in which placebo was substituted for methylphenidate without informing parent, child, or teacher. Sleator, von Neumann, and Sprague (1974) were quite surprised to find that 26% of the hyperactive children in their sample were able to function adequately without medication within 2 years of the start of treatment. Shifting their subjects to placebo after only 3 months of treatment, Gittelman-Klein, Klein, Katz, Saraf, and Pollack (1976) found that only 5% were able to function adequately without medication. This difference in remission rates is not surprising, given the differences in length of treatment and dosage levels. The average dosage used by Sleator *et al.* (1974) was .66 mg/kg, while the Gittelman-Klein *et al.* (1976) average was 1.72 mg/kg. Even the 5% remission rate, however, leads us to wonder how many children continue to take drugs unnecessarily merely because drug-free trial periods have not been attempted.

Another important consideration here is the degree of similarity or dissimilarity in dose–response curves when different target behaviors are assessed. Sprague and Sleator (1973, 1977), for example, suggest that the dosage levels that optimize cognitive performance (as assessed by a picture-recognition, short-term memory task) may be much lower than those that optimize social behavior (as assessed by teacher ratings). Moreover, these investigators contend that if psychostimulant dosage is increased until improvement in social behavior is maximized, cognitive performance may deteriorate to levels equal to or even below those obtained when children are given placebos. Swanson *et al.* (1978) demonstrated acute and transient "overdose" effects in a group of five children known to respond favorably to methylphenidate. When the average dose was increased from 14 to 21 mg for these children, performance on a paired-associate learning task was impaired. In contrast to these curvilinear relationships, side effects apparently show a direct, positive relationship to dosage (Safer *et al.*, 1972; Sprague, 1977), and this pattern must also be entered into the complex decision matrix for individual children. Clearly, there is a need for others to follow this excellent work and to conduct improved studies using multiple performance indicators of dose–response relationships.

Monitoring Drug Effects

The data on physiological side effects, dose–response curves, and drug holidays underscore the need for careful monitoring of children taking stimulant medication. What do we know of clinical practice in this area? Unfortunately, data of this type are extremely difficult to obtain. A study by Solomons (1973), however, gives reason for concern. Solomons' operational definition of "adequate monitoring" could be considered a minimal one: A telephone call or office visit twice in 6 months or three times a year was deemed sufficient. But only 55% of the physicians surveyed met this lenient criterion!

Cantwell (1977) and Werry (1977) recommend scheduled "drug holidays" (preferably using placebos rather than discontinuing medication) as a means of checking a child's response to medication. It is impossible to know, however, how often systematic drug holidays are used. Despite the obvious merits of this procedure, the issue is quite controversial, and many physicians are opposed to any deviation from a prescribed regimen. Interviews with physicians and parents conducted during an ongoing study by the authors indicate that the widespread reluctance to use drug holidays stems partially from concern that progress will be impeded, or that the child will become too aware that he can "be good" only following ingestion of a pill. Indeed, the anticipated negative consequences of short-term discontinuance have been reinforced through the use of clinical labels. One couple earnestly told us that they would never allow their child to go without medication, even for one day, because, on top of all his other problems, they would not want him to develop the "up-and-down syndrome."

Data from recent teacher surveys should also be considered when reviewing monitoring practices. Only 22% of the midwestern teachers queried by Bosco and Robin (1976) reported that physicians had requested school evaluations of children in their class who were taking Ritalin. Data obtained from a survey of New York teachers indicated that direct contact between physicians and teachers of children on medication occurred in only 18% of the cases, and contact with the physician through an intermediary (e.g., parent or school psychologist) occurred in another 39% of the cases (Weithorn & Ross, 1975). Analyzing medical records rather than teacher questionnaires, Loney and Ordoña (1975) also found that physicians rarely contacted teachers for evaluations of the effects of medication. Given recent indications that physicians are often unable to detect behavior problems or changes during a time-limited office visit, and that teachers may be the best source of information for evaluating children's responsivity to medication (e.g., Katz *et al.,* 1975; Sleator & von Neumann, 1974; Sprague & Gadow, 1976; Werry & Sprague, 1974), these findings raise further doubts about the adequacy of behavioral monitoring procedures for children taking psychostimulants.

Apparently, the availability and popularity of the "ready remedy" carries an implicit message—for professionals as well as for parents—that the medication is mild and innocuous, and that comprehensive monitoring may be unnecessary. In an influential book on minimal brain dysfunction, Wender (1971) designated low cost as one major advantage of pharmacological methods, maintaining that adequate evaluation of psychostimulant treatment requires only 4–6 hr the first year and even less time thereafter.

Without careful monitoring, there is a tendency for treatment practices to become functionally autonomous or disengaged from empirical evidence on treatment outcomes. There are reports that some physicians prescribe medication without seeing or examining the child and that, when neither positive nor negative effects are salient, children may be kept on psychostimulants for as long as 6 years without a trial withdrawal period (Browder, 1972; Sroufe, 1975; Stewart & Olds, 1973). In this context, it is instructive to consider the current controversy concerning maintenance psychotropic drug usage with adult mental patients. The long-term use of psychotropic medications with psychiatric inpatients and outpatients is a widespread practice; Lentz, Paul, and Calhoun (1971) found that maintenance psychotropic medications were prescribed for over 80% of "hard core" mental patients with nonorganic problems. This practice continues, apparently uninfluenced by recent findings that both cast doubt on the effectiveness of these drugs and raise grave concerns about potential negative consequences (e.g., Paul, Tobias, & Holly, 1972).

The optimal treatment strategies for chronic adult mental patients are not yet known, and convincing arguments can be mustered for either a prodrug or an antidrug stance (Davis, Gosenfeld, & Tsai, 1976; MacDonald & Tobias, 1976; Tobias & MacDonald, 1974). We have introduced this controversy not to make a case pro or con, but rather to point out the parallels between the recent history of psychoactive drug usage with adults and a nascent trend in the use of psychostimulants with children. The inadequate research methodologies of early drug studies were unfortunate, but the failure of current clinical practice to take into account the results of recent, well-controlled empirical studies is even more disheartening. The routine use of psychoactive drugs with adult mental patients antedated the use of psychostimulants with children by at least a decade, and it is hoped that the knowledge and methodological sophistication spawned by adult drug studies will be put to advantage in acquiring information on psychostimulant effects with children. As the practice of maintaining adolescents and adults on psychostimulants increases in popularity, and the financial costs of alternate interventions become progressively prohibitive, meeting the need for careful and continual assessment of drug effects becomes even more obligatory.

Concern over inadequate monitoring is prompted further by the finding of Rapoport *et al.* (1974) that the only variable to predict side effects was verbal IQ ($r = .33$; $p < .01$), suggesting that frequency counts of side effects based on child's self-report may be underestimates. The Rapoport *et al.* (1974) data also illustrate a further difficulty with self-report. As in other studies, appetite decrease was reported for 23% and insomnia for 16% of children taking methylphenidate. However, the corresponding rates for children on placebo medication were 22% and 33%, respectively. These results raise doubts about the meaning of the usual report that anorexia and insomnia are the two major side effects of methylphenidate. Given the placebo rates, we cannot separate drug effects from cognitive expectancies or non-drug-related causes. Interpretation is clearer for the three side effects that were found significantly more often with children on methylphenidate than with those on placebo: stomachaches (23% versus 0), drowsiness (16% versus 0), and increased blood pressure (26% versus 0).

Other Pharmacologic Agents

In addition to methylphenidate and dextroamphetamine, a variety of drugs have been used to treat hyperactivity. An alternate amphetamine form, *l*- or levoamphetamine (Cydril), has been found effective in some children (Arnold, Huestis, Smeltzer, Scheib, Wemmer, & Colner, 1976; Arnold & Wender, 1974), as has a combination of the two amphetamine forms known as racemic amphetamine or Benzedrine (Gross, 1976). It has been suggested that the subgroup of hyperactive children who are also considered hyperaggressive may respond better to the levo than to the dextro form (Arnold *et al.*, 1976), but there is a paucity of empirical evidence to support this hypothesis. These drugs are being recommended not as the treatment of choice, but rather as an option in cases where (*a*) children do not respond to dextroamphetamine or methylphenidate; (*b*) the side effects of dextroamphetamine or methylphenidate are too severe; or (*c*) there is serious concern about potential abuse of dextroamphetamine.

In 1975 the FDA approved a new stimulant for use with children: magnesium pemoline or Cylert. The direct effects of pemoline are apparently quite similar to those of methylphenidate and dextroamphetamine (e.g., Dykman, McGrew, & Ackerman, 1974). A substantial advantage of magnesium pemoline is that it is a long-acting drug that is effective following a single, early morning dose, thus eliminating the social stigma and logistic difficulties often encountered when children take midday medication at school. Another advantage is that side effects, particularly changes in blood pressure, may be less marked than those found with the other psychostimulants (Page, Bernstein, Janicki, & Michelli, 1974). On the negative side, some investigators have reported that improvement on Cylert is less dramatic and more gradual than on Ritalin or Dexedrine, and that behavioral gains may not be evident until the fourth week of treatment (Conners, Taylor, Meo, Kurtz, & Fournier, 1972; Page *et al.,* 1974). The data reported by Dykman, McGrew, Harris, Peters, and Ackerman (1976) indicate that, in terms of average group performance, methylphenidate was more effective than pemoline on a variety of measures, including teacher ratings and Continuous Performance Test scores. When individual rather than group scores were examined, however, it appeared that pemoline was the superior drug for *some* of the children.

The phenothiazines, particularly Mellaril (thioridazine) and Thorazine (chlorpromazine), have also been used to treat hyperactivity (Greenberg *et al.*, 1972; Saletu, Saletu, Simeon, Viamontes, & Itil, 1975; Weiss *et al.*, 1971). Controlled studies with these antipsychotic agents indicate that the phenothiazines do not consistently improve attention and learning, and may even impair cognitive functioning (Gittelman-Klein *et al.,* 1976; Sprague *et al.,* 1970). In addition, studies of chronic schizophrenic adults have indicated that serious side effects (e.g., blood dyscrasias and extrapyramidal reactions such as dyskinesia or akinesia) may occur with high doses or prolonged usage, and little information is available on side effects following long-term use by children (Kornetsky, 1976; Safer & Allen, 1976). Haldol (haloperidol), an antipsychotic agent that is not a phenothiazine derivative, has also been tested with hyperactive children (e.g., Barker, 1975; Werry & Aman, 1975). Despite uncertainties and concerns about both efficacy and toxicity, Werry (1976) describes antipsychotic drugs as "the second line of defense in the management of the hyperkinetic child [p. 84]."

Imipramine hydrochloride, or Tofranil, is a tricyclic antidepressant that has been used to treat childhood hyperactivity (Greenberg, Yellin, Spring, & Metcalf, 1975; Huessy & Wright, 1970; Rapoport *et al.,* 1974; Waizer,

Hoffman, Polizoes, & Englehardt, 1974; Winsberg *et al.,* 1972) as well as school phobia (Gittelman-Klein & Klein, 1973), enuresis (Werry, Dowrick, Lampen, & Vamos, 1975), and a variety of other childhood disorders (Gaultieri, 1977). In recommending the study of imipramine as an alternate for psychostimulant treatment of hyperactive children, Waizer *et al.* (1974) point out that this drug does not "carry the onus of presumed potential for drug abuse [p. 587]." However, there is substantial concern that cardiotoxic side effects may be both more frequent and more severe than with the psychostimulants, and that imipramine may occasionally induce seizures or systemic toxicity (Brown, Winsberg, Bialer, & Press, 1973; Martin & Zaug, 1975; Petti & Campbell, 1975; Saraf, Klein, Gittelman-Klein, Gootman, & Greenhill, 1978; Saraf, Klein, Gittelman-Klein, & Groff, 1974; Winsberg, Goldstein, Yepes, & Perel, 1975). Few comparative studies of the effectiveness of imipramine and the psychostimulants have been conducted. The conclusions drawn from different studies are contradictory and the results difficult to compare, given the heterogeneous populations and diverse dosage levels studied (e.g., Rapoport *et al.,* 1974; Winsberg *et al.,* 1972).

Other substances used to treat hyperactivity include Deaner or deanol acetamidobenzoate (Coleman, Dexheimer, DiMascio, Redman, & Finnerty, 1976; Conners, 1973a; Lewis & Lewis, 1977; Lewis & Young, 1975; Oettinger, 1977), Benadryl or diphenhydramine hydrochloride (Fish, 1975), Atarax or hydroxyzine (Greenberg *et al.,* 1972), Elavil or amitriptyline (Kupietz & Balka, 1976; Yepes, Balka, Winsberg, & Bialer, 1977), lithium carbonate (Greenhill, Rieder, Wender, Buchsbaum, & Kahn, 1973; Whitehead & Clark, 1970), and caffeine (Conners, 1975c; Firestone, Davey, Goodman, & Peters, 1978; Firestone, Wright, & Douglas, 1978; Garfinkel, Webster, & Sloman, 1975; Gross, 1975; Reichard & Elder, 1977; Schnackenburg, 1973, 1975). In general (and with some important exceptions), it is much more difficult to draw conclusions from studies of these other substances than from research on the psychostimulants. The subjects are diagnostically mixed: Some studies include children diagnosed psychotic or mentally retarded, and others exclude all youngsters with subnormal IQs or severe behavioral deficits. Sample sizes are often small and dependent variables not clearly specified. Dosage patterns also vary considerably. Given this heterogeneity of relevancies, it is difficult to compare results from different studies and to sort out possible reasons for contradictory findings.

To summarize, the research literature on nonstimulant drugs is less extensive, less adequate, and less consistent than that on the psychostimulants. The 10–40% of children who do not respond positively to psychostimulants continue to spur experimentation with alternative chemical agents as well as attempts to differentiate subgroups of children who respond best to each substance. To date, however, little progress has been made in these areas.

The psychostimulants remain the drug treatment of choice for hyperactive children, with methylphenidate the most favored (Krager & Safer, 1974; Millichap, 1973; Safer & Allen, 1976; Sleator & Sprague, 1978). Following a review of pharmacotherapy research with hyperactive children, Cantwell (1975a) concluded that a clinician prescribing nonstimulant medication for a child who has not responded well on psychostimulants "has little other than his clinical intuition to guide him [p. 180]," and must be prepared for what may be a long and frustrating trial and error process. (It is important to note, however, that behaviors commonly subsumed under labels such as "hyperactive child syndrome" or "hyperkinetic reaction" are often associated with mental retardation, organic brain syndromes, psychosis, etc., and that in many such cases psychostimulants may *not* be the drugs of choice [Fish, 1971].)

Long-Term Outcomes and State-Dependent Learning

The data on long-term effects are just beginning to appear in print, and the initial picture is disquieting. Several studies indicate that the immediate gains observed in school-aged children taking psychostimulants do not carry over into adolescence when medication is discontinued (Douglas, 1975; Huessy, Metoyer, & Townsend, 1974; Weiss *et al.,* 1975). Follow-up studies of adolescents and young adults document the persistence or recurrence of serious social and academic difficulties (Ackerman, Dykman, & Peters, 1977). Many of these youngsters have no friends, appear sad and self-deprecating, and engage in relatively high rates of antisocial activities (Mendelson, Johnson, & Stewart, 1971; Minde, Weiss, & Mendelson, 1972; Stewart, Mendelson, & Johnson, 1973; Weiss, 1975; Weiss, Minde, Werry, Douglas, & Nemeth, 1971). For example, in Riddle and Rapoport's (1976) 2-year follow-up study of 72 hyperactive boys, there was no improvement on the reading subtest of the Wide Range Achievement Test and a significant *decrease* in the mathematics scores. High rates of peer rejection and demoralization were also reported at the time of the 2-year evaluation. In summarizing their disappointing results, Riddle and Rapoport (1976) pointed out that "an 'optimally medicated' group . . . had almost identical academic achievement and social acceptance as did a group of drop-outs from drug treatment [p. 126]." Weiss *et al.* (1975) reached a similar conclusion after completing an intensive 5-year follow-up study of a different group of hyperactive children: "Our impression was that methylphenidate was helpful in making hyperactive children more manageable at home and at school, but did not significantly affect their outcome after five years of treatment [p. 159]."

These disappointing results are, of course, derived from average scores of groups of children—a statistical procedure that obscures marked improvements (or deteriorations) in individual youngsters. Another empirical strategy is to relate outcome measures to pretreatment scores on a variety of assessment instruments in an attempt to develop predictive equations. For example, both child aggression and poor family functioning (e.g., poor marital relationship, use of deviant childrearing practices, presence of psychiatric illness in one or both parents) have been found to correlate negatively with improvement following pharmacological treatment (Weiss & Minde, 1974). Reviewing 36 studies involving over 1400 hyperkinetic children, Barkley (1976) concluded that the best predictors of drug response are measures of attention and concentration; children with marked attention problems initially are the most likely to improve following psychostimulant treatment. In general, however, the extensive attempts to predict which children will show good and poor long-term outcomes have not been very fruitful (Mendelson *et al.*, 1971; Werry & Sprague, 1974).

The reasons for poor long-term outcome are unknown. One possible explanation is the phenomenon called "state-dependent learning" or "learning dissociation," in which a response learned under the influence of a drug may not transfer to the drug-free state (or vice versa). In a systematic attempt to test for state-dependent effects of psychostimulants in children, Aman and Sprague (1974) used three drug conditions (placebo, dextroamphetamine, and methylphenidate) and three laboratory tasks (recognition, paired-associates, and mazes). Children learned all tasks under one of the three drug conditions. Subsequent retention tests were administered at 48-hr intervals, with each child tested under each drug condition.

The authors reported no evidence of state dependency on any of the laboratory tasks. In other words, there was no interaction between the drug administered before acquisition of a task and the drug administered before subsequent retention trials. The child's performance was equally adequate whether he received methylphenidate before acquisition and no drug before retention or methylphenidate before each phase.

There is an important limitation of this study, however, that must be considered in interpreting the results: Aman and Sprague found no drug-induced gains on their three tasks during either the acquisition or the retention phases. In other words, children performed equally well whether they were given placebo, methylphenidate, or dextroamphetamine. It may be that state dependency occurs only with tasks for which drugs facilitate *initial* learning. Or, there may be an important person variable here: State dependency may occur only in children who are positive drug responders. It is unfortunate that Aman and Sprague neither included a task on which drug-induced facilitation could be demonstrated nor separated their subjects into those who did and those who did not improve on psychostimulants.

In another study of state-dependent learning, Swanson and Kinsbourne (1976) attempted to improve previous methodologies by restricting their medicated group to children who were "stimulant-responsive," that is, "who had demonstrated a favorable response to an established therapeutic dose of the stimulant methylphenidate [p. 1355]." They also included a group of nonhyperactive or control children who were being seen at the same learning clinic as the hyperactive youngsters.

The study involved a paired-associate learning task that was administered twice daily (morning and afternoon) on 2 successive days, once following methylphenidate administration and once following placebo administration. The result was a bidirectional state-dependent learning effect for the hyperactive group. During the relearning trials on Day 2, under medicated conditions, significantly more errors were made with items initially learned in the placebo (different) than in the drug (same) state. Similarly, during relearning trials under placebo conditions, significantly more errors were made with items initially learned in the drug (different) than in the placebo (same) state.

Another important finding was that the results differed for the two groups of subjects. State-dependent learning was not demonstrated for the nonhyperactive group and, more importantly, the performance of these children under the drug condition showed a trend toward deterioration rather than facilitation.

Preliminary evidence suggestive of state dependency also emerged in a study of the effects of dextroamphetamine and placebo on a classification task (Fisher, 1978). Hyperactive boys given placebo before each of two training sessions showed a substantial practice effect during Session 2. In contrast, no positive practice effect was found for boys in the two "mixed state" groups, that is, either placebo during Session 1 and dextroamphetamine during Session 2, or the two conditions in the reverse order.

It would appear that Aman and Sprague's (1974) conclusion that state-dependent learning does not occur is premature, as is Swanson and Kinsbourne's (1976) warning that because of bidirectional state dependency, medication must be given regularly if behavioral improvement is to endure. In summary, we can neither implicate nor rule out state-dependent learning as a prime factor in the poor long-term outcome of psychostimulant treatment programs. What is needed now is a series of studies in which types of tasks, subject characteristics, dosage levels, and temporal dimensions are varied systematically.

Research Questions

The following set of research questions is presented in order to highlight the information gaps previously discussed. The questions vary markedly in "answerability." For some, particularly those dealing with the nature of hyperactivity, vigorous research efforts along several fronts have not yet produced definitive answers. For others, particularly those concerned with medical practices, the problem appears to be one of low research density rather than high difficulty. It is indeed surprising that only a few physician surveys and archival studies of medical records have been published to date. The answers to these questions have implications not only for individual hyperactive children, but also for broader issues surrounding the labeling and medical treatment of behavioral differences.

1. What behaviors differentiate children labeled hyperactive from their unlabeled peers, not only in the laboratory, but also in their natural environments as they negotiate an ordinary day? Which of these behaviors change with medication?
2. What proportion of the time do hyperactive children behave in ways likely to earn them the diagnostic label? Are 6-hr hyperactives more typical than 24-hr hyperactives?
3. What situational variables (type of task, degree of structure, timing of activities, behavior of other people) are most frequently associated with (*a*) behaviors labeled hyperactive and (*b*) drug-related improvement?
4. In what types of environments are hyperactive children indistinguishable from their peers? Is the inability to distinguish hyperactive and normal children in these settings due to behavior changes in the children labeled hyperactive? In their peers? In the adults who evaluate child behaviors?
5. What are the actual dosage ranges and dosage adjustment rates used in clinical practice, and how do dosage levels relate to (*a*) individual characteristics of physicians, parents, or teachers, (*b*) child behaviors, (*c*) professional "rules of thumb," (*d*) type and prevalence of side effects, and (*e*) situational variables?
6. How flat, steep, or curvilinear are the dose–response curves for diverse measures of attention, academic performance, and social behavior?
7. How often, on what basis, and with what results are second and third drugs added to the initial medication program?
8. How important are physician factors, parent factors, child factors, and situational factors in determining whether or not a child takes medication during weekends and vacations as well as on school days?
9. What are the "catch-up" growth rates not only during drug holidays, but also after medication is discontinued? To what variables are catch-up growth rates related (e.g., length of treatment, age at initiation, or age at discontinuance)?
10. What are the physician's primary data sources for evaluating the child and the treatment, and how widely do assessment procedures vary

from physician to physician? Is there a relationship between prescribing practices and monitoring procedures? For example, do physicians with more objective and systematic assessment procedures prescribe more or less medication for longer or shorter periods of time?

11. What actually occurs during check-up visits? What measures are collected of the child's health, development, and behavior? What kinds of parental reports are solicited and recorded? How often and in what settings are teacher evaluations requested or school personnel contacted? Under what conditions do physicians consult with the child? How systematically are data collected and recorded?

12. How successfully are double-blind codes broken by physicians? By teachers? By parents? By children? What are the cues that signal that the child has not had medication?

13. How many children taking psychoactive drugs are actually placebo responders, and what characterizes these children? How often are placebo responders detected in actual practice?

14. How long are most children maintained on psychostimulants, and what is the range of treatment durations? Again, how important are physician factors, parent factors, child factors, and situation factors in determining length of psychostimulant treatment?

15. Under what conditions, in what settings, with what dosages and dependent variables does state-dependent learning occur in children taking psychostimulant medication?

16. What criteria are used to determine when medication should be discontinued? How often are these judgments based on the child's age or graduation from elementary school, how often are they based on the child's behavior, and how often on other factors such as parental attitudes?

17. What are the salient academic and social behavior changes noted as medication is withdrawn or discontinued?

CIRCLE TWO: SOCIOCOGNITIVE EFFECTS ON THE CHILD AND SIGNIFICANT OTHERS

Thus far the focus has been on Circle 1, that is, the two types of drug response that are the most easily observed and measured: (*a*) direct effects on overt, target behaviors, and (*b*) side effects. This section will consider Circle 2, emanative influences on the child's own cognitive processes and immediate social environments. Of primary concern here is the message value of the medication. The child needs to explain the medication to himself and his peers and to interpret his expectations and behaviors within the context of the chemical intervention. The pills modify the child's self-perceptions and alter the causal attributions he generates to account for what he sees and does. Changes also occur in the way other people view the child and in their expectations for him. Though unintended, these sociocognitive sequels may have pervasive consequences for the long-term impact of medication programs (Whalen & Henker, 1976). In the following paragraphs, two examples of possible emanative effects will be discussed in the context of recent research: self-perceived competence and drug dependence.

Perceptions of Competencies

Drug treatment is never a discrete, isolated event. It is inevitable that when the medication is used, it is accompanied by psychoeducational messages. The clinician always gives the parent, and usually also the child, an explanation of what the drug is for and why it is being prescribed. Some of these explanations are minimal, whereas others are quite intricate. Some physicians emphasize physiological etiology and the power of the medication (Adler, 1972); others portray the drug only as an adjunct to psychological or educational therapies (Stewart & Olds, 1973).

Consider the differential implications of these three statements:[4]

CLINICIAN A (TO THE PARENTS): *Now, I want him to stay with it and take it twice a day, 7 days a week, and exactly at 7:30 and 11:30 in the mornings. Don't let him forget, and don't leave it up to him. Things are looking a lot better and we want them to stay that way.*

CLINICIAN B (TO THE CHILD): *Now remember, Chris, the medicine is like using a crutch when you have a bad ankle. It can help you, but it can't do the walking for you. You're the one that has to do the work.*

CLINICIAN C (TO THE PARENTS): *O.K., we'll put him on Ritalin, but only if Mother goes on Librium. I think what we're seeing is his reaction to some things that might be going on at home, and I'm very glad about that appointment you have with Dr. X* [a family counselor]. *Let's at least check it out and get his suggestions about how you can manage things differently at home.*

The physician's prelude is only one example of the cognitive structuring that inevitably surrounds psychostimulant treatment. Of focal concern here is the impact of drug treatment on causal attributions, or the explanations people generate for the behaviors they observe. How does psychostimulant treatment modify the child's constructions of his world and his perceptions about his own ability to influence people and events? It is usually assumed that once medication is initiated and positive behavior change occurs, the

[4]All of the statements by practitioners, used here for illustrative purposes, are actual quotations from interviews conducted by the authors.

child will shed his "failure image" and begin to see himself as a competent, successful individual (Adler, 1972). The 1971 Report by OCD–HEW illustrates this conviction with the following statement: "The hoped-for secondary consequences are better peer relationships, improved self-image, and pleasure in acquiring competencies [p. 527]."

Though certainly plausible, this positive snowball effect or virtuous cycle has never been tested empirically. Recent research from social psychology laboratories suggests that medication processes influence an individual's perceptions and attitudes in ways that may *either* facilitate *or* interfere with these expected positive self-evaluations (Davison, Tsujimoto, & Glaros, 1973; Valins & Nisbett, 1971; Weiner & Sierad, 1975). School success following medication may be viewed as authenticating the child's developing competencies or proving that he cannot perform adequately without a chemical crutch. The pill regimen may, in fact, place the child in an attributional conflict or dilemma, where causes of success and failure are unclear. The child's significant others may help him or her resolve this conflict by consistent and public ascriptions to the medication (e.g., "Did you take your pill this morning?"). Despite diverse alternatives, such as increased effort on the part of the child or improved child management strategies on the part of the parents, adults often select medication as their attributional anchor for positive behavior change. This ascription may be modeled by peers and eventually accepted by the child. In brief, the corrective value of success cannot be assumed (Bandura, Jeffery, & Gajdos, 1975).

WHAT THE CHILDREN SAY

During a study of causal attributions, the authors are conducting interviews with children diagnosed hyperactive and currently taking psychostimulant medication (see Whalen & Henker, 1976). The following excerpts from these interviews illustrate the ease with which "good" behaviors *may be* attributed directly to medication (rather than to a child's effort or skill), and how "bad" behaviors *may be* attributed to failure to take medication. The first three excerpts are from an interview with an 11-year-old girl:

CHILD: *I wasn't at all—I didn't at all have hardly any friends. I only had two, and that was it. And last year I didn't take it* [the medication] *in the afternoon, but the last time I saw my doctor he said, "Why don't you have her start taking it in the afternoon?" And then since I've been doing that I've gotten about 20 more friends.*

INTERVIEWER: *How can you tell when you forget to take Ritalin?*

CHILD: *When I can tell that I'm not concentrating in school. Like she'll* [the teacher] *give us a half hour to do a math page, like there's about 20 problems, and I'll get about 6 done in 20 minutes, a half hour. But if I take it, I can get them all done in 10 minutes, 20 minutes, and have 10 minutes free.*

INTERVIEWER: *This is an "imagination" question. Let's say you stopped taking Ritalin altogether.*

CHILD: *Oh wow, I'd stay home from school.*

INTERVIEWER: *How come?*

CHILD: *Because I know what would be happening if I didn't. I wouldn't get my work done at all.*

INTERVIEWER: *How about your friends?*

CHILD: *Nobody would like me then, if I didn't take it. They'd think in their minds, "Gosh, she doesn't even want to play. What a baby!"*

INTERVIEWER: *Pretend that a friend of yours was about to start taking Ritalin and she asked you what you thought . . .*

CHILD: *They'd ask me, like "What does it* **do**?" *I'd just tell them, "Well, it helps you concentrate, get more friends, and you want to join in the games more. And you'd be invited more places."*

The following excerpt is from an interview with a 9-year-old boy who described himself as being "on the borderline between a hyperkinetic and a regular person":

INTERVIEWER: *You were giving me a good example of times when you take an extra pill. Can you think back to another time?*

CHILD: *Yes, at Catalina. Another fishing story.*

INTERVIEWER: *Great, another fishing story.*

CHILD: *In the fishing I got bored, 'cause we couldn't catch the goldfish. There's goldfish in the ocean. . . . So we wouldn't catch them and I got bored waiting for another Catalina perch. We were bored. And I needed a pill—so I had to have another pill. And I didn't have one that morning. Then I had two. My Dad brought a case of them.*

INTERVIEWER: *He carries them with him?*

CHILD: *Yeah.*

INTERVIEWER: *So, how did you know you were bored and that you needed a pill?*

CHILD: *'Cause my legs started kicking and my hands got all loose . . . then my feet start kicking all around and stuff. . . . My body gets all out of control and I need another pill.*

The following excerpt is from an interview with a 10-year-old boy:

INTERVIEWER: *How can other people tell when you forget to take Ritalin?*

CHILD: *Yeah, people can tell when I'm not taking it, because I'm running around.*

INTERVIEWER: *Tell me about the last time you remember that happening. When was that?*

CHILD: *Sunday, yesterday.*

INTERVIEWER: *And what happened?*

CHILD: *I was trying to run in the water, swimming pretty fast, bumping into the girls, my sisters, and diving in, and diving in and bouncing in and diving in and turn around and spring off your feet like a bowling pin in the water.*

INTERVIEWER: *And they didn't like it very much?*

CHILD: *Uh uh, and so they told my Mom and my Mom called me in and I had to take my Ritalin.*

The next excerpt is from an interview with an 11-year-old boy.

INTERVIEWER: *How can people tell when you forget to take Ritalin?*

CHILD: *I'm acting horrible.*

INTERVIEWER: *What kinds of things do they see?*

CHILD: *I'll be bouncing the ball all around the room, that kind of stuff. Like say it's past 11:30 and I'm doing "wah-wah-wah"* [pretends to bounce ball], *he* [the teacher] *will ask me if I took my pill.*

INTERVIEWER: *OK, so one thing he* [the teacher] *can see when you forget to take Ritalin is bouncing the ball around, doing that kind of thing. What else, what else does he see?*

CHILD: *Running around the room. Like, like there's a girl named Vicki and sometimes I go, "Sticky-Vicky is very picky about her diet. All she has on her diet is fat." And that really, and then she sometimes goes and tells the teacher.*

INTERVIEWER: *What else, any more samples? Those are good examples for me.*

CHILD: *Running out of the room, kicking people, beating people up, cussing them out, things like that.*

INTERVIEWER: *How come?*

CHILD: [laughs] *I don't know. I just wanna. I just feel like it.*

INTERVIEWER: *What* **does** *that feel like?*

CHILD: *Like, I don't know what it feels like, really.*

INTERVIEWER: *Think about it for a minute.*

CHILD: *I can't. Let's see, how it feels. It feels just like you can't hold it in. It has to come out.*

INTERVIEWER: *How do you know?*

CHILD: *Because, I can tell by the way I'm acting. You know, like if I'm acting really goofy, I know I haven't taken my pill.*

The next excerpts, taken from an interview with a 13-year-old boy, illustrate the fact that medication does not inevitably lead to external attributions and low personal control and may, in fact, serve to enhance self-perceived competencies.

INTERVIEWER: *How well do you think Ritalin seems to be working for you, in general?*

CHILD: *It does, well, a pretty good job, you know, because, altogether it helped me calm myself down and get a chance to think straight before I say something, or do something.*

[Later] *Actually, I don't think it will really help that much because if that child was so determined and stubborn, you know, you could give me 50 pills and it isn't going to do much besides make me ill at ease, you know, because it all depends on if you* ***want*** *to try, you know, because if I want to try to work along with the Ritalin it will help me, but if I don't it will take longer.*

CAUSAL CONSTRUCTS AND TEMPORAL PARAMETERS

Psychostimulant treatment not only has direct message value for the target child, but also exerts subtle effects by altering the expectations and behaviors of the child's significant others. Moreover, there is no *single* message conveyed by medication. Often the reactions of the child, teacher, parents, and peers may be quite disparate, and the child may need to respond to a network of conflicting expectations and reactions. This point was poignantly illustrated by Renstrom (1976) in a discussion of treatment termination: "One 12-year-old, after four years of drug therapy, asked me if his teachers and parents *had* to know that medication was being stopped. He was fairly certain of his behavior, but was afraid of others' [p. 108]."

The point here is that sociocognitive sequels are not usually considered an integral part of the treatment program. Physicians rarely interview children about their attitudes, opinions, and feelings concerning medication, nor does the clinical literature deal with these topics (Loney & Ordoña, 1975; Stewart, 1976a; Werry, 1977). We are suggesting that cognitive variables may interact in complex fashion with the overt behavior changes that are anticipated and observed. It is often assumed that the effects of the medication and the "sales pitch" are additive. When left to chance, however, the direct and emanative effects of psychostimulants may work against each other, diluting the ultimate outcome.

The ethical concerns about long-term effects raised by Stewart (1976b) are particularly pertinent here:

> Specialists see a number of young people who have taken stimulants every day of their lives from, say, ages 10 to 16, at which point both the children and their families are thoroughly dependent on a drug to maintain daily life. These children

> may have forgotten what their original personalities were, and they may feel quite uncomfortable about their natural behavior. They are in the dilemma of having to adjust to being different people if a psychiatrist recommends that they stop taking the drug, and their families are correspondingly troubled. Thus when these children are mature enough to decide for themselves whether or not to accept treatment with a psychotropic drug, they and their families may already be so conditioned to the drug's use that they are no longer free to choose [p. 234].[5]

In a previous paper, we have underscored the importance of perceived personal causation, specifically the extent to which people believe events are under their own (internal or personal) control versus under the influence of external agents such as other people, chance, or fate (Whalen & Henker, 1976). It was hypothesized that psychostimulant treatment often enhances external attributions, conveying the message that the child's problems are biologically based. Neither parent nor child caused the difficulties, and neither parent nor child can be expected to ameliorate them. External ascriptions about problem *source* or etiology were viewed as potentially beneficial, decreasing maladaptive guilt over past transgressions and blame for current inadequacies. In contrast, external ascriptions about problem *solutions* may interfere with long-term gains by causing a deceleration of personal efforts to improve and a perception that drugs are a prerequisite for behavioral adequacy.

The attributional literature from social psychology laboratories suggests the importance of temporal parameters in the development of causal constructs. There are strong indications of a primacy effect: Those causal attributions that are embraced initially tend to be those that endure, regardless of later events (Kanouse, 1971). Apparently, people are likely to accept the first feasible explanation of a phenomenon and retain this initial causal attribution, even when later faced with better alternatives or new data. If these laboratory findings reflect real world phenomena, they suggest that once a child, his parents, and his teachers begin to ascribe positive behaviors to potent chemicals (external agents), it may be quite difficult to effect reattribution to an internal agent, such as a child's developing competencies. Regardless of a child's actual abilities, "good" behavior may continue to be attributed to medication and "bad" behavior to the lack of medication. This reasoning implies that it may be beneficial to undersell medication, that is, to lower expectancies about its potency, rather than to raise expectancies and thus enhance "placebo effects" (Valins & Nisbett, 1971).

One way to decrease the salience of medication is to begin a nonchemical

[5]Reprinted by permission from Stewart, M. A. Treating problem children with drugs: Ethical issues. In G. P. Koocher (Ed.), *Children's rights and the mental health professions*. New York: Wiley, 1976.

training or therapy program before starting medication. Even when medication is construed by the practitioner as the swiftest solution, long-term goals may dictate a prior intervention, such as cognitive self-instructional training, designed to increase a child's capacity for self-control and perceptions of personal causation (e.g., Bugental, Whalen, & Henker, 1977; Camp, Blom, Hebert, & van Doorninck, 1977; Douglas, Parry, Marton, & Garson, 1976; Meichenbaum, 1977). The two-step strategy of beginning with a cognitive intervention program and then adding psychostimulants would provide the child and his significant others with "internal" attributional anchors for behavioral improvement before changes are inexorably ascribed to external causes, that is, to the medication. (Moreover, a side effect of this sequential treatment strategy might be the recognition that, for some children, cognitive training obviates the need for medication.)

Stimulant Use and Drug Dependence

SOCIAL AND COGNITIVE STRUCTURING

Are today's child stimulant users likely to be tomorrow's adolescent and adult drug abusers? Despite 40 years of research with stimulant medication, the answer to this question is unknown (Report, 1971). Eisenberg (1972) draws a sharp distinction between the use of stimulants by adults and by children. Adults experience euphoria when they take stimulants, and presumably it is this "high" that leads to repeated usage. Children are assumed not to experience positive mood changes and may, in fact, show sadness and depression. Eisenberg goes on to suggest that hyperactive children given stimulants may actually have a lower probability of later abuse than children from whom the drugs are withheld, partially because the former group have learned "to take medicine for the proper business of suppressing illness [p. 713]," and partially because the repeated failure and social rejection of untreated hyperactive children may lead these youngsters to seek drugs as anodynes.

Eisenberg's carefully reasoned arguments and predictions, however, do not receive unanimous support from the professional community; some child specialists maintain that hyperactive children treated with stimulants run an increased rather than a decreased risk of later drug abuse. The data indicating that stimulants do not produce euphoric mood states in children are neither consistent nor conclusive (Conners, 1972a). The dependency of drug effects on specific expectancies and social cues is gaining increasing recognition (e.g., Lennard, Epstein, Bernstein, & Ransom, 1971; Schachter & Singer, 1962). Gritz and Jarvik (1975) reviewed the growing body of literature on cognitive and situational factors and concluded that, "Drugs, whether endogenous or exogenous, do not trigger specific emotional states, but rather a more general pattern of physiological response which is interpreted by a person in the framework of his surroundings, and of those cognitions available to him [p. 16]."

Studies of the effects of cognitions and social settings on drug responsiveness have been restricted to adults. No information is available on how a child's constructs or settings might influence his immediate response to medication and, perhaps more importantly, his long-term use of psychoactive agents. It has been suggested that the main reason children taking psychostimulants feel calmed rather than aroused or "high" may be that they are led to expect calmness rather than euphoria (e.g., Sroufe, 1975). However, the practice of conveying expectations of calmness, while common, is by no means universal. It is interesting to note that Bradley (1937), the pediatrician frequently credited with the first published report on the use of amphetamines with children, maintained that youngsters engaged in difficult behaviors because "they were desperately unhappy or unsatisfied in their lives," that amphetamines were euphoriants, and that "as the children were enabled to feel happier as the result of the medication, there was less need for them to display their deviant behavior [Laufer, 1975, p. 107]." Given current societal problems with substance abuse, we wonder about children who are not given "calmness" as a cover story, or for whom this set induction does not "take," perhaps because of contradictory expectancies generated by older siblings or the mass media. The need for information about the effects of cognitions and social cues on children's medication responses is increased by the current trend to maintain children on psychostimulant medication through adolescence—a developmental period when peers become increasingly influential and drug cultures more and more salient (Safer & Allen, 1976). As Ray and Wilson (1975) point out, "there is no clear way to separate medical and recreational use when a drug is obtained medically [p. 400]."

ADOLESCENT DRUG USAGE

A most striking fact is that arguments supporting either a direct or an inverse relationship between childhood psychostimulant use and adolescent drug abuse have received scant empirical support. Only two follow-up studies have been published to date. Surveying 100 former hyperkinetic patients between the ages of 15 and 26 (and obtaining a 57% return rate), Laufer (1971) found that very few were using drugs of any type, and none was "hooked." Similar results were found in a study by Beck *et al.* (1975) comparing adolescents who were diagnosed minimal brain dysfunction and given chemotherapy during childhood to a group of adolescents with no history of psychiatric disorder or chemotherapy. During individual interviews, adolescents in the contrast group reported much more extensive drug use than those who had received chemotherapy during childhood. In fact, only 3 of the 30 adolescents in the latter group reported any illicit drug use, either past or present.

The results of these two studies are difficult to interpret in that both were conducted under medical auspices and neither preserved the anonymity of the subjects. These conditions are certainly not conducive to candid self-report. It is somewhat puzzling that only 5 of the 57 respondents in Laufer's study reported experimentation with drugs such as marijuana or LSD. Perhaps psychostimulant treatment during childhood actually "inoculates" against adolescent drug use. It seems just as likely, however, that individuals who have been treated with stimulants for pervasive behavioral difficulties may be less willing than their peers to provide candid self-reports of drug usage. "Doper" and "pusher" are common epithets bestowed by peers who learn that these youngsters are taking psychostimulants for hyperactivity. Youngsters who had experienced extensive social and academic difficulties but had not been given psychostimulant therapy would comprise a more adequate comparison group than those studied by Beck *et al.* (1975), but such a group would be extremely difficult to assemble.

To summarize, we do not yet know whether the relationship between stimulant use in childhood and later substance abuse is direct, inverse, or nonexistent.[6] Recent evidence of a familial tendency toward alcoholism in families with hyperactive children raises the possibility that hyperactive children may be particularly prone to drug dependence, and that the medical use of psychostimulants with these youngsters may potentiate substance abuse (Goodwin, Schulsinger, Hermansen, Guze, & Winokur, 1975; Satterfield & Cantwell, 1975; Werry, 1976). Until recently, the typical practice was to discontinue stimulant therapy around the age of 11 or 12, and some professionals assert that the drugs *must* be discontinued by puberty because of the potential for abuse (Stewart & Olds, 1973). As it becomes more common to use psychostimulant therapy during adolescence and adulthood (Allen, Safer, & Covi, 1975; Arnold, Strobl, & Weisenberg, 1972; Mackay, Beck, & Taylor, 1973; Maletzky, 1974; Safer & Allen 1975b), the question of drug abuse assumes increasing importance. There is no empirical basis for recent alarmist predictions, but there is also no reason for complacency at this point. The data are just not in.

P.R.N. PRACTICES

Another research need here is the study of p.r.n. drug administration, the practice of having parents or teachers give psychostimulants on the basis of

[6]The only anonymous data to date, however, do indicate little cause for concern (Henker, Whalen, Bugental, & Barker, in press). Additional drug use findings are also presented in Loney, Kramer, and Milich (in press).

perceived need rather than according to a fixed routine. Parents often report that, with or without their physician's approval, they give their child extra medication for special occasions, such as scout meetings or visits from grandparents (Fowlie, 1973; Gadow, 1977; Katz *et al.*, 1975; Stewart & Olds, 1973). One girl interviewed by the authors reported that she had been given an extra pill immediately before coming in for the interview because her mother thought she was "acting weird." Some children themselves admit taking extra medication for such events as school examinations (Sroufe & Stewart, 1973).

The long-range effects of such p.r.n. practices may be detrimental, teaching drug taking as a coping style. Alternatively, the effects may be quite beneficial, particularly if the p.r.n. program includes the possibility of omitting the usual dosage. Thus far, p.r.n. practices have been left primarily to chance or to individual differences among physicians and families. Our information is merely anecdotal; no systematic data are available on either the extent or the impact of self-regulation of drug dosage. These are important empirical questions that deserve careful study.

Research Questions

Once again, a set of empirical questions is provided as a means of summarizing the kinds of information needed on the sociocognitive effects of labeling and medication programs. The major questions here concern the message of the medication and the interactions among cognitive constructs and behavioral outcomes. In a sense, the following is a call to map the social ecology of drug intervention, given that the treatment is a public event which in itself influences the expectations and reactions of the child's family, peers, and teachers.

1. How do physicians actually introduce the topic of medication to parents and children? What is the range of rationales used by physicians, and how often are internal as opposed to external ("magic pill") expectancies induced during this "initiation period." How often is the cognitive structuring aimed at enhancing the potency of the pill, and how often are the child's own efforts emphasized? How much (and what kinds of) responsibility is the child given for his or her own treatment program?
2. What changes in the child's self-perceived competencies and expectancies are induced by the labeling–medication intervention? How does the child explain the medication to himself or herself? To peers?
3. How aware are child and adolescent peers of (*a*) the label "hyperactive," and (*b*) psychostimulant treatment programs? How do peers perceive children labeled hyperactive, and how are peer attitudes expressed in interpersonal behaviors? What (if any) distinctions are made between "bad" or

misbehaving youngsters and those who are publicly labeled hyperactive? How does the introduction of medication enhance or counteract these labeling effects?

4. How do children interpret their own behavioral improvement when taking psychostimulants? When (or for whom) is improvement likely to enhance self-perceived competencies, and when (or for whom) is drug-related improvement likely to be viewed as proof that the child has a serious deficit?

5. What changes in causal attributions and expectancies in significant adults are induced by the labeling–medication intervention?

6. Can measures of the child's expectancies and causal constructs predict long-term outcome once medication is discontinued?

7. How are changes in medication dosage or type interpreted by child and parent? When is a child likely to view the addition of a mid-afternoon dose as a sign that he or she is even more seriously disturbed than previously thought?

8. What long-term effects do nonpharmacologic (e.g., cognitive or behavioral) treatment programs have on hyperactive children? Are the effects of introducing a nonpharmacologic intervention *before* medication different from those of introducing the two programs simultaneously, or in the reverse order?

9. How often do parents give their children psychostimulants p.r.n., and what person and situation factors are related to p.r.n. practices? How often and under what conditions do the children adjust their own medication?

10. How do children and adolescents negotiate the transition from medication to nonmedication? What are their self-expectancies, and how are these cognitive constructs influenced by the attitudes and behaviors of their significant others?

11. What are the attitudes and behaviors of adolescents and young adults who were previously taking psychostimulants toward (*a*) licit and (*b*) illicit drugs?

CIRCLE THREE: PROFESSIONAL PRACTICES, SLIPPERY SLOPES, AND RUNAWAY LABELS

The Assiduous Search for the Syndromes

There is some indication that the incidence of hyperactivity may be increasing (Weithorn & Ross, 1976). Reported increases might result from improved assessment and diagnostic practices, or from actual increases in putative etiological factors including maternal smoking (Denson, Nanson, & McWatters, 1975), and environmental lead acquired from foods, air, dirt, glazed pottery, or gasoline (David, 1974; de la Burdé & Choate, 1975; Needleman, 1973; Silbergeld & Goldberg, 1974; Warren, 1974). It is also quite likely, however, that increased prevalence of the "syndrome" of hyperactivity may result from social and bureaucratic processes quite independent of the children's behavior. In a discussion of "the labeled child," Guskin, Bartel, and MacMillan (1975) provided two examples of such processes:

> Thus, a child who was formerly "difficult" or "hard to control" becomes "emotionally disturbed" when diagnostic personnel and services become available; similarly, hundreds of school systems suddenly had large numbers of "culturally deprived" students when federal funds for such children became available in the 1960s [p. 191].[7]

Safer and Allen (1976) suggest that the availability and viability of lithium treatment for manic-depressive psychosis has increased the frequency with which manic-depressive psychosis is diagnosed; a similar escalation may be occurring with hyperactivity and psychostimulants. Recent reports indicate that in some regular classrooms more than 50% of the children are labeled hyperkinetic (Arnold, 1973b). Moreover, psychostimulant treatment is no longer restricted to school-aged children clinically diagnosed as hyperkinetic. More problem domains are being subsumed under the hyperactivity–psychostimulant rubric, and the age range deemed appropriate for psychostimulant intervention is creeping down to the toddler level and up through adolescence and adulthood (Allen *et al.,* 1975; Conners, 1975a; Lerer & Lerer, 1977; Mackay *et al.,* 1973; Maletzky, 1974; Mann & Greenspan, 1976; Safer & Allen, 1975b; Schleifer, Weiss, Cohen, Elman, Cvejic, & Kruger, 1975; Wood, Reimherr, Wender, & Johnson, 1976). The greater the apparent effectiveness of psychostimulants, the greater the number of people for whom this treatment is prescribed; the greater the number of people treated with psychostimulants, the more effective the medication appears to be.

This "slippery slope" in the use of psychostimulant treatment is facilitated by the semantic elasticity of the term "hyperactivity." Although it is assumed that everyone knows a hyperactive child when he or she encounters one, there are few exclusionary criteria for this diagnostic category and no unequivocal positive markers (Conners, 1975c). When professionals from

[7]Reprinted by permission from Guskin, S. L., Bartel, N. R., & MacMillan, D. L. Perspective of the labeled child. In N. Hobbs (Ed.), *Issues in the classification of children* (Vol. 2). San Francisco: Jossey-Bass, 1975.

diverse health and education disciplines are asked to indicate the traits most characteristic of hyperkinesis, they show remarkable consensus. Schrager, Lindy, Harrison, McDermott, and Killins (1966) found that at least 75% of the individuals from each of five disciplines agreed on the primary characteristics of the hyperkinetic syndrome (i.e., fidgets, restless, inattentive, hard to manage, cannot sit still, easily distracted, and cannot take frustration). However, when investigators attempt to operationalize these trait labels and obtain multimodal assessments of children identified as hyperactive, they are often unable to achieve satisfactory reliability and validity, particularly when ratings or observations of presumably identical behaviors are obtained from more than one source (Blunden *et al.*, 1974; Klein & Gittelman-Klein, 1975; Langhorne *et al.*, 1976; Rapoport & Benoit, 1975; Werry & Aman, 1975; Yepes *et al.*, 1977). Routh and Schroeder (1976), for example, found that activity room measures of hyperactivity did *not* correlate with parent ratings of hyperactivity, even though the activity room measures did distinguish reliably between children referred for clinical evaluation of hyperactivity and a normal comparison group. Data from an intensive study of 84 hyperkinetic boys are also illustrative (Loney, Langhorne, Paternite, Whaley-Klahn, Broeker, & Hacker, in press). Ratings made by mothers correlated positively but modestly with those made by trained examiners; the strongest relationship was found for aggressive interpersonal behavior ($r = .50$, $p < .001$) and the weakest for hyperactivity ($r = .11$, ns). Moreover, the various behavioral signs considered characteristic of hyperactivity fail to cluster together when subjected to empirical scrutiny (e.g., Routh, Chapter 2 of this volume; Werry, 1968b). Knowing that a child is inattentive does not tell you whether or not he is impulsive (Routh & Roberts, 1972), and knowing how many times he changes quadrants in a specially marked playroom tells you nothing about how much he will fidget or squirm while being tested (Barkley & Ullman, 1975).

In summary, children labeled hyperactive and treated with psychostimulants are a heterogeneous bunch whose commonalities elude empirical specification (Conners, 1975b; Lambert, Windmiller, Sandoval, & Moore, 1976). The more successful the drug treatment appears to be, the greater the propensity for labeling, and the higher the tolerance for diagnostic ambiguity. The circularity is further entrenched by the tendency to use a positive drug response as confirmation of the diagnostic label (Wender, 1971). The logical fallacy inherent in this approach is underscored by the Rapoport *et al.* (1978) findings of improved performance in *normal* prepubertal boys following a single dose of dextroamphetamine (versus placebo). (See also Rapoport, Chapter 9 of this volume.) Ironically, it is the short-term success of the drugs that appears to be diverting attempts to understand the interactions among child behaviors, adult perceptions, and situational factors that lead to the identification of large numbers of children as hyperactive, and to the socialization of many of these youngsters and their families in psychostimulant treatment programs.

It should be noted, however, that the early warning signals are starting to be heard. In a recent follow-up survey, Krager, Safer, and Earhart (1979) found that medication use for hyperactive children seems to be leveling off (see also Bosco & Robin, Chapter 6 of this volume; and Sandoval, Lambert, & Sassone, Chapter 5 of this volume).

Self-Fulfilling Prevalence Rates

A related emanative effect of drug treatment is the propagation of mythical prevalence rates for hyperkinesis. Once a specified prevalence rate is accepted or expected, failure to find this rate in a geographical region may lead to "case hunts" in which health and education professionals search for unrecognized, masked, or latent instances of hyperactivity. A case in point is the following statement by a well-known and respected physician:

> The prevalence rate of four percent can often help decide doubtful situations. For example, if a school already has 15% of its students diagnosed and/or medicated, the probability that another child should be so diagnosed plummets to near zero. The pool of undiagnosed hyperkinetics in that school should be exhausted already. (Of course, it is possible that the wrong ones have been diagnosed and the real hyperkinetic children missed thus far, but this would be betting against the odds.) On the other hand, if few students (much less than four percent) in a school have been diagnosed, we may assume the presence of a residual pool of undiagnosed hyperkinetics. In such circumstances, the appropriateness of diagnosing a given suspected child soars [Arnold, 1973b, p. 511].[8]

Although intended to encourage early intervention, this statement could easily be misconstrued as a recommendation that we "play the numbers game" in identifying hyperkinetic children. Given our ignorance about the etiology and correlates of hyperactivity, coupled with the subjectivity and bias inherent in the identification process, this clinical variant of the "gambler's fallacy" is quite alarming. The refutability of the diagnostic label, once given, is still an open question and should lead to great caution in any search for untreated cases.

[8]Reprinted by permission from Arnold, L. E. Is this label necessary? *Journal of School Health,* 1973, *23,* 510–514.

The Masking Effects of Medication

Another potential emanative effect on professional practices is the gradual placing of more and more eggs in the medication basket until the importance of nonpharmacologic influences fades. When medication increases manageability, health and education professionals may relax their efforts and overlook important problems that may be obscured, temporarily, by drug-related changes. One concern is that giving a child drugs to control his restless or unruly behavior deprives him of opportunities to use his own "executive powers" and develop effective modes of self-control (Grinspoon & Singer, 1973; Ladd, 1970). A second concern is that when a child begins to behave better, attempts to deal with his academic underachievement are curtailed (Rie, 1975). Reading failure is certainly less salient and less irritating than disruptive behavior, although the long-term consequences may be equally detrimental. A third example occurs when a child does not respond positively to medication; in these cases physicians are often encouraged by their colleagues to increase the dosage or to add a second drug rather than to seek alternate solutions for the difficulties observed (Cantwell, 1975b; Katz *et al.*, 1975). This increasing reliance on chemical solutions to problems in living will be discussed further in the following section.

Social System Interdependencies and the Medical Decision Matrix

Within the field of social ecology, it has become pro forma to point out the interplay among social systems; a shift in one system produces reverberative shifts in other systems. As noted before, we do not know whether the true prevalence of hyperactivity is increasing or whether the reported increases index a system shift. Parents who are dissatisfied with the educational system responsiveness to their child's problems often find relief by shifting to a medical paradigm. The connotations of the term "hyperactive," with the implicit message that the problems are biologically based and will disappear at adolescence, are more palatable and benign than alternative labels such as "learning disabled," "emotionally disturbed," or "antisocial." Parental guilt diminishes as parents begin to attribute the problems to the child's physiology rather than to their own feelings or inadequacies, and the ever-present burden of finding help for their child is lessened considerably once psychostimulant treatment begins. In some ways, the diagnosis of hyperactivity and the use of psychostimulants also aid school personnel, reducing their need to juggle budgets, alter didactic approaches, or change educational priorities in order to accommodate to children labeled hyperactive.

In response to this microcosm of imperatives, the physician has few options for action other than psychoactive medication. Despite a flurry of demonstration programs using alternative intervention strategies, such as parent management training and cognitive behavior modification (e.g., Ayllon, Layman, & Kandel, 1975; O'Leary, Pelham, Rosenbaum, & Price, 1976; Varni & Henker, 1979), the area of nonchemical treatments remains in its early infancy. Case studies are appearing, but encouraging gains from programmatic efforts have been limited and very difficult to document (see Camp *et al.*, 1977, and Chapter 7 of this volume), and only one large-scale test has produced a globally positive verdict (see Douglas *et al.* 1976, and Chapter 11 of this volume). The promise is high, but the gains documented thus far from nonpharmacologic interventions are neither as impressive nor as reliable as drug-related changes (e.g., Gittelman-Klein, Klein, Abikoff, Katz, Gloisten, & Kates, 1976, and Chapter 8 of this volume). Perhaps even more to the point, the practicing physician rarely has access to one of these alternative programs.

The physician is hampered further by the fact that hyperactivity is unlikely to materialize in the office. Clinical lore is replete with examples of the "model" behavior of hyperactive children during brief visits to their pediatrician. Typically, physicians must rely on the observations of other people rather than on their own assessments or the results of laboratory tests. Sleator and von Neumann (1974) reported that only 10 of the 46 hyperkinetic children in their study could have been diagnosed hyperkinetic by the physician alone. Physicians must rely on the observations of others, yet they have no knowledge of the histories, values, expectancies, objectivity, or other individual differences among their reporters, primarily parents and teachers. A further impediment is the lack of articulation among the several social systems involved with hyperactive children (Robin & Bosco, 1976).

Finally, those committed to primary health care delivery cannot afford the luxury of an exclusive focus on the defects of our society. To improve the fabric of social institutions and systems is certainly a lofty goal, but one that the child experiencing difficulties *today* cannot await (Whalen & Henker, 1977). Given these potent social forces and constraints, along with economic exigencies, it is somewhat surprising that medication is not prescribed even more frequently!

Research Questions

1. For children experiencing academic and/or social difficulties, how often is the diagnostic label "hyperactive" or "hyperkinetic" applied? What

proportion of children in regular school programs is considered hyperactive, and how do current prevalence rates compare with those of 3, 5, or 10 years ago?

2. What alternative labels are used for children experiencing academic and/or social difficulties, and what is the probability associated with each label that the child will be given psychoactive medication?

3. What characteristics distinguish teachers, psychologists, and physicians who identify or nominate many children as hyperactive (high-rate nominators) from those professionals who identify relatively few (low-rate nominators)? Do children respond differently to high-rate and low-rate nominators? In other words, do high- and low-rate nominators elicit different behaviors from children labeled hyperkinetic?

4. How often is the diagnostic label "hyperactive" or "hyperkinetic" applied to adolescents and adults, and how do current rates compare with those of 3, 5, or 10 years ago?

5. What are the exclusionary criteria used most frequently by professionals in diagnosing hyperactivity? What are the most frequently used positive markers?

6. How are most families "recruited" into psychostimulant treatment programs? How often are school personnel, family physicians, relatives, friends, or neighbors the first to suggest medication?

7. What happens when parents refuse medication for their child? How many of these parents eventually accept a trial medication program, and what are the influences that lead to this eventual acceptance? What distinguishes families who accept medication immediately from (*a*) those who refuse at first and later accept, (*b*) those who refuse and enroll their child and/or family in alternative treatment programs, and (*c*) those who refuse and seek no help for their child or family?

8. How do expected and actual prevalence rates for hyperactivity vary according to (*a*) geographical region, (*b*) profession and institution (e.g., schools versus child guidance clinics versus pediatricians), and (*c*) socioeconomic and ethnic subgroups?

9. What characteristics (e.g., personal, professional, experiential) distinguish physicians who frequently prescribe psychoactive medication for children from those who rarely prescribe medication?

10. How many children currently taking psychoactive medication are enrolled in other treatment programs (e.g., psychoeducation, behavior modification, family counseling), and for how many is medication the sole treatment?

11. What is the natural history of intervention for children labeled hyperactive? How often are drugs the first resort, and how often are they the last resort?

12. What is the actual role of schools in encouraging medication for hyperactive children? How likely are teachers and school psychologists to recommend medication, and in what ways is the recommendation given?

13. What is the actual role of physicians in encouraging nonchemical intervention to complement or replace drug therapies? How often and how explicitly are alternative strategies recommended, and what types of follow-through measures are instituted?

14. How do informal networks from schools to physicians or from non-prescribing to prescribing physicians develop, and how is the existence of these networks communicated to troubled parents?

CIRCLE FOUR: THE SOCIAL MATRIX

The effects of psychopharmacologic treatments diffuse far beyond the child and his immediate interpersonal and professional environments to influence broad social phenomena, including subcultural life styles and public modes of coping with problems in living. Such wide-ranging effects are often quite difficult to detect, and even more difficult to link directly to specific drug treatment practices. In recent years a few attempts have been made to chronicle or anticipate how psychopharmacological treatment trends influence the larger social matrix. In a disquisition on drugs and society, for example, Freedman (1973) described possible effects of methadone maintenance programs on the community, suggesting that the availability of these programs may effectively decrease the large number of heroin addicts who "mature out" (estimated at 30–50% of the addict population) and simultaneously increase the quantity of heroin available for the recruitment of young addicts. Moreover, by fabricating personal histories, individuals who may be deterred by the need for criminal involvement or hustling can use methadone maintenance programs as a route of entry to the drug culture. Freedman further questions "whether the enthusiasm and the evangelical endorsement of methadone maintenance by important figures somehow legitimized, if not glamorized, opiate use [p. 282]."

Freedman affirms that there are no ready relationships and that we do not know how prevalent or important such effects may be. He concludes his intriguing analysis with a plea that we study the psychoecological consequences of drug intervention programs. To date, such effects have eluded systematic examination. The following discussion of potential emanative effects on society is intended as illustrative rather than definitive or comprehensive. The two focal examples will be (*a*) opportunistic drug use and abuse, and (*b*) the medicalization of problems in living.

Opportunistic Drug Use and Abuse

The concern that a child treated with psychostimulants may develop attitudes and habits leading to later drug dependence was discussed in the context of Circle 2. The focus here is on the impact psychostimulant treatment may have on those who interact with the target child and also on society at large. In both direct and indirect ways, psychostimulant treatment of school children may increase drug use in adolescents and adults. Anecdotal reports that a child's relatives or friends may abuse his supply of psychostimulants are finding their way into the literature (Arnold, 1973a; Stewart & Olds, 1973). One teenager we interviewed recently related how she hated taking the medication, a phenomenon quite common among adolescents (Safer & Allen, 1975). This young girl faced a dilemma: She did not want to anger her mother by refusing the pills, but she was also quite adamant about not taking them. Her solution was to remove the pills from their container—so that her mother would think she was taking them regularly—and then to give them to an eager friend. To cite another example, a pediatrician recently told the authors that the father of one of his young patients had, by repeatedly refilling his child's prescription for methylphenidate at different times of the day at a 24-hr pharmacy, amassed 540 tablets before his ruse was discovered. Here we have an unheralded example of what has been labeled the "gray market," casual and informal channels for obtaining prescription drugs without prescriptions (Brecher, 1972).

The abuse potential of dextroamphetamine has long been recognized, and a similar potential for methylphenidate has emerged. "Exotic" abuse of Ritalin, involving intravenous injection of whole tablets dissolved in water, was reported first in Seattle and is evidently on the increase (Omenn, 1973; Willey, 1971). In a study of heroin addicts, Raskin and Bradford (1975) found a high frequency of Ritalin abuse among methadone maintenance patients, presumably because Ritalin provides a euphoric psychological "high," counteracts the sedating effect of methadone, and is not detected in standard urine tests. These investigators found that methadone maintenance patients were developing Ritalin habits that cost them between $25 and $100 per week on the streets.

Following a study of nonmedical drug use conducted in 1975–1976, Abelson and Fishburne (1976) estimated that stimulants have been used (at least once) by 16.6% of 18–25-year-olds and by 4.4% of 12–17-year-olds in the United States. The door is open for adolescents such as the one described above, who are involuntarily taking Ritalin under medical prescription, to find a financially rewarding means of disposing of their pills.

Medical Solutions to Problems in Living

Psychostimulant medication is relatively inexpensive, readily available, and easily administered. No nonchemical intervention can be applied at a cost of approximately 20¢ and 5 or 10 min per day, and no other intervention can claim documented success rates ranging from 60 to 90%. When alternatives or concomitants to drug therapy are considered, a huge gap between policy and practice is apparent. In the literature, many professionals emphasize that stimulant drugs should constitute only one element in a total treatment program (Anders & Ciaranello, 1977). Physicians have been careful to point out that drugs can change specific behavioral symptoms but cannot, in themselves, improve a child's self-esteem, reading skills, or relations with peers (Eisenberg, 1972; Fish, 1975; Greenberg & Lourie, 1972; Sandoval, Lambert, & Yandell, 1976; Schain, 1973; Stewart & Olds, 1973). Despite widespread dissemination and acceptance of this caveat, one frequently finds, in practice, reliance on medication as the sole agent of change (Sroufe, 1975).

As Stewart and Olds (1973) observe, successful drug treatment is seductive. In the previous section, it was suggested that the very effectiveness of psychostimulants may foster an exclusive focus on this one intervention strategy, to the neglect of interpersonal, educational, or environmental changes that might have a greater positive impact and fewer negative sequels in the long run. There is danger not only that individual children will be denied optimal treatment packages, but also that the need for improvements in social and educational practices will be obscured by the success of the pill. Clinical concerns over the exclusive use of medication in the treatment of hyperactivity blend readily into ideological and sociopolitical concerns over the medicalization of deviant behavior in a more pervasive sense. To facilitate discussion, we shall divide this topic into two interrelated problem areas: "chemical coping" and "institutional somatarchy." The first term refers to society's increasing dependence on and expectations for easy (chemical) solutions to everyday problems; the second refers to the role of various power groups—including the medical profession, the pharmaceutical industry, and public policymakers—in maintaining and expanding this biochemical dependence.

CHEMICAL COPING

There is increasing concern among health professionals and social commentators that, by adopting medical solutions to problems, we may be substituting chemistry for coping. This process could impede the development of interpersonal strategies that might, in the long run, be more satisfying and effective than pharmacologic agents (Lennard *et al.*, 1971; Rogers, 1971; Silverman & Lee, 1974). Here distinctions begin to blur between licit and illicit drug use. In an intriguing and somewhat alarming analysis, Silverman and Lee (1974) maintain that:

> To some clinicians and pharmacologists the utilization of psychoactive agents represents a highly satisfactory if temporary solution. These drugs are not illegal, immoral, or fattening. They enable many patients to live with such problems as an unhappy marriage, a frustrating job, the fear of getting a tooth extracted, a snub at the country club, the generation gap, racism, pollution, and war. They help frantic mothers cope with young children who insist on behaving like children. They let many individuals stay awake all day and sleep all night. They serve as an antidote to emotional tension—as if emotional tension always calls for an antidote. They alleviate depression. In some cultures or subcultures, their use serves as a mark of belonging. They can bring peace and tranquility to a household, a schoolroom, an old people's home, a psychiatric institute, an entire hospital ward. Such a result may be viewed as a blessing by parents, teachers, nurses, hospital attendants, and other caretakers, but the value to the children or patients concerned may be seriously questioned [p. 272].[9]

Lennard *et al.* (1971) use a pollution metaphor to describe the spread of psychoactive drugs, and warn us that we may be precipitating an ecological catastrophe by giving up self-regulation and interpersonal problem solving in favor of chemistry and technology. There is concern that we are turning into a society of prescription shoppers, expecting a pill not only for every ill, but also for every discomfort or inconvenience (Silverman & Lee, 1974). Similar concerns are expressed by Bok (1974) in a cogent discussion of the expanding use of placebo measures in reaction to the desire for "instant push-button alleviation of symptoms." Some observers of the contemporary scene are predicting a growing drug problem as the distinction between "well" and "sick" becomes more blurred, and as society increases quasi-medical use of drugs to cope with daily problems and anxieties (Newitt, Singer, & Kahn, 1971). Those who share this view point out that drugs change nonusers as well as users and lead society to new and less human modes of transaction (Lennard & Bernstein, 1974). Opponents label this position "pharmacologic calvinism," ask where the evidence is that social solutions are superior to chemical ones, and suggest that the failure to use medication when indicated is "just as criminal as treating the difficult child with drugs rather than with good teaching [Kornetsky, 1976, p. 248]."

The concern is that society may be falling into a "social trap" in which immediate, individual "goods" are pitted against long-term, collective

[9]From Silverman, M., & Lee, P. R. *Pills, profits, and politics*. Berkeley: University of California Press. Copyright © 1974 by the Regents of the University of California; reprinted by permission of the University of California Press.

"bads." In many ways, Platt's (1973) insightful analysis of social traps fits the current concerns with psychoactive drug use patterns. Once set in motion, the process assumes a self-accelerating character as society pushes for drugs of increasing potency to solve problems of expanding complexity. A core concept here is disjunction between short-term, predictable benefits, and delayed, less certain detriments.

INSTITUTIONAL SOMATARCHY

In the past few years, several publications have appeared depicting the use of psychostimulants with hyperactive children as a form of insidious somatarchy, or rule by biochemicals (Lasswell, 1961). In a milder form, the concern is that reliance on medical solutions diverts our attention from pervasive and perhaps pernicious deficiencies in our social systems and institutions (Eisenberg, 1976; Grinspoon & Singer, 1973). According to this view, we may be treating the wrong patient, the individual child, rather than the total social milieu (Conrad, 1975). Banks (1976) discusses our cultural proclivity to sidestep troublesome moral and social dilemmas by blaming the victim and using drugs as escape mechanisms; Smith (1975) asserts that by using psychostimulants for troublesome children, we obviate the need to reassess educational curricula and teaching philosophies. Broudy (1976) attributes to "counterculturists" the argument that the hyperkinetic child "is a defensive invention of the hypokinetic teacher, an excuse for pedagogical and personal inadequacy [p. 47]."

The portrayal of psychostimulants as medical incursions upon individual freedoms creates a fertile field for hyperbole. Schrag and Divoky (1975) maintain that, "It is the ideology of drugging, the idea that people can and should be chemically managed, that represents the most pervasive imposition on personal liberty and the most dangerous extension of authority [p. 106]." Witter (1971) expresses the concern that "human rights will be drowned in an exotic brew of biochemical manipulators, stirred and watched by an untouchable medical-educational complex [p. 34]." Child health specialists are accused of violations of children's rights, wholesale drugging, professional child abuse, chemical violence, and sedating the opposition with a heavy chemical hand (Bendix, 1973; Brown & Bing, 1976; Jackson, 1976; Messinger, 1975; Walker, 1975). Psychoactive drug treatment has been depicted as a minatory vehicle for maintaining the status quo by suppressing sensitive reactions to intolerable social conditions. Conrad (1975), in fact, has suggested that the use of psychostimulants with hyperactive children in the United States is analogous to the commitment of political dissenters to mental hospitals in the Soviet Union.

These arguments often reflect errors of logic as well as errors of evidence. The either–or thinking, which leads some people to insist that the problem resides in the child and others to insist that it resides in society, is neither logically tenable nor empirically functional. Children labeled hyperactive have difficulties in some but not all settings. Particular settings create difficulties for some but not for all (or even most) children. Youngsters have been engaging in the behaviors we now label "hyperactive" for centuries; they encountered serious learning and interpersonal difficulties before the advent of current educational philosophies and medical practices. To insist that change efforts should be targeted exclusively on troubled children, or on faulty environments, or on sick societies, is to engage in a useless debate while diverting attention from the more promising study of person-by-situation interactions, and the development of equations for predicting and enhancing the match among diverse response styles in children, alternative learning and living environments, and society's multifarious rules for accepting and changing behaviors. (See Whalen and Henker, 1977, for a more complete discussion of these issues.)

Children's Rights[10]

Another critical issue that surfaces here is that of a *child's* right to accept or refuse treatment. Many children who take psychostimulants are quite neutral about both process and outcome, and some actually extol drug effects. But how about those who fear or detest the medication? In a thoughtful discussion of legal issues, Wells (1973) points to a child's rights to "mental autonomy," "mind privacy," and freedom from "chemical intrusions." Maintaining that we should be guided by the legal doctrine of the least restrictive alternative when making intervention decisions for individual children, Johnson, Kenney, and Davis (1976) assert that, "The use of psychoactive chemicals is typically not the least restrictive alternative if one's goal is to change observable behavior rather than ameliorate or eliminate a suspected physiological condition or psychiatric disorder [p. 93]."

In its extreme form, the view that the child labeled hyperactive has a right to engage in the behaviors that generated the label carries an implicit assumption of infinite elasticity in social environments. The rights of hyperactive children must be balanced against the rights of the community, and pharmacologic intrusions must be weighed against social intrusions. How do we balance one child's right to engage in unconventional classroom behavior against his classmates' right to experience an harmonious learning environment? What are the rights of unlabeled children to receive as much individual teacher attention as labeled children? What about the rights of

[10]See also Chapter 12 of this volume.

teachers to design a productive classroom without having to cope with constant conflict, guilt, and intimations about their own competence (Renstrom, 1976)?

The other side of the medical–nonmedical coin presents an equally perplexing set of issues. Do educators or other responsible adults who hold antidrug attitudes have the right either to withhold medication or to exclude medicated children from their schools or programs? In California, for example, there are several school programs, most of them private, that insist on drug discontinuance as a condition of admittance. Often the administrators are those who believe that interventions should be focused on the educational system rather than on the children. What are the rights of the child, particularly a child who is known to respond well to medication, in these settings? Do not the child and family, as Wells (1973) suggests, have a right to medical treatment that is parallel to their right to refuse it?

Related to this focus on children's rights to receive or refuse treatment is the current controversy over pediatric research (Sprague, 1978). Concerns about the ethics of human experimentation led to the establishment of the National Commission for the Protection of Subjects of Biomedical and Behavioral Research in 1976 (Hershey & Miller, 1976), and a much needed set of guidelines is under development. There is apprehension, however, that pediatric drug testing is at risk, and that new human subjects regulations may pose such serious impediments that important research with children will not be attempted. Since research regulations are likely to be far more restrictive than treatment regulations, we may be moving toward the absurd situation in which clinicians continue to prescribe drugs with impunity, but research investigators are unable to study their effects (Lockhart, 1977; Sprague, 1978). The crescendo of concerns over the widespread use of psychoactive medication with institutionalized children and adults (e.g., Marker, 1975; Sprague, 1977), the growth of the Children's Rights Movement (Feshbach & Feshbach, 1978; Gross & Gross, 1977; Koocher, 1976), the pending class action suit against the school district of Taft, California, charging that children were coerced into taking Ritalin (Bruck, 1976), all foretoken weighty litigation and, perhaps, resolution of some of these thorny legal and ethical dilemmas.

Research Needs

While some of the preceding apprehensions and warnings may be dismissed as alarmism, others are well-reasoned and quite compelling. One question that arises here concerns the pervasiveness of psychostimulant usage. Although no conclusive answer can be given, the evidence available suggests that while the absolute percentage is quite small, the absolute number is quite large. Two surveys have suggested that between 1.7 and 2% of school-aged children in the United States are taking psychostimulant medication (Krager & Safer, 1974; Stephen cited in Sprague & Sleator, 1973). On the basis of these survey data, Sprague and Gadow (1976) estimate the actual numbers to range between 595,000 and 688,000 (although they are concerned that these figures may be overestimates). Despite uncertainty about the actual numbers, there is good reason to predict that the probability of a person—child or adult—coming into contact with a child on stimulant medication during any given year is quite high. There is no evidence, however, that psychostimulant treatment has had or will have wide-ranging, toxic effects on society. Nor is there a means of evaluating the trade-offs between immediate and long-term, or individual and social, outcomes. Those who dramatically impugn the motives of the drug giver and predict calamitous consequences for drug giver and drug taker alike do so unhampered—and unenlightened—by an empirical data base. The problem is that we just do not know how drug giving and drug taking affect society as a whole.

Drugs are here to stay. Twenty thousand tons of aspirin are consumed annually in the United States, almost 225 tablets per person (Brecher, 1972). Consumers spend over $1 billion a year for nervous system drugs alone (Goddard, 1973). A "street" sample of American adults in 1968 contained 14% who had taken a centrally active drug within the previous 24 hr (Parry, 1968). It has been estimated that 1 in 10 adults in the United States uses Valium or Librium each year, typically for periods of a few weeks to a few months (Waldron, 1977). In a national survey conducted during 1970–1971, Parry, Balter, Mellinger, Cisin, and Manheimer (1973) found that 1 in 3 American adults had used some type of psychotherapeutic drug at least once during the past year. Moreover, one-third of the people who had used prescription psychoactive drugs were classified as high level users, meaning regular daily use for at least 2 months. Data from another recent survey suggest that 7% of people above the age of 13 "are regularly using at least one of these prescription psychoactive drugs to stimulate, sedate, and tranquilize themselves [Chambers, Inciardi, & Siegal, 1975, p. 50]." According to estimates by Joyce and Hammond (1975), "the probability at an encounter between no more than two people that one of them will have taken at least one drug (including alcohol) is at present between 50% and 80% [p. 266]." Clearly, drugs are a compelling fact of modern life. There is every indication that new drugs will continue to be synthesized and used ever more widely to regulate the stresses and strains of daily life (Lennard *et al.*, 1971) as well as to improve specific intellectual functions (Dimond, 1976).

What is needed is not a ban on psychopharmacologic agents, but rather an empirical look at the multidimensional consequences of drug treatments, a social cost accounting, or cumulative benefit–cost analysis. Such an analysis must identify outcomes at each of the four levels of direct and emanative effects, and then estimate the differential desirabilities and the varying probabilities associated with each identifiable outcome.

One key feature of the social ecological model developed in the preceding paragraphs is that the various personal, social, and organizational spheres are highly interdependent; we are dealing with an extended family of variables, and a change within one sphere results in readjustments in others. The use of psychostimulant medication to modify the personal characteristics of 1–2% of our school-aged population alters the social system as a whole. Moreover, these changes are not always mutually congruent. A child whose school performance improves with stimulant treatment (Circle 1) may, for example, start thinking of himself as a more competent individual who is learning how to succeed at difficult tasks (Circle 2). At the same time, his parents or teachers may interpret the improvement as proof positive that the child has a disability, assuming that drugs work only for children who have organic brain damage (again, Circle 2). The results might be a more positive and realistic view of his behaviors and abilities, or an unwarranted and unsalutary assumption that he will be unable to acquire age-appropriate academic and interpersonal skills.

Changes within professional and societal spheres may also occur. Educational specialists, viewing drug-facilitated improvement as evidence that hyperactivity is curable, may construe more classroom problems as manifestations of the "hyperkinetic syndrome," and request that more children be placed on medication (Circle 3). Society's expectations for easy (chemical) solutions may creep into more domains of everyday life (Circle 4). The initial positive impact on the child may have negative impacts not only on his significant others and his own long-term adaptation, but also on more pervasive social structures and public policies. The net consequences may be far from optimal. Ironically, the more positive the immediate impact on the individual child, the more toxic may be the ultimate outcome for society.

A second feature of this systems approach is that changes within and across these four realms may follow different timetables. The immediate impact may occur in the overt behavior domain, whereas changes in cognitive structures and professional practices may be somewhat delayed. Alterations in the fabric of society may be the last to surface and perhaps also the most durable.

II

HYPERACTIVITY IN CONTEXT: DIFFERENTIATING CHILDREN AND ENVIRONMENTS

2

Developmental and Social Aspects of Hyperactivity

DONALD K. ROUTH

INTRODUCTION

This chapter is essentially the history of a research program on the relationship of hyperactivity to normal child development and social behavior. It describes a series of research findings, places these within a larger context, and suggests some future research directions. In order to provide the reader with some background, the chapter begins with a working definition of the hyperactive child syndrome, a description of the naturalistic situations in which hyperactive behaviors are typically observed, and a description of some of these behaviors.

The research program described in this chapter began with a search for what turned out to be a will-o'-the-wisp, minimal brain dysfunction (MBD). This search led to a narrower focus on "hyperactivity," which is one salient item listed under the more global heading of MBD.

The initial search for MBD had involved the use of a variety of clinical measures, including psychological tests, teacher ratings, and information from a multidisciplinary examination of each child. No identifiable MBD cluster emerged from this study, which was not designed to reveal whether a hyperactive subgroup existed. The second study in the series adopted a simpler, and as it turned out, more productive method, namely behavioral observation of normal and hyperactive children in a standardized playroom.

In the initial series of playroom studies, a number of interesting findings emerged. First, systematic developmental changes were found in children's

HYPERACTIVE CHILDREN
The Social Ecology of Identification and Treatment

ISBN 0-12-745950-2

playroom behavior, and the playroom method was indeed found to provide some suitable indices of hyperactivity. A number of experimental variables was found to influence children's playroom activity, including instructions to the child, reinforcement, and modeling.

Since the playroom research began, the major shift in direction has been from the study of the individual child to the study of the child in social interaction. This change came about in several steps. First, it was found that 3-year-old children often became upset when observed alone in the playroom. Studying this more systematically, we discovered that the easiest way to prevent such distress was to have the mother in the playroom too. In contrast to the mother, persons unfamiliar to the child did not share this ability to prevent distress. Our observations in this respect thus linked up directly with those of students of attachment. In trying to extend our findings regarding the development of activity to a broader age range, we discovered that the presence of the mother in the playroom, at least for 5-year-old children, increases the level of playroom locomotor activity. We are still trying to understand the meaning of this finding.

Once we began observing mother–child dyads, it made sense to pay attention to the mother's behavior as well as the child's. We were thus led step by step into the study of other dyadic relationships as well, such as teacher–child interaction. Coming full circle, the author is now beginning to see how important the child's social relationships are to the understanding of hyperactivity. It was in this rather serendipitous way that a researcher who began trying to study aberrant behavior in the individual child found himself becoming interested in the social ecology of hyperactivity.

A WORKING DEFINITION OF THE HYPERACTIVE CHILD SYNDROME

Definition

It is felt that the following definition of hyperactivity will be acceptable to the majority of reseachers in this field. "Hyperactivity" refers to a child's frequent failure to comply in an age-appropriate fashion with situational demands for restrained activity, sustained attention, resistance to distracting influences, and inhibition of impulsive response. At least for research purposes, the term is restricted to describing children whose behavior problems are severe enough to have come to professional attention, and whose difficulties are manifest in several situations over a considerable period of time. It is true that our own research has focused on preschool age children, and that we have viewed the behavior of the young child as a sort of model for hyperactivity. Nevertheless, if one is interested in studying hyperactivity in its more typical form, it might be wise to exclude children under 6 or over 12 years of age, as well as those with mental retardation, unequivocal evidence of brain damage, chaotic family situations, or accompanying psychiatric disorders. Specific learning difficulties (e.g., in reading), conduct disorders (such as aggressive or destructive behavior), and "soft" or equivocal neurological signs are not unusual among hyperactive children; however, these traits are not considered necessary to the definition of hyperactivity. It is becoming increasingly common to confirm the clinical diagnosis of hyperactivity with standardized teacher rating scales, such as the one developed by Conners (1969, 1973c). As a rule of thumb, a score of 15 (or a mean rating of 1.5) on the 10-item abbreviated version of this scale is often taken as sufficient confirmatory evidence.

Observations of Hyperactive Behaviors and Hyperactive Children in Naturalistic and Laboratory Settings

Despite the usefulness of teacher and parent rating scales in diagnosing hyperactivity and assessing treatment effects, the researcher can hardly be satisfied with an understanding of hyperactivity obtained only through the filter of parents' and teachers' interpretations. What do these children actually *do* in the classroom and at home that causes so much trouble? Can the same kinds of behaviors be elicited under more controlled conditions in the psychologist's laboratory? Because of the lack of consensus in the field and the scarcity of relevant research, many of the following studies cited are ones that have used definitions of their populations of children somewhat at variance with the strict one advocated here.

OVERACTIVITY

In the classroom, a child's overactivity might be manifested by the child's restlessness in his or her chair, by standing up, running, jumping, or remaining out-of-seat without permission (Abikoff, Gittelman-Klein, & Klein, 1977). The parents might be concerned about overactivity in other settings, for example, a child's tendency to run up and down the aisles of a supermarket (Barnard, Christopherson, & Wolf, 1977). Whether a child's activity in a particular natural setting is considered to be deviant may depend not only upon the behaviors per se, but also upon whether restraint of activity is demanded in that situation. Jacob, O'Leary, and Rosenblad (1978) carried out classroom observations of hyperactive children in "formal" and "informal" (open) classrooms. The hyperactive children behaved in about the same way in both types of classrooms, while nonhyperactive children were much less active in the more restrictive "formal" classroom.

Overactivity has also been found to be characteristic of hyperactive children's behavior in standardized playroom settings, where it is often measured simply by the child's crossing the lines of a grid on the playroom floor (Hutt & Hutt, 1964; Montagu, 1975; Pope, 1970). In a playroom, just as in the classroom, the overactivity of hyperactive children is more likely to be at a higher level than that of nonhyperactive children, if observed under conditions in which the child is asked to restrict his or her activity (Routh & Schroeder, 1976). Scott is hot to do what he wants, doggeys.

SHORT ATTENTION SPAN

In the classroom, a child's inattentiveness is defined typically in terms of "time off task," that is, time engaged in attending to stimuli other than assigned work (e.g., Abikoff et al., 1977). A child's attention span at home might be defined in terms of the frequency of switching play activities (Rapoport & Benoit, 1975), or length of sustained TV watching time (Anderson & Levin, 1976). Hyperactive children have been noted to show inattentiveness in a number of different settings; indeed, this is regarded as their most characteristic behavioral difficulty.

The laboratory task most commonly used in the study of inattentiveness of hyperactive children is the Continuous Performance Task. This task requires the identification of certain infrequent events, usually visual displays such as a particular letter of the alphabet or a pattern of flashing colored lights. Hyperactive children make consistently more errors of omission (failing to note instances of the event in question) and errors of commission ("false alarms") than matched control children (Anderson, Halcomb, & Doyle, 1973; Sykes, Douglas, & Morgenstern, 1973).

DISTRACTIBILITY

Observing the child in a natural setting, it is difficult to separate distractibility caused by external stimulation from inattentiveness due to other factors. In fact, for a long time there were few convincing demonstrations even in the laboratory that hyperactive children were excessively distractible, despite the fact that clinicians thought they were (e.g., Schrager, Lindy, Harrison, McDermott, & Killins, 1966). It has been possible to demonstrate that hyperactive children are indeed more distractible than other children (Bremer & Stern, 1976; Doyle, Anderson, & Halcomb, 1976). Bremer and Stern (1976), for example, had hyperactive and non-hyperactive boys read stories to themselves under quiet and distracting conditions. The hyperactive boys reacted more to the distracting events, such as a ringing telephone, and were less attentive to task relevant stimuli than were control boys.

IMPULSIVITY

According to the temperament theory of Buss and Plomin (1975), the component of personality most important in defining hyperactivity, besides activity itself, is impulsivity. (As stated previously, most other researchers, including the author, regard inattentiveness as more definitive of hyperactivity than is impulsivity.)

In the classroom, the most common "impulsive" behavior observed in children seems to be "interference," such as calling out, interrupting others during work periods, and clowning (Abikoff *et al.*, 1977). As judged from the content of parent rating scales (e.g., Werry, 1968a), talking out at inappropriate times and interrupting others is often observed among hyperactive children at home as well.

As far as laboratory measures are concerned, one might list here Kagan's Matching Familiar Figures Test (MFFT), since it has consistently been found to differentiate hyperactive children from others (Campbell, Douglas, & Morgenstern, 1971; Juliano, 1974). On this matching-to-sample task, "impulsivity" refers to fast response latencies in combination with high error scores. Impulsivity on the Matching Familiar Figures Test (MFFT) has been found to be correlated with similar types of fast-inaccurate performance on reading tasks (Kagan, 1965) and in inferential reasoning (Kagan, Pearson, & Welch, 1966). There is currently controversy over the meaning of children's scores on the MFFT (e.g., Block, Block, & Harrington, 1974). Whatever the outcome of this controversy, however, there is no doubt about the empirical relationship of MFFT scores to hyperactivity (e.g., Messer, 1976).

Exclusion Criteria

AGE

Hyperactivity in its most characteristic form seems to be seen in children of elementary school age. Some attempt has been made to identify hyperactivity in preschool children (Schleifer, Weiss, Cohen, Elman, Cvejic, & Krueger, 1975). However, although behavior problems continued to exist among these children at school age, only 1 mother out of 20 complained specifically about hyperactivity at follow-up (Campbell, Schleifer, Weiss, & Perlman, 1977). The problem may be that most, if not all, young children manifest overactive, inattentive, and impulsive behaviors. Thus, these behaviors among children who will (at school age) be identified as "hyperactive" may not be as differentiating at age 2 or 3 as they will be later on.

Although ex-hyperactive children continue to have problems of various kinds in adolescence and adulthood, their activity level tends to wane, and the main complaints concern other types of problems (Minde, Weiss, & Mendelson, 1972; Weiss, Minde, Werry, Douglas, & Nemeth, 1971).

MENTAL RETARDATION

Although hyperactive behaviors unquestionably exist among mentally handicapped individuals, the behaviors may have a different significance in many cases than among children of average ability. For example, Jenkins and Stable (1971), in a study of 3847 mentally retarded persons, found that the presence of a severe problem with hyperactivity was associated with all kinds of other difficulties, ranging from cerebral palsy to psychosis. Such strong relationships between hyperactivity and other problems are not typically found among persons of average intelligence, although relationships among hyperactivity, learning disabilities, and aggression have been documented.

BRAIN DAMAGE

The Isle of Wight study (Rutter, Graham, & Yule, 1970) showed that children with neurological impairment were about five times as likely to have behavior disorders as children who were neurologically intact. However, the particular kind of behavior disorder was not predictable from knowledge of a child's neurological status. This and other studies indicate that the relationship between damage to the brain and hyperactivity is nonspecific. Thus, unless one has a specific interest in brain damage, it is reasonable to exclude children with gross brain damage when the focus of research is on hyperactivity.

CHAOTIC FAMILY SITUATIONS

If the child's behavior problems seem explainable primarily on the basis of the way the child is being treated by family members, there seems to be little advantage to adding the label "hyperactivity" to the child's and the family's difficulties.

PSYCHOSIS

Fish (1971) convincingly makes the point that "hyperactivity" may be merely one more symptomatic aspect of a more complicated behavior disorder. For example, "disturbances in motility" are one defining characteristic of certain types of child psychosis (Creak, 1964). Research on "hyperactivity" is concerned principally with children for whom the hyperactive syndrome is their primary difficulty.

Associated Features Not Essential to Definition

SPECIFIC LEARNING DIFFICULTIES

Poor achievement in school is clearly a significant problem for many hyperactive children. For example, Mendelson, Johnson, and Stewart (1971) in a follow-up study found that 58% of a sample of hyperactive children had failed one or more grades in school by the time they reached their teenage years. However, learning difficulty is by no means universal among hyperactive children; conversely, specific learning difficulties often exist apart from any hyperactive behavior.

CONDUCT DISORDERS

Hyperactivity was once defined, only partly in jest, as "those aspects of a person's behavior which annoy the observer [Buddenhagen & Sickler, 1969, p. 580]." Its similarity to conduct problems is thus quite evident. Indeed, Abikoff *et al.* (1977) found hyperactive children to show significantly more physical and verbal aggression in the classroom than comparison children. The Mendelson *et al.* (1971) study cited before also found delinquent behavior to be a common problem among adolescents who had been hyperactive children. Nevertheless, to the author the conceptual distinction between impulsive misbehavior in a child with poor sustained attention, and aggressive or destructive acts carried out by a child with intact attentional processes, seems an important one. Although some hyperactive children become antisocial adults, not every antisocial adult was a hyperactive child.

EQUIVOCAL NEUROLOGICAL SIGNS

The frequent existence of "soft" neurological signs does not seem to be specific to hyperactivity, but also characterizes some children with other kinds of behavior problems, such as neurotic difficulties or conduct disorders (Chess, 1972; Shaffer, McNamara, & Pincus, 1974).

AN UNSUCCESSFUL SEARCH FOR MINIMAL BRAIN DYSFUNCTION

Is There Such a Behavioral Syndrome?

In the Child Development Clinic at the University of Iowa where the author once worked, the diagnosis "minimal brain dysfunction" or its equivalent "minimal cerebral dysfunction" was very frequently applied.

However, there seemed to be no consensus in the literature as to the precise criteria for defining this condition. Thus, the research project described in this chapter began with an attempt to clarify the diagnostic criteria for MBD.

The historical precursor of the MBD concept was no doubt Strauss and Lehtinen's (1947) concept of the "brain-injured child," also sometimes labeled the "perceptually handicapped child." By the time the task force convened by Clements (1966) tried to introduce some order in the terminology, there was quite an extensive literature on the topic. As a result of reviewing this literature, Clements listed 99 purported symptoms of MBD, with the 10 most frequently cited ones being as follows: (*a*) hyperactivity; (*b*) perceptual–motor impairments; (*c*) emotional lability; (*d*) general coordination deficits; (*e*) disorders of attention; (*f*) impulsivity; (*g*) disorders of memory and thinking; (*h*) specific learning disabilities; (*i*) disorders of speech and hearing; and (*j*) equivocal neurologic signs and electroencephalographic irregularities.

Our initial study (Routh & Roberts, 1972) concerned the covariation of these deficits among a sample of 89 school-age children attending the Child Development Clinic. Most were referred for evaluation of poor school performance. All children with either mental retardation or gross neurologic defect were excluded from the sample, as the review done by Clements' (1966) task force suggested. Some of the deficits of these children were defined by teacher ratings (e.g., attentional problems), others by psychological tests (e.g., the Bender Gestalt Test), and others by consensus based on multidisciplinary examination of each child. After partialling out the covariation among the aspects of MBD due to age and IQ, we found that there was virtually no common variance left among the measures of different types of behavioral deficit. Thus in this sample, one could not predict from the degree of rated hyperactivity how much visual motor difficulty a child might be having, or predict how much of a reading problem a child had from knowing the child's degree of incoordination, and so on. The results of the study were considered "somewhat damaging" to the idea of an MBD syndrome. In fact, the author considered the study a clear signal that his approach was too global and went on to narrow the focus of his research to hyperactivity.

One negative study does not destroy a concept. In the case of the concept of MBD as a behavioral syndrome, however, there seem to be many negative studies (Dreger, 1964; Paine, Werry, & Quay, 1968; Rodin, Lucas, & Simson, 1963; Werry, 1968b), and no positive ones. Before I will seriously wish to use the concept of MBD again, I will wait to be *shown* that such a syndrome exists.

Is There a Hyperactive Child Syndrome?

From definition given in the second section of this chapter, it is probably clear that I still believe in a syndrome of hyperactivity, more narrowly defined than MBD. The evidence supporting this concept will now be discussed.

GENERALITY OF BEHAVIORS ACROSS SETTINGS AND SOURCES

One study that seemed particularly damaging to the notion of even a hyperactive behavior syndrome was that of Langhorne, Loney, Paternite, and Bechtoldt (1976). In studying ratings of hyperactive children's behavior by different observers, they found mainly "source" factors: That is, clinicians described one subgroup of children as most hyperactive, teachers another, and parents another, with no real agreement among these sources of information.

A problem in this and other studies may be with the types of ratings parents are asked to do. They are asked, for example, to say whether their child engages in some particular behavior "just a little," "pretty much," or "very much," when they really have no basis for comparison to make such judgments. Probably as a result, parental ratings have often shown no significant relationship to objective measures and ratings done in settings outside the home (Langhorne *et al.*, 1976; Rapoport & Benoit, 1975; Routh & Schroeder, 1976). However, Rapoport and Benoit (1975) found that objective observations of hyperactive children at home *did* correlate with clinic and school ratings. Also, when parents were asked to keep a 4-day diary describing their children's actual behaviors (instead of rating them "very much," etc.), their observations also correlated with information from other settings and sources.

GENERALITY ACROSS BEHAVIORS

Research discussed earlier in this chapter already documented the relationships between a number of different laboratory measures and hyperactivity. Some linkages among different "hyperactive" behaviors also seem to be present in observations in a single setting. Thus, in a playroom study of hyperactive and nonhyperactive children, Barkley and Ullman (1975) found mostly low, though significant, correlations among multiple measures of activity and distractibility, including actometer scores, quadrant entries, and toy changes.

In summary, although the concept of an MBD syndrome does not currently seem justified, there is at least some positive evidence for the generality of hyperactivity across settings, sources, and behaviors.

REVIEW OF STUDIES USING A STANDARDIZED PLAYROOM

Developmental Changes in Playroom Activity

The pioneering study of human locomotor activity under controlled conditions was that of Ellis and Pryer (1959), in which severely "neuropathological" children were observed under standardized conditions; the study showed that measures of gross bodily activity could be quite reliable from day to day. A number of other investigators have studied differences between clinically selected groups of children (hyperactive, retarded, epileptic, etc.) and controls in playroom settings. Hutt and Hutt (1964) found that in terms of amount of locomotion, hyperkinetic children were practically indistinguishable from normal or nonhyperkinetic brain damaged children in an empty room. However, when the environment was structured by the addition of toys and particularly by the presence of adult, the nonhyperkinetics stopped moving around so much, while the hyperkinetics kept moving. Pope (1970) found that "brain-injured" hyperactive boys showed significantly more locomotor activity in a playroom than nonhyperactive control subjects.

Our own research has examined the effects of age upon the playroom activity of normal children, the use of a standardized playroom in diagnosing hyperactivity, the effects of several experimental variables on normal children's playroom activity, the effects of drugs, and the effects of social factors on normal children's playroom behaviors.

The study by Routh, Schroeder, and O'Tuama (1974) differed from previous work in focusing upon age changes in activity among normal children in such a playroom. This study and several others following it were based upon a developmental approach to the problem of hyperactivity. Eisenberg (1966) hypothesized that hyperkinesis resembled the activity pattern of normal children, but the level of activity was "displaced chronologically to the right by four to six years [p. 593]." Kinsbourne (1973) similarly described MBD, including hyperactivity, as a neurodevelopmental lag, stating that the diagnosis is based on findings that are abnormal *only* with respect to the age of the child. That is, a younger child with the same findings would be normal. In the Routh *et al.* (1974) study, 140 children aged 3–9 years were observed individually in a playroom divided into four quadrants by strips of black tape on the floor, with a table, chair, and standard toys available in each quadrant. Each child participated in a 15-min free-play session and in a session under instructions to avoid crossing lines on the floor. (Half the children got these sessions in the reverse order.)

The results showed a systematic decrease with age in children's gross motor activity, as measured by crossing the lines between the different quadrants in the playroom. A decrease with age was also found in parent ratings of the children's activity levels, on an adaptation of the Werry (1968a) scale. Both of these findings agree with the view that the hyperactive child may be like younger, normal children in activity, attention, impulsivity, and distractibility. Indeed, a subsequent study of hyperactive children and controls matched in age, race, sex, IQ, and socioeconomic status showed that the hyperactive children resembled younger normal ones in playroom quadrant entries, toy change scores (under restrictive instructions), and parent-rated hyperactive behaviors (Routh & Schroeder, 1976). Another study of children's classroom behaviors (Abikoff *et al.*, 1977) confirmed this developmental decline in activity level with age in both hyperactive and comparison children.

Use of the Playroom as a Diagnostic Tool

Like other researchers before us, we found that children referred for evaluation of hyperactivity differed significantly in their playroom behaviors from community children with similar demographic characteristics (Routh & Schroeder, 1976). However, only about one-third of the children so referred (11 of 32) were found to meet an arbitrary cut-off point of two standard deviations above the mean for their age on playroom activity scores. After the original collection of preliminary normative data by Routh *et al.* (1974), and in response to requests from colleagues in the medical center at the University of North Carolina, we put the "activity room" into preliminary use in the evaluation of children for hyperactivity. Referral sources such as pediatricians, child psychiatrists, and teachers began to send a steady stream of children for such evaluations; they seemed to find the scores reported back to them an aid in their evaluation of the children. However, there are many questions that remain to be answered about the diagnostic use of such playroom observations. High interobserver reliabilities have been found for the scores reported (quadrant entries and toy changes). However, the test–retest reliability is unknown, as are questions of validity, such as relation of playroom scores to home and classroom hyperactive behaviors, and the utility in differential treatment decisions.

Effects of Experimental Variables on Playroom Behaviors

In the first of our playroom studies (Routh *et al.*, 1974), we found that children of all ages were markedly and significantly less active and changed toys less frequently when they were asked to avoid crossing lines and changing toys, than when under free-play instructions. Once the restrictive instructions had been given, their effects carried over to influence behavior in a second session, despite the fact that the child was then instructed to play freely. These were the first of many additional findings suggesting that these playroom behaviors were remarkably sensitive to a variety of experimental manipulations. One subsequent study of normal children (Barkley & Routh, 1974) showed that both modeling (watching an adult play in attentive fashion with a single toy) and the promise of contingent reward (pennies) could influence 4- and 5-year-old children in the direction of low activity and low toy-switching scores. These effects were in addition to those produced by restrictive instructions.

The preceding results are in broad agreement with a variety of behavior-modification studies in showing that children's out-of-seat behavior can be reduced, and that their attentive behavior can be increased through a variety of behavioral techniques (Barrish, Saunders, & Wolf, 1969; Hall, Lund, & Jackson, 1968; Jacobson, Bushell, & Risley, 1969; Osborne, 1969; Packard, 1970).

There has been very little experimental study of the differential effects of variables such as instructions, modeling, reinforcement, and punishment on hyperactive as compared to nonhyperactive children. What observational research there is, for example the studies of Hutt and Hutt (1964) and Jacob *et al.* (1978) already discussed, suggests that hyperactive children may be less sensitive than others to some types of situational influences. Some other research we have done on impulsive behavior is at least tangentially relevant to this issue. Errickson, Wyne, and Routh (1973) devised a procedure in which mentally retarded children's incorrect responses on the MFFT were punished by withdrawal of a token for each error. This response–cost procedure and the standard procedure were given in counterbalanced order to two groups of 15 children. Subjects showed significantly longer latency to first response under the response–cost procedure; they also made fewer errors under this procedure when it was the second one administered. When response–cost was given first, the subjects tended to carry over their relatively low error rates to the subsequent trials under the standard procedure. A subsequent study (Brent & Routh, 1978) applied a similar response–cost procedure to impulsive word recognition errors among 30 fourth graders with reading disabilities. Each child was given two word-recognition lists, the first one as a pretest, and the second list under one of three different experimental conditions: control; positive reinforcement (one nickel for each word read correctly); and response cost (1 of 40 nickels taken back for each word read incorrectly). Relative to the control condition, positive reinforcement led to a significant increase in response latency but no change in errors; response–cost led to both a significant increase in latency and a significant decrease in reading errors. This was a very strong effect, with every child in the response–cost condition showing a reduction in error rate. The effects of response–cost on impulsive behavior may depend crucially on the characteristics of the child; that is, some children may be differentially sensitive to the effects of response–cost, and others more affected by positive reinforcement. Nelson, Finch, and Hooke (1975) found, for example, in a study of the MFFT, that impulsive children made significantly fewer errors under response–cost, whereas reflective children made fewer errors in a positive reinforcement condition.

Use of Playroom Observations in Drug Research

As Cantwell (1975a) points out, most of the research literature on the treatment of the hyperactive child syndrome consists of drug studies. Thus, even though the emphasis of our playroom research has not been on psychopharmacology, some comment should be made on the sensitivity of playroom observational measures to the effects of drugs.

The only published drug study coming out of our own laboratory is that by O'Tuama, Swisher, Reichler, and Routh (1977). This double-blind crossover study of 10 hyperactive children found no significant effects of thyrotropin releasing hormone (TRH), a result in conflict with a previous study on this drug by Tiwary, Rosenbloom, Robertson, and Parker (1975).

Given the current uncertainty about whether TRH has effects on hyperactive children's behavior, the O'Tauma *et al.* (1977) study provides little useful information about the drug sensitivity of our playroom measures. More relevant is Barkley's (1977) dissertation, a double-blind crossover study of 36 hyperactive boys that found significant effects of methylphenidate as compared to placebo on playroom quadrant changes and toy changes. Barkley used a playroom observational procedure modeled very closely on that of Routh *et al.* (1974). The findings of Rapoport, Buchsbaum, Zahn, Weingartner, Ludlow, and Mikkelson (1978) that normal boys respond to dextroamphetamine in much the same way as hyperactive children do, support one main point of this chapter: There is much continuity between hyperactivity and normal child behavior.

Effects of Social Factors on Playroom Behaviors

The author began the present series of studies with minimal interest in the social behavior of children and has been led by the outcome of one study after another to become more deeply enmeshed in trying to understand the effects of the child's social ecology.

In the initial playroom study (Routh *et al.*, 1974), it had been planned to observe each child alone. This plan worked out well for children 4 years old and older, but about one-third of the 3-year-olds were replaced in the study by other children the same age, until the required number had been obtained.

The next study (Belkin & Routh, 1975) attempted to resolve the problem of the distressed 3-year-old and ended up finding that the phenomenon of the child's attachment to the mother extends beyond the ages at which it is usually investigated. In this study, children were observed initially in the playroom under one of four different experimental conditions: alone; mother present; unfamiliar adult female present; or unfamiliar adult male present. The mother or other adult was given a magazine to read and asked to interact with the child as little as possible. In the mother-present condition, no child became distressed during the session; the children tended to vocalize or talk a lot and spent a certain amount of time in physical contact with the mother. The other experimental conditions differed significantly in those respects from the mother-present condition, but did not differ from each other. In each of these non-mother-present conditions, about a third of the children became distressed before the session was over; the children spent little time vocalizing or talking, and no child touched one of the unfamiliar adults or the adult chair in the room. These findings were found to fit nicely into Ainsworth's (1964) catalog of attachment behaviors, that is, separation protest, maintaining physical proximity, and differential vocalization.

With slight modifications in furnishings and in the instructions to the child, the standardized playroom was transformed into a small classroom. In a study by Watkins, Routh, and Arendshorst (1975), 4- and 5-year-old normal children were observed individually in such a "classroom" setting. They were introduced to the "teacher," a woman previously unfamiliar to them, and the teacher then instructed the child in the task to be performed (copying a large number of pages of geometrical designs) before play with several nearby toys was allowed. The study was complex in its procedures, involving, for example, a videotape modeling manipulation. But for present purposes, the finding worth emphasis was that the presence of this "teacher" during a subsequent 30-min work period prevented distress, compared to the same situation with the teacher absent after initially instructing the child. Apparently the ability to prevent young children's distress in a laboratory situation is not restricted to the mother or even to a familiar person. Future research must explore the reasons why an unfamiliar adult prevented distress in this study, but not in the Belkin and Routh (1975) study with younger children. Perhaps the "teacher" label imparts a greater potency as a parent surrogate to an unfamiliar person.

Having learned something about preventing distress in preschool children in our laboratory, we felt ready to extend the playroom observation downward into infancy. Routh, Walton, and Padan-Belkin (1978) studied, individually, 100 infants and children ranging in age from 10 months through 5 years. To adapt the playroom for this age group, three changes were introduced. The tables and chairs were replaced by four rugs on the floor, one centered in each quadrant. Some of the toys were replaced by others of greater interest and safety for infants. Also, a small open closet adjacent to the playroom was set up as a place for the mother to be present,unobtrusively, near the child during the session. The mother was not visible unless the child chose to enter the closet. The main rationale for this study was an interest in the early development of activity level. It was thought that activity level would begin at a low point in infancy, rise to a peak at some point in the preschool years (perhaps at age 3, perhaps earlier), and then decline. The major results of the study were unanticipated, but have proved to be reproducable ones. Activity, as measured by quadrant entries, did rise and then fall during the infant age range, but over the ages of 3–5 years, there was a significant *rise* in activity.

Routh *et al.* (1978) then studied normal children aged 3, 4, and 5 years old,once more, systematically varying the three procedural differences between the previous studies, with conflicting results. Every combination of mother presence and absence, type of furniture (tables and chairs versus rugs), and type of toys ("child" versus "baby" toys) was present in the design. The divergent findings of the two previous studies were basically replicated, and a somewhat unexpected interaction was found. The presence of the mother was the factor that has produced the anomalous results. With the mother absent, playroom activity decreased with age and was lowest in the 5-year-olds (as in the Routh *et al.,* 1974 study). With mother present, 5-year-olds were significantly more active than with mother absent, and activity was higher in 5-year-olds than in 3- or 4-year-old children (as in the Routh *et al.,* 1978 study). No ready theoretical explanation has been found for these results. Neither attachment theory predictions nor those derived from the social facilitation literature seem to fit a detailed analysis of these data. But clearly, social variables are proving to be crucial in understanding children's playroom behavior.

Looking at the literature on hyperactivity after these eye-opening experiences with the importance of social variables, the author finds much emerging evidence for the importance of social factors. One striking example is the study of Kaspar and Lowenstein (1971). They observed school-age boys individually in a free-play situation, and then retested low-activity children alone or together with a highly active child. The presence of a high-activity child markedly increased the observed activity of the low-activity child. In parent–child interactions also, the hyperactive child may often be the one influencing rather than the one influenced. Using videotapes of an overactive child, an underactive child, and an average-active child, Stevens-Long (1973) documented such an effect: Refusals by the child to allow the adult to join in the child's play elicited more severe disciplinary reactions from adults when the child was portrayed as overactive. Bell's (1968) conclusion that the child's behavior may affect the parent as well as the other way around may turn out to be applicable especially to hyperactive children.

The author is, in fact, coming to understand hyperactivity as not simply a developmental lag in the ability to restrain activity, distractibility, and impulsiveness. Hyperactivity is also a problem for the student of social development and behavior.

SUGGESTIONS FOR FUTURE RESEARCH

Planning studies is a somewhat hazardous venture in this burgeoning new area of research. Our own research program has been full of surprises and serendipitous new leads. There do seem to be at least three types of studies in need of particular emphasis by researchers in this field: Namely, better definition of what hyperactive children actually *do* in different situations; further examination of the question of whether there really is a hyperactive behavior syndrome; and finally the exploration of new models of hyperactivity in relation to normal social development.

Identifying Specific Hyperactive Behaviors

Up to the present time, hyperactivity has been diagnosed mostly on the basis of teacher ratings and interviews with parents. Studies now need to be carried out comparing the actual behaviors of hyperactive children (for example, as defined in the second section of this chapter) with matched controls, in situations commonly referred to in the major parent and teacher rating scales. One list of such situations, derived from the Conners (1969) and Werry (1968a) scales, is as follows:

1. In the classroom
2. At mealtime
3. Watching television
4. Doing homework
5. At play with other children and alone
6. At bedtime
7. During travel
8. During shopping

9. At church
10. In the movies

The interesting behaviors in each situation include those presently emphasized in the definition of hyperactivity—excessive activity, inattentiveness, distractibility, and impulsiveness—plus behaviors alluded to in commonly used rating scales, and no doubt other behaviors not captured by any of the present rating scales. A question that might be asked repeatedly in such studies would be, do hyperactive and control children actually behave differently in this type of situation? In what particular ways? The answers would come in the form of group differences in frequencies or durations of the observed behaviors.

For many of these situations, there already exist observational or intervention studies (e.g., attempts at behavior modification) which have done some of the necessary groundwork, but not many with children specifically bearing the label "hyperactive." A recent example of the kind of study needed is the classroom observational work of Abikoff *et al.* (1977). It should be possible to build on this work in studying the situational expressions of hyperactivity.

Testing the Generality of the Hyperactive Child Syndrome

The model for a study of this type might be provided by previous efforts, such as that of Routh and Roberts (1972) or Langhorne *et al.* (1976) already discussed, but hard observational data would be used in addition to ratings. This would involve collecting information about different behaviors, across different settings, by different methods of assessment, and by varied observers including the major "significant others" in the child's environment.

A sample of hyperactive children (selected according to the above definition) and a sample of matched control children might be observed in 2 or more of the 10 settings listed above. Behaviors of three kinds would be recorded: (*a*) hyperactive behaviors (i.e., activity, inattentiveness, distractibility, and impulsivity); (*b*) behaviors questionably related to hyperactivity (i.e., aggressive–destructive behaviors, learning behaviors such as academic performance or amount retained from a TV program); and (*c*) behaviors traditionally considered as having little to do with hyperactivity (i.e., positive social interaction, emotional reactions). The strongest support for the idea of a syndrome would consist of higher correlation among the hyperactive behaviors, within and across situations, than between hyperactive behaviors and behaviors of the other two types (at least among children labeled hyperactive). Of course the problem of identifying a syndrome becomes more complicated if there turn out to be several types of hyperactivity.

Hyperactivity as a Lag in Social Development

Among children seen in the standardized playroom over the last several years, it has been rare to see separation protest or discomfort in a normal child over the age of 3. In our initial playroom study (Routh *et al.*, 1974), not 1 of the 120 children over that age cried. Yet it has not infrequently happened that children aged 4, 5, 6, and occasionally even older referred to the clinic for the evaluation of hyperactivity have become upset during a playroom observation, requiring mother or another familiar person to be present in the playroom before the observation could be completed. This informal observation might suggest that the waning of attachment behaviors may occur more slowly in hyperactive children than in others. An alternative possibility is that children brought in for clinical evaluation are more likely to become upset than those simply coming in to participate in a playroom study. If the former interpretation is correct, it means that hyperactive children are immature in their social development as well as their motor behavior, attention, etc. This general hypothesis is worthy of systematic study.

Upon presenting the results of the Routh *et al.* (1978) study in Cleveland, Ohio, the author received an interesting communication from a teacher in the audience, Ms. Rae Jacob. She said that she found the puzzling "mother presence effect" on normal 5-year-olds very much in line with her experience. The special education class she taught (for children at risk for learning disabilities) often had mothers of the children as observers. It was found that the children were more likely to "act up" when their own mothers were present, and that this disruptive effect of mothers' presence continued for weeks before the children adapted to it. Perhaps when we come to understand better the "mother presence effect" in the laboratory playroom, we will find that it, too, has some relevance to hyperactivity. It is too early to say.

In summing up, we would list the following as conclusions that seem to follow from our published studies:

1. The existence of MBD as conventionally defined is in doubt.
2. Activity level decreases with age in normal children, under certain specifiable observational conditions.
3. Hyperactive children often resemble younger normal children in their activity level in a standardized playroom.
4. Certain experimental variables such as instructions, modeling, and

reinforcement have systematic effects on the playroom activity levels and play of young normal children.

5. Attachment behaviors such as maintaining physical proximity to the mother, differential vocalization, and separation protest are found in 3-year-olds as well as the younger children usually studied.

To conclude, this research program is still in midstream; it has generated some answers but many more questions about hyperactivity in relation to normal child development. One certainty is that the research can never again proceed without due regard for the importance of the social environment of the child.

3

Defining Hyperactivity: Psychophysiological and Behavioral Strategies

STEPHEN W. PORGES
KAREN M. SMITH

INTRODUCTION

Despite years of research, the meaning of hyperactivity as a diagnostic classification remains obscure. During most of this time, hyperactivity has been assumed to be a neurological disease entity caused by specific injury or dysfunction that required treatment with pharmacological agents. Increasingly, this disease model has been called into question; extensive research has failed to pinpoint either a clear-cut set of diagnostic signs or a plausible etiological sequence. It is the goal of this chapter to examine critically the assumptions that have been made about hyperactivity, particularly about the relationship between neural function, or dysfunction, and behavior. We propose an alternative model for this relationship, a model based on an interaction between organic and situational factors.

Hyperactivity is usually defined as a collection of symptoms including abnormally high levels of motor activity, short attention span, low frustration tolerance, hyperexcitability, and an inability to control impulses (e.g., Stewart, Pitts, Craig, & Deirut, 1966). These symptoms are often regarded as a syndrome, a set of behaviors that correspond to a single underlying dysfunction, and for that reason are expected to be seen in combination in most hyperactive children. Based on the traditional disease model of hyperactivity, treatment with pharmacologic agents is expected to bring about a reduction in the problem behaviors through the normalizing effect such treatment may have on the physiological substrate of those behaviors.

HYPERACTIVE CHILDREN
The Social Ecology of Identification and Treatment

ISBN 0-12-745950-2

Is hyperactivity a manifestation of pathology in the nervous system? An organic source for the disorder is often used to justify pharmacologic treatment, and the success of pharmacologic treatment is sometimes taken as confirmation of the existence of an organic disorder. Brain damage, prenatal and perinatal stress, maternal smoking, lead poisoning, diet, and heredity have all been implicated as organic causes of hyperactivity, with some empirical support for each. A portion of the samples of hyperactive children studied for each possible etiology, however, have shown no history of organic insult or genetic predisposition. For this reason, a formerly popular assumption of a common etiology for all hyperactivity has been discarded by most investigators.

At present there seem to be two major views, not mutually exclusive, on the etiology of hyperactivity: the organic disease model and the social–environmental model. The organic disease model tends to encourage pharmacologic treatment in order to remediate an inferred dysfunction in the nervous system. The social–environmental approach views hyperactivity as a response to various constraints, contingencies, or demands in the environment. To control the hyperactive child's disruptive behavior, the social–environmental approach tends to encourage behavior modification and other psychological treatments. Of course, there may be situations in which a behavioral treatment might be used, even though there are clear signs of an organic etiology. The reverse might also be true.

Multiple etiologies could possibly produce an identical syndrome in different individuals. In the case of hyperactivity, a general description of fidgetiness, impulsiveness, and short attention span may apply to most diagnosed hyperactive children, but a closer analysis of specific behavior patterns has usually revealed a very heterogeneous group (Baxley & LeBlanc, 1976). Even the existence of a well-defined syndrome may be questioned. Attempts at cross-validating measurements of hyperactive behaviors have produced rather mixed results (Sandoval, 1977), and intercorrelations among categories of "hyperactive" behaviors within the same observation period may be low (Barkley & Ullman, 1975; Werry & Quay, 1969).

The diagnosis of hyperactivity has been applied to various groups of children. This population heterogeneity seriously impairs interpretation of research results. Specifically, results of studies done at different times and under different circumstances may not be comparable because different types of individuals may have been included under the categories of hyperactivity, minimal brain dysfunction, or learning disability.

The complex etiology of hyperactivity includes continua of organic and environmental factors. It is our belief that the interaction of these two continua cause, to varying degrees, the collection of behaviors associated with hyperactive children. Thus, if one could identify the individual organic and situational factors associated with the specific etiology of hyperactivity in a child, a more individualized treatment might be developed. The treatment might consist of pharmacologic agents, behavioral methods, or a unique combination of the two. Measurement of physiological activity may provide an index of the state of the central nervous system, and, in combination with a behavioral–situational analysis, may lead to a more precise, individualized diagnosis and treatment. It is possible that only for a subset of hyperactive children is there an organic abnormality paralleling behavioral abnormality. We will speculate that the parallel is not causative, but places the child "at risk" in specific situations.

In this chapter we will discuss behavioral and physiological strategies for studying hyperactivity. We will describe the development of a model of hyperactivity that has been derived from empirical work using both strategies. More emphasis will be given to introducing the psychophysiological orientation than to the behavioral since the latter is well-represented elsewhere in this volume.

THE BEHAVIORAL RESEARCH STRATEGY

Hyperactivity is primarily a dysfunction of behavior. This is true despite the evidence that at least some hyperactive children may be physiologically dysfunctional as well. Hyperactive children are identified by their consistent behavioral patterns, and treatment for hyperactivity is evaluated in terms of its effects on those patterns. Given such an elementary premise, it is surprising how difficult it is to formulate a reliable definition of hyperactivity and to obtain consensus on criteria for treatment outcome. The reason for this confusion may lie in not recognizing the different levels at which the behavior of hyperactive children can be defined and the many sources of behavioral variability within the hyperactive population. In the following sections, three levels of behavioral analysis of hyperactivity will be discussed: behavioral patterns reflected in adult ratings; description and measurement of behavior and performance directly observed; and behavioral response to controlled contingencies.

Formerly it was common to assume that hyperactivity was a behavioral syndrome found consistently in all or most children diagnosed hyperactive. The behavioral research strategy that grew from this assumption used group designs in which one group of hyperactive children served as controls. Similarly, comparisons of hyperactive and nonhyperactive subjects were made in which only a few characteristics of the subjects were matched or measured such as diagnostic categories, IQ, and the standard age and demographic data. In other words, it was assumed that hyperactive children formed a homogeneous group, consistently different from *normal*. Not surprisingly, a number of studies that employed this assumption found that the treatment had very few effects on a large number of seemingly important measures (e.g., Conners, 1975a); others found the instrument that distinguished hyperactive from nonhyperactive subjects in some studies did not do so in others (Sandoval, 1977). This lack of consistency and predictive power within the hyperactive diagnostic category has led to greater emphasis on looking at treatments within subjects (Sprague & Sleator, 1975), studying behavioral syndromes within subjects in order to identify more homogeneous subgroups (Marwitt & Stenner, 1972; Ney, 1974), and looking for variables within the hyperactive population that predict response to medication (Halliday, Rosenthal, Naylor, & Callaway, 1976).

Ratings and Labels: Adult Evaluations

Establishing the existence of a syndrome, or a set of syndromes, within a heterogeneous hyperactive group is complicated by the kind of information most often gathered about hyperactive children's behavior. Many studies rely exclusively on ratings by teachers, parents, and clinicians, rather than on direct observation or measurement of the child. This procedure has the advantage of economically reflecting stable patterns across a variety of situations, but has the disadvantage of including both variability and individual response biases due to raters. Too often, variability or consistency in ratings has been attributed solely to the child's behavior patterns. Without cross-validation with other data sources and without examination of interrater reliability, it is methodologically questionable to make inferences based exclusively on adult ratings about stable behavioral patterns, or about situational influences on the child's behavior. It should be kept in mind that the variability being studied is due to both child and rater.

Although the idea of a hyperactivity syndrome was largely developed from adult ratings of children's behavior, the existence of a genuine syndrome remains in doubt even after extensive research of this type. Situational variables may account for some of this discrepancy, with some situations evoking more hyperactive behavior than others. There are also likely to be differences in the composition of behavior patterns within individuals, and different degrees to which individual children display consistent patterns. An additional factor, not always recognized, is the effect of the label "hyperactivity" on the rating process itself. In studies that show inconsistencies between raters, parents and teachers seem especially likely to disagree, despite their having the most contact with the child. Most children are diagnosed as hyperactive after they begin school; many parents up to that point do not perceive any striking abnormality in their child's behavior.

With the more stringent demands of school, and perhaps with the teacher's different outlook, children who ultimately are labeled hyperactive begin to have either academic or social problems, or both. Clinically, rating scales are generally employed only after the child's problem has reached the stage at which he or she is thought of as possibly hyperactive. The application of the label "hyperactive" could influence adult evaluations; a syndrome may be perceived where none was seen previously. This effect of labeling, in combination with raters' own response biases, could tend to exaggerate the correlations among rated behaviors within a checklist, and make the diagnosis of hyperactivity a self-fulfilling prophecy. Interrater reliability is typically rather low (Sandoval, 1977). This, along with labeling, response bias, and the well-known halo effect of drug treatment (Gittelman-Klein & Klein, 1975), could produce the anomalous situation in which there are seemingly clear indications of a syndrome, and no clear agreement on the syndrome's symptoms and composition.

Description of Behavior: Direct Measurement

A number of specific behavioral characteristics of hyperactive children are often cited in the literature, among them high levels of motor activity, impulsiveness, distractibility, emotional lability, and restlessness. Most of these well-known hyperactive characteristics were originally derived from adult evaluations of children labeled hyperactive. Efforts to describe the behavior of hyperactive children directly, rather than through adult-derived ratings, have led to results that do not necessarily support traditional definitions of hyperactivity. As an example, the idea that hyperactive children show more motor activity than nonhyperactive children has received fairly consistent support from adult ratings of behavior (Conners, 1969; Werry, 1968), and plays a central role in many definitions of hyperactivity (Werry & Sprague, 1970). Attempts to validate this finding with direct observation and measurement, however, have produced equivocal results. Some studies have found significantly higher levels of motor activity in hyperactive children when compared to nonhyperactive children (Barkley & Ullman, 1975; Routh & Schroeder, 1976); others have found no differences between groups in some situations (Douglas, 1974; Weiss, 1975). Parent and/or teacher ratings have been found to be relatively unrelated to activity scores assigned on the basis of direct observation (Klein & Gittelman-Klein, 1975; Weiss, 1975), or measurement (Barkley & Ullman, 1975). This inconsistency is surprising in light of the widespread acceptance of a high activity level as a key symptom of hyperactivity. We must conclude that a high level of motor activity alone may not be a reliable variable for distinguishing hyperactive from nonhyperactive children.

The preceding paragraph illustrates a very important aspect of behavioral research strategies: Description of the behavior that constitutes hyperactivity is not meaningful without some reference to the *situational* context. It is difficult to distinguish, on the basis of activity level during free play, diagnosed hyperactive from nonhyperactive children (Weiss, 1975). Only when the constraints of the classroom or other structured situations are imposed do hyperactive children tend to behave differently from their nonhyperactive peers. This difference in behavior, which may stem from impulsivity or lack of behavioral inhibition, could result in higher measured, or perceived, activity in groups of hyperactive children in restrictive situations. Other aspects of hyperactivity may also be situation specific, such as the inability to sustain attention over prolonged periods. Some hyperactive children who generally show this deficit in the classroom can attend to television programs for quite a while (Ross & Ross, 1976, p. 79).

It seems reasonable to conclude that circumstances and context determine the extent to which hyperactive children are noticeably active, impulsive, and distractible. Sources of variance at the descriptive level can include heterogeneity in the population, adult perceptions and attitudes, situational constraints, and the stable behavioral predispositions of the child himself.

Analysis of Behavior: Contingencies and Performance

There is a third level at which hyperactivity can be defined behaviorally: analysis of behavioral predispositions within varied contingencies or contexts. Unlike the descriptive level, the analytic level is not concerned so much with the behavioral acts themselves, but rather with the underlying processes they reflect. Reaction time studies are an example. The interest is not so much in learning how quickly and accurately hyperactive children typically respond to stimuli, but in using reaction time performance as an index of attentional abilities under various task presentation formats. A number of very interesting results have come out of studies using this type of strategy. Douglas and her colleagues (Douglas, 1974) have performed a series of experiments that varied reinforcement contingencies, feedback, and presentation format in reaction time and concept formation tasks; the results indicated that hyperactive subjects showed different sensitivity to these manipulations than nonhyperactive subjects. Specifically, the hyperactive children's performance was optimized when the task was self-paced, when respond signals in reaction time tasks were contingent on the subjects' apparent attention to the signal source, and when accurate feedback, both positive and negative, was provided during the task. Hyperactive subjects' performance was debilitated by cessation of reinforcing feedback, when reinforcement was all positive and generalized, and when warning and respond signals in reaction time tasks were not contingent on the subjects' actions.

Hyperactive subjects' evident dependence on immediate feedback for maintenance of performance appears in social contexts as well; Campbell (1975) has reported that hyperactive boys asked for and received more feedback, both positive and negative, from their mothers in a laboratory problem-solving task than did either normal or learning disabled subjects. The source of this sensitivity to certain types of feedback and reinforcement is not known, but such research could serve as a starting point for very useful and interesting experimental questions. Is the format of classroom instruction such that inappropriate behavior provides more of this potent reinforcement than does appropriate activity? Is parent–child interaction related to hyperactive children's response to feedback, as suggested by the Campbell study? Could neural organization be related to greater sensitivity to some stimulus contingencies than to others? Can we distinguish subgroups of hyperactive children, and predict treatment outcomes, from knowledge of their performance under various experimental conditions?

Use of analytical strategies gives an insight into the functional organization of hyperactive children's behavior and helps to circumvent the problem of bias in adult evaluations of behavior. This is not to say, however, that the definition of hyperactivity should be confined to this level. Hyperactivity is in part a dysfunction of adaptation to adult-defined social constraints and expectations. Any valid understanding of the problem must provide a link between the artificial conditions of the laboratory and the real world situations in which the child must function. An adequate definition of hyperactivity will have to encompass all levels: social interactions, consistent behavioral patterns, specific predispositions, and contextual determinants of behavior.

THE PSYCHOPHYSIOLOGICAL RESEARCH STRATEGY

The psychophysiological approach to the study of hyperactivity has evolved from two major sources. The first is the traditional medical concept of hyperactivity as a manifestation of specific organic damage, disorder, or dysfunction. Hyperactivity was first identified as a behavioral syndrome in brain-damaged individuals (Still, 1902), and until quite recently many investigators assumed a direct correspondence between the behavioral symptoms of hyperactivity and an inferred organic pathology.

A number of different theories have been advanced that consider physiological function the explanatory basis of hyperactivity; treatment with sympathomimetic (stimulant) drugs is grounded ultimately in this theoretical viewpoint. Pathophysiological views of hyperactivity mandate direct alteration of the biochemical activity of the nervous system as the only effective treatment, since behavioral problems are assumed to arise directly from nervous system dysfunction. The pathophysiological models run the gamut of possibilities. A high-activity level has been interpreted as a parallel to an overaroused or highly aroused central nervous system (Freibergs & Douglas, 1969; Laufer, Denhoff, & Solomons, 1957), as a compensatory behavior to arouse a suboptimally stimulated individual through an increase in proprioceptive sensory input (Satterfield & Dawson, 1971; Stewart, 1970; Werry, Sprague, Weiss, & Minde, 1970), or as a correlate of defective cortical inhibitory mechanisms (Dykman, Ackerman, Clements, & Peters, 1971; Porges, 1976).

An explanation of how the stimulant drugs function is also associated with each pathophysiological model of hyperactivity. The "overaroused" models assume that the stimulant drugs elicit an inhibitory rebound (Anisman, 1975). The "underaroused" models assume that the drugs increase central arousal (Satterfield & Dawson, 1971; Stewart, 1970; Werry *et al.*, 1970). The "weak inhibitory systems" models view the drug as directly increasing the activity of the central inhibitory systems (Shih, Khachaturian, Barry, & Reisler, 1975; Shih, Khachaturian, Barry, & Hanin, 1976). Models such as these are indispensable to the psychophysiological approach to hyperactivity, but supporting evidence for each is at best fragmentary at this point.

As with the behavioral research on hyperactivity, clearly no one model applies to all children diagnosed as hyperactive. Large individual differences in physiological function and behavior seem to indicate that very different subgroups exist within the hyperactive population. Pathophysiological models may, therefore, be most useful in helping to identify those subgroups and to formulate appropriate treatments, pharmacological or otherwise. It has also become clear, as will be illustrated later, that drug treatment cannot be construed as having all-or-nothing effects. Within individuals, different aspects of hyperactive behavior may or may not respond to drug treatment. This fact points to differences in the type of syndrome found in different individuals and to situational influences on hyperactive children's behavior, both with and without drug treatment. In other words, both the physiology and behavior of the hyperactive child are evidently not as invariable or immune to the effects of situation, experience, or learning as many pathophysiological theories seem to imply.

The second basis for psychophysiological research in this area is the empirical evidence for a parallel between certain physiological measurements (most notably heart rate, respiration, and some aspects of electroencephalographic [EEG] measurement) and the attentional and cognitive demands of experimental tasks. This research has been carried out most often with nonhyperactive subjects—both children and adults—but has proven useful in investigations of hyperactivity by providing a "normal" theoretical standard against which to compare our results.

If attentional or cognitive difficulties characterize some groups of hyperactive children, we might reasonably expect to find disturbances in the physiological and behavioral responses of these children to the same types of demanding tasks in which "normal" patterns have been studied extensively. The information thus gained adds to our understanding of hyperactivity as an organic syndrome, and also increases our knowledge about the fundamental relationships between physiology and behavior.

The Continuity Assumption

Many prevalent theories on the etiology of hyperactivty link hyperactive behavior to specific pathologies in the nervous system. On the surface this relationship is plausible. The basic assumption is that of *continuity* among various levels of functioning. The inability to control, inhibit, or mediate behavior is assumed to be a peripheral manifestation of an imbalance in the central inhibitory–excitatory systems. Peripheral physiological responses in the autonomic nervous system should also be part of this continuous function, and thus reflect the same central mechanisms. Unfortunately, measurement is rarely as adequate as theory. Direct measurement of the key variable, central nervous system function, is difficult and elusive at best. As a result, it is necessary to construct and test hypotheses using a chain of inference and indirect measurement, which may lead the research into blind alleys and logical traps. Researchers have leaned heavily on the continuity assumption, coupled with observations of behavior, to formulate theories that assume a direct *correspondence* between hyperactive behavior and central nervous system dysfunction.

Correspondence between variables is a more far-reaching and difficult claim to substantiate than is continuity of function. Essentially, a correspondence assumption requires that we accept behavior or peripheral physiological activities as uncontaminated indices of the individual's central nervous system function—independent of situational constraints or interactions among systems at different functional levels. Clearly, this assumption is entirely too simplistic to apply to something as complex and finely attuned to the environment as a human child. It may ultimately prove to be ethically untenable as well, for it leads to a circular argument supporting the use of pharmacological treatment for any child who exhibits "hyperactive" behavior. The reasoning is that the behavior is an unequivocal sign of central nervous dysfunction, and that drug treatment is the most effective means of dealing with organic dysfunction—a conclusion that tends to preclude other forms of treatment. If drug treatment changes behavior in a desired direction, as it may do even if the main outcome is only sedation or a placebo effect, then a diagnosis of organic dysfunction is considered supported. As a result, the correspondence assumption may seduce us into prescribing drugs for any child who frequently misbehaves. In a later section, we shall discuss how correspondence assumptions can also lead to errors of inference from physiological data.

Making a continuity assumption, we may ask a number of valid questions about hyperactivity that are empirically answerable. For instance, an attentional deficit has been identified as a source of some hyperactive children's difficulties both in school and in reaction time and vigilance tasks in the laboratory (Douglas, 1974; Dykman *et al.,* 1971; Keogh & Margolis, 1976). Sustained attention to environmental stimuli has been shown to produce, with a fair degree of reliability, heart rate deceleration and a decrease in heart rate variability (Lacey, Kagan, Lacey, & Moss, 1963; Obrist, Webb, & Sutterer, 1969; Porges, 1972); respiration and muscular activity have also been shown to be affected by performance on attention-demanding tasks (Obrist, Webb, Sutterer, & Howard, 1970; Porges & Raskin, 1969). These attention-linked physiological responses have been found in both adults and children, and have been shown to be correlated with performance scores in the reaction time paradigm (Coquery & Lacey, 1966; Holloway & Parsons, 1972; Porges, 1972). The hypothesis, based on a continuity assumption, is that all of these measures—performance on reaction time, vigilance, and some school tasks, as well as changes in heart rate, respiration, and muscular activity—reflect the central processes that control sustained attention. If at least some hyperactive children are less able to sustain attention than nonhyperactive subjects, then we might expect to find in those children inappropriate or disturbed performance and physiological responses under attention-demanding conditions. If we find both behavioral and physiological dysfunction, our diagnostic technique may be strengthened. Such disturbances of both behavioral and physiological responses have been found in hyperactive children. There is evidence, discussed in a following section, that these may be very useful in identifying functionally different subtypes of hyperactivity.

Other leads into the central functioning of hyperactive children can be developed in the same way. A complex of physiological and behavioral responses to novel, interesting, intense, or otherwise attention-provoking stimuli has been called the orienting reflex (OR) (Sokolov, 1963). Measurement of the OR to signal and nonsignal stimuli may indicate the attentional state of the subject and the meaning the stimuli have for the subject (Lynn, 1966). Studies of the OR in hyperactive children often compare their responses to those of nonhyperactive subjects (Boydstun, Ackerman, Stevens, Clements, Peters, & Dykman, 1968; Cohen & Douglas, 1972). The results have not been entirely consistent, but seem to indicate that the hyperactive children studied did not show an abnormal OR to stimuli. In at least one study (Cohen & Douglas, 1972), they also did not show a strengthened OR, as nonhyperactive subjects did, when the stimulus acquired signal value. The implication is that the hyperactive subjects perceived the stimuli normally, but did not respond as much to the added information as the nonhyperactive subjects. This line of research could be helpful in determining the extent to which distraction, an overresponse to nonsignal stimuli, determines hyperactive children's attention problems. The possibility that the informational content of signals is not processed by some hyperactive children could be further investigated using both behavioral and physiological indices of the OR.

A third example of the use of a continuity assumption involves deriving certain measures from EEG recordings. For example, Satterfield and his colleagues (Satterfield, Cantwell, Saul, Lesser, & Podosin, 1973) have reported that subjects with an abnormal EEG had significantly more improvement on methylphenidate than did the borderline EEG group. When EEG is recorded over numerous repetitions of a stimulus, and then averaged across trials, a pattern of short-term shifts in electrical potential, called the average evoked potential (AEP), is observed. Both stimulus and individual characteristics are thought to be differentiated by AEP latency and amplitude. One application of AEP measurement has been the attempt to distinguish hyperactive children who respond favorably to drug treatment from those who do not. Halliday *et al.* (1976) have reported that the children judged by their pediatricians to have shown significant improvement on methylphenidate also exhibited greater AEP variability across trial blocks. In this experiment, the children who showed a poor or marginal clinical response to the drug responded across trial blocks with a very consistent AEP pattern. Other studies have sought differences in AEP between hyperactive and nonhyperactive subjects (Buchsbaum & Wender, 1973; Hall, Griffin, Moyer, Hopkins, & Rappaport, 1976) and differences induced by treatment with methylphenidate and by task variations (Halliday *et al.*, 1976; Prichep, Sutton, & Harkarem, 1976). Interpretation of this area of research is at this point highly speculative. Clear indications of the meaning of AEP measurement for hyperactivity await more study of the behavioral significance of the AEP itself.

This section has not intended to be a complete review of psychophysiological research on hyperactivity. Rather we gave an overview of the potential information to be gained through the use of psychophysiological measurement when the hypotheses are derived from a continuity assumption. In the next section some of the specific methodological and inferential problems of psychophysiological research will be discussed, with special reference to the questions asked about hyperactivity.

Experimental Control and Multimodal Designs

The experimental strategy for studying behavior places great emphasis on appropriate control of the laboratory context. It is expected that in this context, any behavior other than the dependent variables, and any potentially confounding circumstances, will be controlled, held constant, or randomized. Experimenters can rely on prior research to identify the variables that require control, and they can usually devise procedures to attain a constant, neutral background for the effects of their manipulations. The treatments and dependent variables of psychophysiological researchers, by contrast, cannot be isolated from the biological context in which they occur. The baseline rate at which the heart beats, for instance, can affect the probability, size, or even direction of an event-related change in heart rate. Other physiological activity, such as respiratory rate and vasoconstriction, can have direct and indirect effects on heart rate. Depending on the question to be asked, recording of at least some of these contextual variables may be mandatory for understanding the data.

Psychophysiological research requires that same controls over the external context that are used in purely behavioral research. Even with the most stringent controls over the external context, however, the internal context is not amenable to routine control. The methods of control that are available—drugs, selective sampling of baseline, paced respiration—often are not desirable in light of experimental goals. They are relatively drastic solutions in which either the function of the entire organism is radically altered, as with drug administration, or the external context is changed in a fundamental way, as in paced respiration. Or the sample can be biased in a way that may not be appropriate, as in selective sampling. The usual response to the control difficulties is to monitor those aspects of the biological context that are thought to influence the variable of interest. Essentially this strategy is a multimodal design: One studies the effect of treatments on a chosen dependent variable, the effect of contextual variables on the focal variable, the effect of treatments on those contextual variables, and the effects of treatments on the relationship between contextual and focal variables.

A multimodal approach leads quite naturally to a design in which the dependent variable of interest is not a function of a certain activity at a given time, but is a function of several activities at a given time.

Multimodal designs have developed from theoretical sources as well as from considerations of adequate experimental procedure. Most psychophysiological theories concern the functional organization of the brain, as reflected in both behavioral and physiological activity. If the central organization of the entire organism can be studied indirectly, then establishing relationships among various types of activities controlled by the nervous system is a good place to start the analysis. The theories that serve as a basis for the psychophysiological study of hyperactivity—those having to do with arousal, inhibitory–excitatory balance, or optimal stimulation—all predict differences in the way that both behavioral and physiological variables covary over time, depending on the situation, individual, or treatment. In a sense this is an examination of the continuity assumption. Information about the underlying functional organization of behavioral and physiological activity is gained by investigating the relationships among these variables under different conditions.

Inference from Physiological Data

Once a significant effect has been found in a psychophysiological experiment, there are very specific kinds of inferences that may or may not be reasonably drawn; the limits and possibilities of interpretation of this type of data are often unrecognized and are rarely stated explicitly. First, it cannot be assumed that by measuring physiological variables one has somehow bypassed the behavioral or cognitive characteristics of the subject. Given a continuity assumption,this should be common sense, but interpretations of physiological responses are frequently made as if circumstances that might affect behavior will not affect physiological response systems. The assumption seems to be that physiological activity is a direct pathway to brain function, independent of the attitudes and perceptions of the subject, or of the subject's behavior or behavioral predispositions at the time of measurement. For most physiological variables of interest, it makes a great deal of difference whether the subject is alert and attentive, uncertain and apprehensive, or bored and fidgety at the time of measurement. It hardly needs saying that the last possibility is very likely when the subjects are hyperactive children. To compare those subjects' physiological responses with the responses of alert and attentive children or adults, without any reference to the quality of behavior or performance at the time, is to use only a part of the necessary information. To infer from the comparison that stable differences in neural structure or organization somehow *cause* behavioral differences is unjustified; it is based on an incomplete account of the circumstances in which the recording was made.

This kind of inference shows up in the literature on hyperactivity in conclusions about organic damage or dysfunction, or genetic predisposition based, for instance, on one sample of EEG recording made under unspecified conditions. Very few researchers would be willing to make this kind of inference based on a single observation of behavior. Some special assumptions have been made about the kind of information an EEG contains. It is assumed that an EEG reflects fixed structural differences that are chronic and unmalleable, impervious to the effects of learning, experience, or the immediate context in which the measurement is made. This is, in essence, the physiological form of a correspondence assumption, and as such needs much more substantiating evidence.

Another way in which psychophysiological data can be misinterpreted is the attempt to trace causal pathways wholly within the organism. Even if one does obtain a fair representation of the central organization that presumably predisposes a given subject to exhibit certain behavior, the analysis cannot end there. Most behavioral predispositions are not thought to be continuous, automatic, or invariable. Hyperactive children do not literally fidget constantly; their fidgeting has different forms and qualities at different times. Even given a predisposition to fidget, there are precipitating circumstances that determine the time, intensity, and quality of fidgeting. An adequate understanding of a hyperactive child's fidgeting and of the functional organization that determines fidgeting requires information about the precipitating circumstances. We cannot conclude that any given behavior observed was *caused* by a certain neural organization, any more than we can say it was caused entirely by circumstances.

This discussion is not meant to imply that psychophysiological research on hyperactivity need be purely descriptive and correlational. As mentioned before, multimodal designs and current theory both tend to emphasize the effects of experimental treatments on the relationships among variables. With a continuity assumption, the several dependent variables of interest may be either behavioral or physiological, and the treatments can be anything validly derived from theory: reinforcement schedules, drugs, social interactions, and so on. Probable causal effects can be demonstrated as long as the limits of causal inference are respected, and the design and control are appropriate to the hypothesis. In this sense psychophysiological research is no different from behavioral research. The misunderstandings of physiological data stem from assigning special meanings to physiological activity that are not assigned to behavior, and from not recognizing, as a consequence, potential sources of confounding.

PSYCHOPHYSIOLOGICAL STRATEGIES: THE IDENTIFICATION OF PATHOPHYSIOLOGICAL FACTORS

It is possible that some of the children categorized as behaviorally hyperactive do indeed have identifiable patterns of organic dysfunction. Clarification of this pathophysiological view requires, first, the development of physiological assessment techniques that precisely evaluate individual differences in nervous system function. Then, if reliable differences in CNS patterns can be documented, one can show how these patterns relate to behaviors, and test each pattern for drug responsiveness.

Since other sections of this chapter and other chapters in this volume have discussed the interpretation of hyperactivity as a behavioral pathology, this section will focus on the possible identification of physiological states unique to hyperactive children. In this chapter we question a common physiological substrate for all hyperactive behavior. Behavior may be treated as a geometric resultant of various underlying physiological vectors; hyperactive behavior may be a function of a variety of vector combinations. A conservative approach, acknowledging the above problems, first accepts the possibility that some hyperactive behavior might have a pathophysiological basis, and then focuses on more detailed analysis of the relative contributions of the nervous system and the environment to this maladaptive behavior. In our laboratory, psychophysiological techniques have been employed to identify a subcategory of hyperactive children who exhibit a physiological parallel of their behavioral pathology. In the following pages, data from these studies will be described.

Experiment I: A Psychophysiological Study of Sustained Attention

To assess whether the hyperactive child exhibited physiological responses consistent with his poor performance, our first experiment (Porges, Walter, Korb, & Sprague, 1975) utilized a well-tested paradigm demanding that subjects sustain attention (Cheung, 1973; Porges, 1972; Porges & Raskin, 1969). The experiment also examined the influence of methylphenidate on both the behavioral and physiological indices of attention. If a pathophysiological state paralleled the behavioral diagnosis, some support would be generated for the suggestion that individual differences in the nervous system might be implicated in the diagnosis and objective subclassification of hyperactivity. The study could also assess whether there is a parallel influence of methylphenidate on behavior and on physiological activity.

In a series of psychophysiological studies (Porges, 1972, 1974; Porges &

Raskin, 1969), different heart rate response components have been associated with attention, and a two-component model of attention has been postulated (see Porges, 1976). The first component is associated with reactive attention and is indexed by short latency, directional heart rate responses to changes in stimulation. This component is similar to William James' (1890) definition of passive reflexive attention. The second component is associated with sustained or tonic attention. This component is correlated with a reduction of heart rate variability (the interbeat intervals of successive heart beats become more constant), and a generalized inhibition of motor and respiratory activity (either reduced respiratory amplitude or a temporary cessation of breathing). This response persists as long as the subject elects to attend, and is very similar to James' (1890) definition of active voluntary attention.

In this experiment, the two-component model of attention was tested with hyperactive children. It was hypothesized that the hyperactive child would perform poorly during tasks that demand sustained attention; this performance would be paralleled by an inability to exhibit the heart rate response associated with sustained attention. Moreover, it was hypothesized that the behavioral improvement associated with methylphenidate would be paralleled by changes in the heart-rate components of sustained attention.

Sixteen children (15 male and 1 female) between 6.5 and 12 years of age, diagnosed by clinical ratings (Conners, 1969, 1970) as hyperactive, served as subjects. To avoid the situational problem of task motivation, a reaction-time task was masked in a race track game. A button press, following a sequence of illuminated ready and go signals, released a toy Matchbox car onto a specially constructed race track. The preparatory interval between the ready and go signals varied randomly among 10, 15, and 20 sec. The subject was instructed that his or her car would be competing with an experimenter-controlled car. If the subject's responses were rapid enough to win most of the races, the subject would receive a Matchbox car as a prize. The experimenter's car, however, was programmed to be released independently of the experimenter's response latency. This automation enabled the experimenter to appear to press his response button rapidly while maintaining the subject's motivation by allowing the subject to win most of the time. There were no complaints about the task, and the children appeared enthusiastic about participating. All subjects were tested in the morning approximately 2 hr after receiving orally either .3 mg/kg of methylphenidate or placebo. Each subject was tested on the last day of both a 3-week drug period and a 3-week placebo period. The order of drug treatment was random.

The reactive component of attention may be examined by analyzing the heart rate response to the warning signal in the reaction time paradigm (the first 5 sec of the preparatory interval). The hyperactive subjects exhibited a normal response characterized by a biphasic heart rate response, a slight deceleration followed by an acceleration. Methylphenidate had no influence on this response. This is not surprising, since the characteristics of hyperactivity generally do not include deficient responses to external stimuli. Of more interest to us was the physiological activity associated with sustained attention, since defective sustained attention is a central characteristic of hyperactivity. Most theories (e.g., Douglas, 1972), definitions, and assessment scales emphasize an inability to inhibit ongoing spontaneous behavior. Therefore, the inability to inhibit spontaneous physiological activity may be a parallel of behavioral hyperactivity.

We have hypothesized that reductions in heart rate and heart rate variability during a preparatory interval in a reaction time task are physiological responses that are parallel to sustained attention. Figure 3.1 illustrates the influence of the drug treatment on the pretrial (5 sec prior to the warning signal) and on-task (the second 5 sec of the preparatory interval) levels of heart rate and heart rate variability. There were significant Drug treatment × Period (pre versus on-task) interactions for heart rate and heart rate variability. During the drug condition, heart rate and heart rate variability were suppressed on task, during the tonic period, relative to a pretrial level.

Although the unmedicated hyperactive subject exhibited normal heart rate responses associated with *reactive* attention, the subject's difficulty in sustaining attention was paralleled by physiological responses theoretically incompatible with *sustained* attention (increases in heart rate and heart rate variability). If one views the hyperactive classification as homogeneous, then these findings would support the notion of a common pathophysiological condition. However, based upon the overall group data presented above, there is no evidence to believe that all hyperactive children have the same etiology or will respond identically to drug treatment. By investigating the individual differences in responsiveness, it may be possible to gain a more precise understanding of the physiology–behavior–medication interaction.

On placebo, not all the children exhibited performance decrements. When the group was divided into a fast and a slow subgroup, based upon the median reaction time on placebo, only two of the eight subjects in the fast group improved on methylphenidate, in contrast to seven of the eight in the slow group. Moreover, the performance difference between the two subgroups on placebo disappeared on methylphenidate. This may suggest that some of the children did not exhibit a behavioral deficit on task. If the task were sensitive to the appropriate behavior dimensions, these children were not deficient in the ability to inhibit spontaneous behavior. In order to develop a model of nervous system influence and a pathophysiological basis for specific forms (or perhaps causes) of hyperactivity, it is necessary to

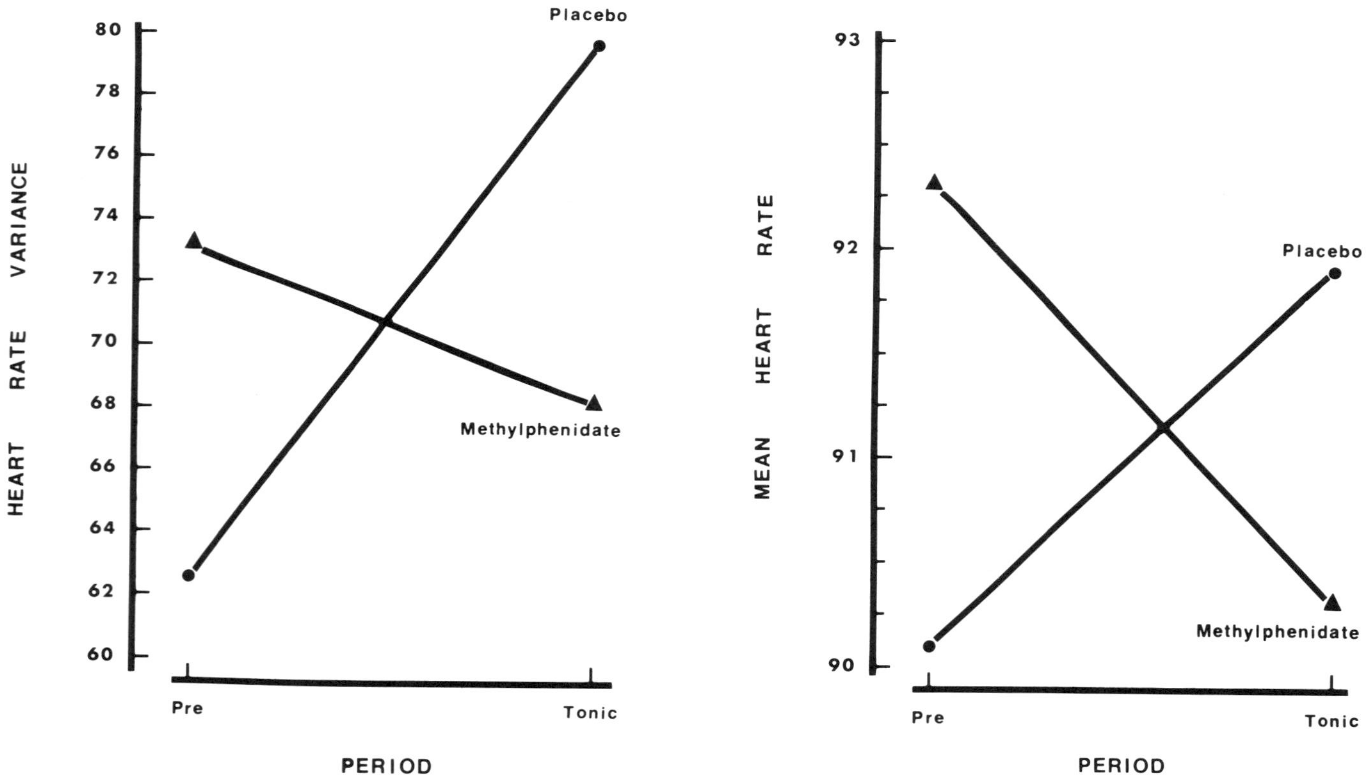

FIGURE 3.1. Heart rate components of sustained attention: The change in heart rate and heart rate variability is from a pretrial level (**pre**) to an on-task level (**tonic**).

distinguish on a physiological level the differences between these subgroups. For example, a physiological response, such as suppression of heart rate variability, might be postulated as a substrate of sustained attention. If the two subgroups exhibit differential suppression of heart rate variability, the possibility exists that this type of psychophysiological assessment might distinguish various types of hyperactivity with either situational or organic bases.

An analysis of the reduction of heart rate variability including a subgroup factor (fast or slow performance on placebo) resulted in a significant Group × Drug × Trial block interaction. The main source of this interaction was the changing reduction of heart rate variability, as a function of drug treatment, for the slow group. On the later trials, the slow group changed from large increases on placebo to large decreases on methylphenidate. As performance significantly improved for the slow group on methylphenidate, there was a tendency to reduce heart rate variability. The fast group, who exhibited no change in performance, tended not to show a drug influence on the reduction of heart rate variability. In essence, the subjects in this study performed as if belonging to two separate subgroups: either (*a*) deficient in performance, with improved reaction time, and a parallel increase in the suppression of heart rate variability with drug treatment; or (*b*) adequate in performance, and relatively insensitive on a behavioral and physiological level to the drug treatment. When the data were collapsed across subjects, it appeared that the drug was having a beneficial effect on all subjects, which, of course, is misleading.

Ratings of improved social behavior in the classroom diametrically differed from the changes in reaction time performance. An interpretation of the reaction time changes in the laboratory would suggest that the poor attenders were aided the most by methylphenidate. Changes in social behavior in the classroom were rated as a function of methylphenidate, and the subjects were categorized into low or high social improvement groups. There was a tendency for subjects who were classified as low social improvers to have also been classified in the slow reaction time group. Six of the eight low social improvers were classified in the slow reaction time group. Thus, subjects who improved the most on reaction time performance improved the least socially, whereas those who improved socially did not have initial attention deficits.

The data suggest that although both attention and behavioral hyperactivity may be influenced by methylphenidate, the response affected may be a function of the individual's specific deficit. It is possible that the influence of methylphenidate on hyperactive behavior may follow a hierarchy. Influences on attentional behavior may precede influences on social behavior; if attention is adequate, social behavior may be influenced. An alternative explanation might link diagnosis and treatment to specific target behaviors. If a psychophysiological diagnostic approach were used, the existence of a parallel physiological component for target behaviors could be tested. In the preceding experiment, the children who had fast reaction times and the appropriate physiological response on placebo might have been placed in a category of situational hyperactivity, unencumbered by the organic parallels assessed in this experiment. Thus, the researcher's selection of a specific target behavior might determine whether a specific treatment were evaluated as effective. In the study described, depending upon whether classroom behavior or laboratory responses were the target behavior, different subjects would be identified as positive methylphenidate responders.

Experiment II: Underlying Physiological Mechanisms of Sustained Attention

In Experiment I, hyperactive children who exhibited attention deficits, defined by long response latencies, also exhibited heart rate responses that were theoretically incompatible with sustained attention. Heart rate responses, such as decreases in heart rate and heart rate variability, have been theoretically associated with sustained attention and are believed generally to be controlled through the parasympathetic nervous system (Graham & Clifton, 1966; Lacey, 1967; Obrist, Lawler, Howard, Smithson, Martin, & Manning, 1974; Porges, 1976).

One may hypothesize that (*a*) some untreated hyperactive children exhibit less parasympathetic, relative to sympathetic, influence on the control of cardiac activity than nonhyperactive children; and (*b*) methylphenidate, a drug that facilitates normal behavior, might result in an increase in parasympathetic, relative to sympathetic, influence. This would be consistent with the *continuity assumption,* which relates inferred individual differences in excitatory–inhibitory balance in the central nervous system to measurable peripheral parallels in the autonomic nervous system, and in behavioral activity. Behavioral inhibition necessary for optimal sustained attention is deficient in some hyperactive children, and may have a parallel in the autonomic nervous system. This parallel may be characterized by a deficiency in the inhibitory control system of the heart. In other words, a continuum of individual differences in parasympathetic influence on the heart may parallel the continuum of excitatory–inhibitory balance in the central nervous system, which is thought to be a determinant of specific types of hyperactivity.

A crude estimate of parasympathetic influence may be obtained from spontaneous heart rate variability (Katona & Jih, 1975). In the study described in the preceding section (Porges *et al.*, 1975), methylphenidate increased the pretrial level of heart rate variability, changed the directionality of heart rate, and altered heart rate variability responses during the task. In other research, individual differences in pretrial and baseline heart rate variability have been shown to be related to reaction time performance in adults (Porges, 1972, 1973) and to physiological response patterns associated with attention (Porges, 1972, 1974).

The relative contribution of the excitatory (sympathetic) and inhibitory (parasympathetic) branches of the autonomic nervous system to the neural control of the heart may be assessed by investigating the rhythm of the heart. The rhythm (fluctuations in the time between successive heartbeats) is determined primarily by a combination of sympathetic and parasympathetic influences. The respiratory influences on heart rate activity (reflexive increases and decreases in heart rate paralleling inhalation and exhalation) are mediated by the parasympathetic nervous system through the vagus (Chess, Tam, & Calaresu, 1975; Eckholdt & Schubert, 1975; Katona & Jih, 1975). We have developed a technique that uses time series statistics to estimate the relative parasympathetic influence on heart rate activity by quantifying the respiratory influence on heart rate (Porges, 1976; Porges, Bohrer, Cheung, Franks, & Drasgow, 1977).

STATISTICAL TECHNIQUES

Spectral analysis (a time-series statistical procedure) may be used to study rhythmic physiological patterns, such as a pattern of changes in heart rate or in respiration amplitude. Spectral analysis detects rhythmic variations in a series of sequential observations, by decomposing the series into constituent sinusoidal functions of different frequencies. When two variables are recorded simultaneously, as in the case of heart rate and respiration, cross-spectral analysis may be used to assess the relationship of frequency components in the two processes. An observed rhythm in one variable may influence an observed rhythm in the second; the measure of influence is the coherence function. Coherence, like the correlation coefficient, is a normmalized function with values between 0 and 1. We have developed a modification of the coherence measure (Porges, 1976; Porges *et al.*, 1977), which is weighted as a function of the actual heart rate activity occurring at the specific frequencies associated with respiration. The coherence statistic derived from the cross-spectral analyses produces an estimate of respiratory–cardiac coupling which may be interpreted as an estimate of parasympathetic control of the heart. For statistical equations see the appendix to this chapter.

In our research, weighted coherence is a statistic that describes the percentage of shared variance between the pattern of changes in heart rate and in respiration. The statistic is derived by dividing the amount of heart rate activity shared with respiration by the amount of heart rate occurring at the normal respiratory frequencies, between .2 and .5 Hz (cycles per second) in children. The interpretation of weighted coherence as a measure of parasympathetic influence is based on the assumption that respiratory activity results in a rhythmic *inhibition* of the parasympathetic input to the heart during inhalation. Inhalation inhibits the parasympathetic influence on the heart, causing a reflexive heart rate acceleration followed by a parasympathetically mediated deceleration during exhalation. Therefore, the greater the respiratory activity influences on heart rate activity, the greater the parasympathetic influence.

PARASYMPATHETIC CONTROL OF THE HEART

Earlier we speculated that individual differences in the nervous system might be manifested peripherally in autonomic activity and in observable behavior. We have also speculated that the tandem use of physiological and behavioral assessment might result in a more precise diagnosis of underlying etiology and a more efficient mode of treatment. Within this framework of speculation, we have attempted to identify a physiological substrate that might index individual differences in hyperactive children's nervous systems. We have theorized that the difficulty shown by hyperactive children in inhibiting spontaneous behavior may parallel a physiological dysfunction that manifests itself, in a subset of children, in the inhibitory control of the heart (showing low parasympathetic influence relative to sympathetic influence). Moreover, the methylphenidate-induced behavioral improvement in these children may be associated with increased parasympathetic control.

If these postulated parallels between behavioral pathology and neural control are correct, some hyperactive children should exhibit deficient parasympathetic control and sympathetic dominance.[1] To test this proposed model, a sample of 16 hyperactive children (13 males, 3 females) diagnosed by the Conners (1969) scale was studied.[2] Experiment II (Porges *et al.*, 1977) was designed to answer two questions: First, do dose levels of methylphenidate differentially influence the parasympathetic component of spontaneous heart rate activity; second, is there an indication of autonomic dysfunction in the hyperactive child prior to the drug intervention? Electrocardiogram (EKG) and thoracic respiration were sampled before and after an attention-demanding task while the child was on the following treatments: prior to drug treatment, .5 mg/kg methylphenidate,

[1]If these physiological assumptions are correct, the hyperactive child may mature into a hyperactive or a hypertensive adult at risk for myocardial infarction (heart attacks). Limited parasympathetic control of the heart is associated with increased probabilities of a heart attack (Katona & Jih, 1975), and this may compound the effect of stimulant drugs on blood pressure.

[2]All subjects prior to drug manipulation scored 15 or higher on the Conners Abbreviated Teaching Rating Scale, $X = 19.56$, $\sigma = 3.92$. All subjects were at least 1.96 standard deviations above the mean of a normative sample of children (Sprague, Cohen, & Werry, 1974).

1.0 mg/kg methylphenidate, and placebo. All conditions except predrug were randomly ordered.

As illustrated in Figure 3.2, the weighted coherence was significantly higher with the low dose of methylphenidate than in the other conditions, which did not differ from each other. Of interest is the differential effect of the two doses of methylphenidate; the low dose increased the weighted coherence, whereas the high dose did not change the weighted coherence from predrug or placebo treatments.

Behaviorally, the preferred drug dosage has been between .3 and .5 mg/kg. This low dose has had positive influences on cognitive performance and social behavior, whereas higher doses often result in lethargic behavior (Sprague & Sleator, 1977). Like the improvement in cognitive performance, the weighted coherence measure peaked at low doses of methylphenidate. Moreover, when the weighted coherence has been assessed for nonhyperactive children, their level tends to approximate the level the hyperactive children reach on the low dose of methylphenidate (see Porges, 1976). This suggests that some hyperactive children, prior to pharmacological treatment, may exhibit a dysfunction in the neural control of the heart that might, in some subjects, be remediated by methylphenidate.

Caution must be exercised regarding the homogeneity of any population diagnosed as hyperactive. Some subjects classified as hyperactive actually exhibited a weighted coherence in the range of nonhyperactive subjects;

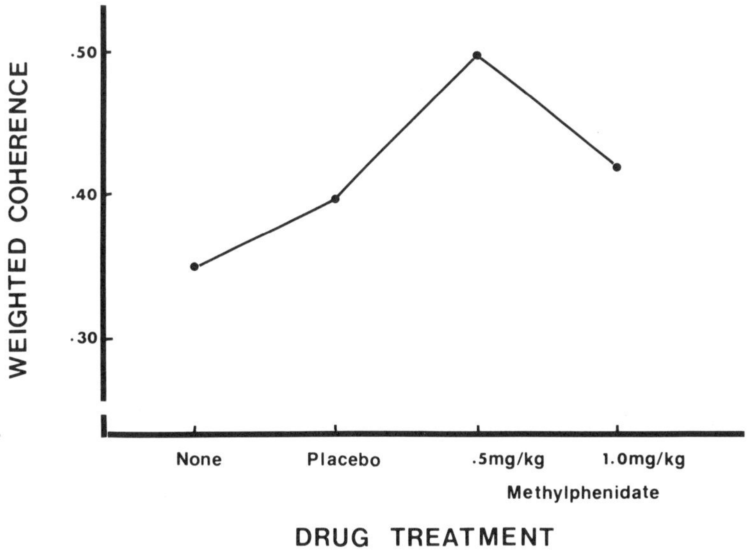

FIGURE 3.2. Weighted coherence shown for 16 hyperactive children in the following conditions: No drug (none), placebo; .5 mg/kg methylphenidate, and 1.0 mg/kg methylphenidate.

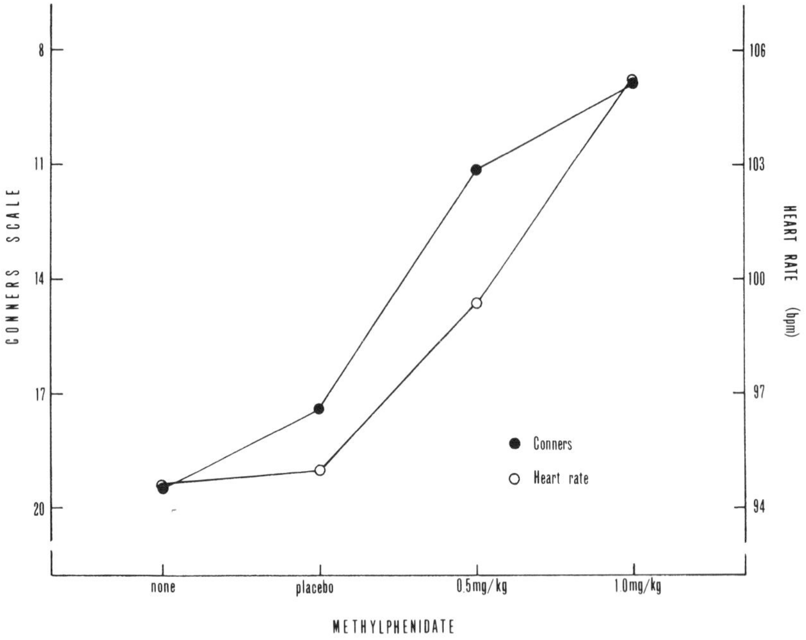

FIGURE 3.3. Changes in heart rate and scores on the Conners scale seen as a function of methylphenidate dosage.

methylphenidate treatment tended not to increase the weighted coherence or improve attentional performance for these subjects. The weighted coherence may be useful in identifying a homogeneous subgroup of hyperactive children, whose attentional deficit and behavioral lack of impulse control may have a clear autonomic parallel, and for whom methylphenidate may be the treatment of choice.

In contrast to the weighted coherence function, the Conners scale (1969) may be sensitive to a much broader category of behaviors. The weighted coherence may be sensitive to behaviors associated with the ability to *mediate* ongoing bodily activity and to facilitate the intake of information. The Conners scale, on the other hand, may be assessing the degree of classroom-disrupting behavior exhibited by the child. By reducing overall activity (an effect of high doses of methylphenidate), independent of quality, the rate of disruptive behaviors may decrease for these children; however, their performance on many cognitive tasks may not improve. As illustrated in Figure 3.3, for the group of subjects in our study, there was a significant reduction in scores on the Conners scale for both doses of methylphenidate. The heart rate significantly increased with increasing dosage. However, consistent with the dose–response relationships of methylphenidate for cognitive behavior (Sprague & Sleator, 1977), the weighted coherence peaked at the low dose.

Experiment III: Hyperactivity and the Continuum of Impulsivity-Reflectivity

In previous sections, we have referred to the impulsive quality of hyperactive children's behavior in terms of the parallel between a lack of behavioral inhibition and autonomic and CNS excitatory–inhibitory imbalances. Another concept of impulsivity is of a response set that grows out of an individual's cognitive style. Kagan and his associates have developed this view of impulsivity and have devised a test, the Matching Familiar Figures Test (MFFT) (Kagan, Rosman, Day, Albert, & Phillips, 1964), to distinguish individuals with impulsive and reflective cognitive styles. The MFFT has been used extensively in research on children's cognitive styles and their relation to behavior and performance (Messer, 1976). The fact that hyperactive subjects tend to be more impulsive on the MFFT than nonhyperactive subjects (Douglas, 1974; Sandoval, 1977) lends credence to the idea that cognitive impulsivity is a major factor in hyperactivity. It has also prompted the question of whether the physiological indicants of excitatory–inhibitory imbalance, thought to be related to impulsive behavior in hyperactive subjects, might also be related to impulsivity in nonhyperactive children. The rationale for investigating this question depends upon two assumptions about the nature of the physiological substrate of impulsivity in hyperactive children.

The first assumption is that the organic syndrome does not, by itself, cause deviant behavior. The maladaptive behavior diagnosed as "hyperactivity" reflects more than simply impulsivity or a lack of behavioral inhibition. The etiology of hyperactive behavior is complicated by unique combinations of situational and organic factors; the organic factors may serve to place the child "at risk" for hyperactivity in specific situations, but the actual development of hyperactivity depends on an interaction of these organic risk factors with specific environmental demands.

The second assumption is that the physiological parallels of impulsive behavior often are distributed across the nonhyperactive as well as the hyperactive population. The physiological substrate of impulsive behavior in some hyperactive children is not a discrete, qualitatively different, or aberrant pattern found only in "pathological" populations. "Normal" children might also show the same relationship between the physiological pattern and impulsive behavior, without necessarily showing severe behavioral maladaptation.

The above hypothesis about the physiological similarity between hyperactive and impulsive children was tested in our laboratory. Leta Secker, in her dissertation research, investigated the relationships between the weighted coherence function and the dimension of impulsivity–reflectivity. Using the MFFT (Kagan *et al.*, 1964), she identified a significant correlative relationship between reflective (slow accurate) or impulsive (fast inaccurate) categories and the amount of parasympathetic influence on heart rate activity; reflective children exhibited more parasympathetic control of the heart. The impulsive children exhibited physiological patterns similar to those of the hyperactive group in the earlier study. Thus, the physiological activity associated with inhibitory autonomic control of the heart paralleled the behavioral assessment of inhibitory control. It is of interest that the population of children selected for this research had not been classified as deviant. For these normal children, there were parallel continua of behavior and physiological activity.

Research is in progress in our laboratory aimed at describing the characteristics of behaviors that are dependent upon the inhibitory systems reflected in the coherence measure. The weighted coherence might be sensitive to an individual's predisposition to perform a broad category of voluntary behaviors requiring some form of mediation of motor activity. One common example, which may represent the core of the behavioral characteristics associated with the hyperkinetic syndrome, is the lack of ability to inhibit spontaneous activity and to sustain attention. It is possible that the weighted coherence measure may develop into a diagnostic instrument to detect individuals who have a predisposition for attention deficits.

We have been emphasizing throughout this chapter that, based on the continuity assumption, parallel assessment of physiological activity and behavior might be a more precise method of identifying those hyperactive children whose behavior has a possible organic parallel than either assessment alone. Consistent with this notion, the physiological basis of hyperactivity, rather than being viewed as a disease entity, should be conceptualized as a characteristic distributed along a continuum. Parallel to this physiological continuum, a behavioral continuum associated with the ability to inhibit spontaneous activity or impulse control could be identified. Thus, within a population of children not categorized as hyperactive, as Secker's dissertation suggests, there should be parallel continua of individual differences of impulsiveness and of physiological activity.

Experiment IV: Hyperactivity and Somatic–Cardiac Coupling

The use of the coherence measure to identify a physiological parallel of hyperactive behavior has been based on the assumption that behavior and peripheral physiological activity are parallel output channels which convey information from the central nervous system. By observing both channels, more information is gained about the status of the central nervous system. Statistically, the spectral analyses decomposed complex physiological response patterns in order to identify a component associated with the inhibitory pathways of the autonomic nervous system. The same spectral techniques could be applied to the rhythmic activity in motor behavior and used to test a similar hypothesis of pathological "linkage" between rhythmic activity in heart rate and motor activity in hyperactive children.

Experiment IV (in collaboration with Dr. Michael Wade) was undertaken to assess rhythmic heart rate and motor activity while hyperactive children attempted to keep a stabilometer in balance. Each of five hyperactive children was tested for two sessions of 30 trials, during periods on placebo and on methylphenidate. Each trial was 30 sec long, during which time the subjects attempted to balance the stabilometer. Following each trial, the subjects were told their results to the nearest .1 sec of the time in balance. Intertrial intervals were approximately 30 sec.

The stabilometer platform (3 × 3 ft) rotated (± 10° from horizontal) on a steel shaft centrally mounted on ball bearings. A potentiometer was attached to the front of the shaft. The output of this potentiometer monotonically varied over the 20° of displacement of the platform. This voltage output represented the shifting rotation of the balance board by the hyperactive child during the attempt to maintain the board in balance. Positioned on either side of the platform were switches that were sensitive to contact when the platform was out of balance. Total time in balance could be estimated by connecting a clock to the switches. For a more detailed description of the apparatus and the performance criteria, see Wade and Newall (1972).

To assess the shared influence of motor and heart rate rhythms, cross-spectral analyses were calculated on the changing heart rate pattern and the changing rotation of the balance board during each trial. These analyses detected the degree that a specific rhythm in one response system was influenced by the other response system. If there were an indication of a high degree of shared activity, one might infer either a common central generator, or a temporal coupling between the peripheral outputs through feedback of motor activity on heart rate. For all five of these children, the relative degree of heart rate activity shared with motor activity increased from approximately 20 to 23% during the drug manipulation. Although this was only a slight increase, it was statistically significant. The performance of four of the five children, measured in time in balance, also tended to improve on drugs. On the average, the children were in balance 44% of the trial duration on placebo and 52% on methylphenidate.

The data from the preceding studies analyzing rhythmic motor and physiologic activity suggest that methylphenidate treatment, which in other studies appears to facilitate classroom behavior and cognitive performance, also tends to increase the linkage or integration among the various peripheral output systems through enhanced feedback (e.g., increased respiratory feedback on heart rate or increased motor feedback on heart rate). From the stabilometer data, we may speculate that the observed behavior of the hyperactive child, often labeled as uncoordinated, awkward, or out of control, might be in part a function of faulty feedback from the peripheral motor systems to the central control systems. The data presented in this series of studies tend to suggest that the control systems in nonhyperactive children are more tightly integrated with peripheral output. The hyperactive child may have less central control of all peripheral output channels because of this weak linkage. Moreover, the weak linkage may reduce the normal homeostatic effects of kinesthetic and visceral feedback.

CONCLUSION

The preceding sections of this chapter have presented arguments for identifying situational and pathophysiological factors that influence the manifestation of hyperactive behavior. Careful analyses of situations indicate that the behaviors associated with hyperactivity may have had various psychological (nonorganic) origins. There is evidence to suggest that social situations, emotional problems, and social learning may produce hyperactive behaviors. Caution must be exercised in interpreting the physiological data presented in this chapter. Even when there is a clear pathophysiological state associated with hyperactivity, the question of the genesis of hyperactivity is not resolved. A physiological substrate of hyperactivity is not equivalent to genetic or physiological determination. The physiological state could have been influenced through environmental manipulations, such as perinatal hypoxia, stress, diet, or even autonomic conditioning. Furthermore, the existence of a pathophysiological correlate of hyperactivity does not imply that potentially successful treatments will be pharmacological. It is conceivable that interventions such as behavior modification or increasing emotional support for the child might have successful influences on behavior, and perhaps, through complicated feedback mechanisms, on the associated physiological state. Of course, those hyperactive children who respond most beneficially and efficiently to pharmacological intervention may be the individuals who exhibit a specific pathophysiological state; this possibility is indeed worthy of investigation.

The usefulness of hyperactivity, as a diagnostic category may be limited, since the category does not provide clear insight into the etiology or the predictability of treatment. In our critique of the area, we assume that effective treatment is a qualitative function of the diagnostic procedures. We have attempted to argue that the use of a multichannel psychophysiological and behavioral assessment strategy might improve diagnosis and facilitate the classification of hyperactive children into various etiological groups. One goal of this research is to provide a clearer understanding of the etiology of hyperactivity. A second goal is to apply this information to facilitate the administration of the most efficient treatment. Given the knowledge that all children diagnosed as hyperactive do not respond well to all treatments, the etiological information may help provide a better match between the individual child and the treatment. Moreover, given the public concern about drug abuse, research that justifies the mode of treatment, whether that treatment is behavioral or pharmacological, is extremely important. With the tools of psychophysiology and behavior analysis, the researcher studying hyperactive children may produce an effective assessment instrument in order to index individual differences in the nervous system, observe the behavioral manifestations of these differences, and assess intervention strategies.

APPENDIX

The following equation may be used to define C_W, the weighted coherence measure:

$$C_W = \frac{\int_{\lambda_1}^{\lambda_2} \rho^2(\lambda) F_H(\lambda)\, d\lambda}{\int_{\lambda_1}^{\lambda_2} F_H(\lambda)\, d\lambda}$$

when coherence (ρ^2) is the shared variance of heart rate and respiration and F_H is the power density of heart rate (a measure of variance) at each frequency (λ) at which respiration normally occurs (in hyperactive children between .2 and .5 Hz, or between 12 and 30 times a minute). The integral, over the dominant respiratory frequencies, of the product of the coherence squared and the power density of heart rate, represents the variance of heart rate shared with respiration. Weighted coherence is this number divided by the integral of the power density of heart rate over these same frequencies. It is possible, as presented below, to simplify the statistics by substituting summations for integrals.

$$C_W = \frac{\Sigma[\rho^2(\lambda) F_H(\lambda)]}{\Sigma[F_H(\lambda)]}$$

This ratio represents the relative contributions of respiration to heart rate activity.

ACKNOWLEDGMENTS

The research described and the preparation of this chapter were supported, in part, by Research Scientist Development Award K02-MH-0054 and Grant 717 from the State of Illinois Department of Mental Health and Developmental Disabilities awarded to S. W. Porges. Grant MH 18909 from the National Institute of Mental Health awarded to R. L. Sprague contributed to the described research. K. M. Smith was supported by post-doctoral research fellowship MH-05773 from the National Institute of Mental Health during the preparation of the manuscript. The weighted coherence formula and time series analyses described in the manuscript are products of interactions with R. E. Bohrer.

4

Childhood Hyperkinesis: Relationships between Symptomatology and Home Environment[1]

CARL E. PATERNITE
JAN LONEY

INTRODUCTION

The clinical problems subsumed under the heading of childhood hyperactivity have generated a great deal of public and professional interest over the past several years. Much of this interest is understandable for very practical reasons. Although prevalence figures vary greatly, depending on diagnostic criteria and the population being studied, an estimated 4–10% of school age children (primarily boys) are affected, accounting for approximately 50% of childhood behavior problem referrals (Huessy, 1967; Miller, Palkes, & Stewart, 1973; Prechtl and Stemmer, 1962; Stewart, Pitts, Craig, & Dieruf, 1966; Wender, 1971; Werner, Bierman, French, Simonian, Connor, Smith, & Campbell, 1968). Futhermore, based on findings from the few follow-up studies that have been conducted, it appears that the adolescent and adult prognosis for many such children, with or without treatment, is discouraging.

The most frequently cited view of a presumed hyperkinetic syndrome is of a condition that begins early in life, affects more boys than girls, and involves a symptom complex of hyperactivity and associated behavioral and learning disorders. Werry (1972) has noted that there is considerable agreement on a descriptive clinical level across observers, who emphasize

[1]The research reported in this chapter was partially supported by NIMH Grant 22659 to Jan Loney.

HYPERACTIVE CHILDREN
The Social Ecology of Identification and Treatment

ISBN 0-12-745950-2

short attention span, impulsivity, distractibility, hyperactivity, excitability, clumsiness, and difficulty with schoolwork as central behavioral symptoms (Bakwin, 1949; Burk, 1960, Cantwell, 1975c; Ebaugh, 1923; Laufer & Denhoff, 1957; Stewart *et al.,* 1966; Werry, 1968b). Additional frequently cited symptoms include aggressiveness, antisocial behavior, poor peer relationships, and low self-esteem (Cantwell, 1975c; Clements, 1966, Laufer & Denhoff, 1957; O'Malley & Eisenberg, 1973; Stewart *et al.,* 1966). Descriptive reports also have suggested that hyperkinesis is associated with a high frequency of soft or equivocal neurological signs and mild electroencephalograph (EEG) abnormalities (Burke, 1960; Clements, 1966; Clements & Peters, 1962).

Unfortunately, this prevailing view of a hyperkinetic syndrome includes a broad set of global and poorly defined attributes, perpetuating a variety of definitional and diagnostic problems. Several of these problems are dealt with in detail in other chapters of this volume. Both systematic empirical studies and literature reviews suggest that the hyperkinetic label is applied to a group of children whose clinical symptomatology is variable not only when they are young, but also when they are adolescents and adults. Little attention has been directed either to empirically deriving clinical components of hyperkinesis, or to examining cross-sectional and longitudinal correlates of symptomatology.

Reflecting the view of several investigators, Cantwell (1975c) has urged the identification of factors that mediate the clinical picture of hyperactivity, concurrently and over time. He believes that factors in the family and the larger social milieu may prove to be important correlates of clinical symptomatology and/or indicators of prognosis. Safer and Allen (1976) have suggested that a "family support factor" may be a significant indicator of the outcome of hyperactive children. Lambert, Windmiller, Sandoval, and Moore (1976) have argued that a basic step to further understanding of childhood hyperactivity is to examine carefully the home environment and demographic factors. Likewise, investigators such as Dubey (1976), Rie (1975), and Whalen and Henker (1976) have stressed the need to examine sociofamilial influences as part of a multimodal assessment and treatment of hyperactive children.

The potential importance of environmental influences seems clinically and intuitively obvious; in fact, the relationships among a wide variety of environmental factors and child development and childhood psychopathology in general have been extensively studied and critically reviewed (Becker & Krug, 1965; Bell, 1968; Brim, 1975, Brook, Whiteman, Peisach, & Deutsch, 1974; Deutsch, 1973; Herzog & Lewis, 1970; Hess, 1970; Hetherington & Martin, 1972; Kagan & Moss, 1962; McDermott, Harrison, Schrager, Wilson, Killins, Lindy, & Waggoner, 1967; Morrison, 1974;

Murrell, 1974; Rutter, 1966; Yarrow, Campbell, & Burton, 1968). However, much of the knowledge gained from this work has been applied only on a very limited basis to the study of childhood hyperactivity. Systematic efforts have not often been directed toward examining the interrelationships among child symptomatology and environmental influences, particularly those associated with the home environment.

Cantwell (1972) and Morrison and Stewart (1971) have investigated the relationships between parental psychopathology and childhood hyperactivity. In the Morrison and Stewart study, the parents of 59 nonretarded hyperactive children and 41 normal controls were compared. Cantwell studied the parents of 50 nonretarded hyperactive boys from intact, two-parent families and 50 age-matched normal control boys also from intact families. The information gained about the parents was based on structured interviews, and the results of both investigations were similar. Morrison and Stewart (1971) reported that 33% of the patients' parents and 16% of the control parents were psychiatrically diagnosable. The comparable results reported by Cantwell were 45% and 18% respectively. In both studies, the differences between the hyperactive and control groups were primarily for rates of paternal alcoholism, paternal sociopathy, and maternal hysteria. In addition, both authors reported that approximately 20% of the hyperactive children's parents would have been diagnosable themselves as hyperactive when they were children, compared to less than 1% of the control parents.

In another widely cited study, Conrad and Insel (1967) reported a positive relationship between quality of parenting and short-term response to stimulant drug treatment. Using case record information, the disorders of 31 drug-treated hyperactive children were classified into one of three broad diagnostic categories: organically based, organically–emotionally based, or primarily emotionally based. Although the entire group of patients was considered hyperactive, subject selection criteria were not described. The parents were classified dichotomously on each of three interpersonal–social dimensions: gross deviance, social incompetence, and quality of the parent–child relationship. Case record material, together with information gained from telephone interviews with the parents, were used to make global clinical ratings of the children's improvement with drug treatment. A significant relationship between response to treatment and child classification was demonstrated; 63% of the organic group, but only 16% of the emotional group, were rated as improved or greatly improved. Sixty-seven percent of the emotional group and none of the organic group, were rated as worse. Ratings of gross deviance, social incompetence, and poor parent–child relationship for either parent were significantly related to unfavorable drug response; ratings on the first two parental dimensions also related to child classification.

Loney, Comly, and Simon (1975) also examined the relationship between quality of parental management and initial response to psychostimulant treatment. From children being seen in an outpatient child psychiatry setting, the authors limited their study to 50 boys who were under 11 years old, had Wechsler Intelligence Scale for Children (WISC) full-scale IQs above 80, were not in special education classes, and had been placed on stimulant drugs because of symptoms suggestive of minimal brain dysfunction. For each boy, drug response and quality of parental management were independently rated on dichotomous scales. Response to medication varied, depending on parental management. Whereas 40% of the 25 poorly managed children were rated as positive responders, 72% of the 25 well-managed subjects were rated as positive responders. In addition, the authors reported a positive relationship between quality of parental management and child self-esteem inferred from a projective test; no relationship was found between parental management and child impulse control inferred from the same projective test.

A few investigators have examined the relationships between more directly assessed hyperkinetic symptomatology and environmental influences. As part of their report on the status of 750 Kauai 10-year-olds participating in a longitudinal study, Werner *et al.* (1968) examined relationships among four types of emotional problems and the quality of the children's home environments. Identified from projective tests and behavior checklists completed by teachers, emotional problems were classified as chronic nervous habits (tics, nailbiting, etc.), withdrawn symptoms (shy, lack of self-confidence, etc.), hyperkinetic symptoms (extremely hyperactive, distractible, irritable, etc.), and persistent overaggressiveness (constant quarreling and bullying, stubbornness, destructiveness, etc.). The category labeled hyperkinetic by Werner *et al.* included measures of what frequently have been referred to as primary or core symptoms of hyperkinesis. The category labeled "persistent overaggressiveness" included symptoms that are often considered secondary; they are either less salient features of the hyperkinetic syndrome, or they develop secondarily as a result of the negative interaction between the child's primary symptoms and aspects of his or her social environment (Loney, 1974; Mendelson, Johnson, & Stewart, 1971; Palkes & Stewart, 1972; Paternite, Loney, & Langhorne, 1976; Stewart, Mendelson, & Johnson, 1973; Wender, 1971).

Werner *et al.* (1968) then rated the quality of the children's home environments on 5-point scales for each of three dimensions: socioeconomic status (SES), educational stimulation, and emotional support. The SES rating considered the condition of family housing, paternal occupation, income, and steadiness of employment. The rating of educational stumulation took into account such factors as parents' educational levels, availability of reading materials, and general intellectual opportunities provided in the home. Emotional support ratings were based on several aspects of the parent–child relationships, as reflected in parent interviews.

Examination of a series of chi-square analyses suggested that both chronic nervous habits and persistently withdrawn symptoms were significantly associated with low emotional support in the home, but were unrelated to SES and educational stimulation. Hyperkinetic symptoms did not vary with SES or emotional support, but there was a negative relationship between hyperkinesis and educational stimulation. Persistent overaggressiveness was negatively associated with each of the three environmental dimensions. The authors concluded that "environmental casualities" played an important role in the type of emotional problems that the Kauai children displayed. The extent to which the findings can be generalized is unknown because most of the sample is of Japanese or Hawaiian ancestry and, therefore, culturally different from most hyperkinetic samples that have been studied.

Brandon (1971) examined a number of family environment variables for 71 overactive, 77 physically timid, and 105 normal control children. Compared to the timid and control subjects, the overactive patients came from worse home environments, as indicated by lower physical standards in the home, poor parent–child relationships, broken or never established homes, psychiatric disorder in the mother, use of physical means for discipline, and noninvolvement of the father. Unfortunately, Brandon provided few details regarding identification of the three groups of children and the definitions and measurement of the environmental variables.

Paternite *et al.* (1976) examined the relationships among measures of hyperkinetic symptomatology, SES, and several parenting variables. The study concerned 113 nonretarded, nonpsychotic, 4–12-year-old hyperkinetic–MBD boys who had been treated with Ritalin and were living in families with two parents or parent figures at the time of their outpatient evaluation. Information about the patients and their parents was obtained from case record material. The authors computed an SES index based on a combination of paternal and maternal data. Maternal education and paternal education and occupation were measured using the scales originally developed by Hollingshead and Redlich (1958), and elaborated by Lesser, Fifer, and Clark (1965). In addition, family income and the clinic payment plan chosen by the families of the patients (no-pay, part-pay, or full-pay) were included as part of the SES index. Several parenting variables were also examined, including self and spouse reports of parental shortcomings (e.g., too strict), as well as separate research staff ratings of each parent along nine dimensions (e.g., gross deviance, consistency, love–hostility) derived from previous investigations (Conrad & Insel, 1967; Loney *et al.*, 1975; Schaefer, 1965). Consistent with recent trends to discriminate between primary and secondary hyperkinetic symptoms, severity ratings by research staff were obtained for each of six primary and three secondary symptoms. The primary symptoms were hyperactivity (e.g., always on the go, overactive, restless), fidgetiness (e.g., cannot sit still, fiddles with objects, shifts in his seat), inattention (e.g., cannot concentrate, distractible, forgetful), judgment deficits (e.g., acts on impulse, immature, lacks good judgment), negative affect (e.g., excitable, irritable, low frustration tolerance), and uncoordination (e.g., awkward, messy, poor drawing and handwriting). The secondary symptoms were aggressive interpersonal behavior (e.g., bullies, fights, will not mind), control deficits (e.g., delinquent acts, does not control self, evasion of rules), and self-esteem deficits (e.g., self-blame, self-pity, does not feel worthwhile).

High and low SES groups differed on each of the three secondary symptoms, with boys from low SES homes showing more severe symptomatology. In contrast, no consistent differences resulted for any of the six primary symptoms. Differences between SES groups were also identified for several parenting variables. In a series of stepwise multiple regression analyses, it was found that for each of the three secondary symptoms, the most important independent predictors were parenting variables rather than SES. The conclusion drawn was that SES and parenting styles may be related to hyperkinesis in potentially important ways. It was suggested that more attention be directed toward differentiating types of hyperkinetic symptomatology and identifying their cross-sectional and longitudinal environmental correlates.

Additional evidence for the potential importance of environmental influences on childhood hyperactivity is provided by a limited number of long-term follow-up studies. Several groups of authors have reported notable prospective follow-up studies of the adolescent adjustment of hyperkinetic children originally evaluated in their own clinics. The Montreal group (Minde, Lewin, Weiss, Lavigueur, Douglas, & Sykes, 1971; Minde, Weiss, & Mendelson, 1972; Weiss, Kruger, Danielson, & Elman, 1975; Weiss, Minde, Werry, Douglas, & Nemeth, 1971) have published several progress reports of the results of their 4–6-year follow-up study. The published reports are based on overlapping groups of children, with sample sizes ranging from 64 to 91. At referral, the children were approximately between 6 and 13 years old, had WISC full scale IQs above 84, were not suffering from known brain damage, were not psychotic, and were living at home with at least one parent. A primary complaint of parents and teachers for all the children was long-term, sustained hyperactivity. The children's ages at follow-up ranged approximately from 10 to 18, and the majority had been treated initially with chlorpromazine and/or a variety of cerebral stimulants. The measures obtained at referral and follow-up were based on interviews, psychological tests, neurological examinations, and ratings by psychiatrists, teachers, and parents. Examination of their results has led the Montreal group to conclude that hyperactive individuals do not completely outgrow their problems from the time of referral to follow-up.

Weiss *et al.* (1971) examined several referral variables in an attempt to identify prognostic indicators of satisfactory school performance, good emotional adjustment, and antisocial behavior at follow-up. Those succeeding in school at follow-up (20%) had obtained higher full scale IQs at referral. No predictors of emotional adjustment were identified, but overt antisocial behavior at follow-up was related to child aggression and family pathology at referral. The three discriminating items on the family pathology rating scale were poor mother–child relationship, poor mental health of the parents, and punitive childrearing practices.

Minde *et al.* (1972) also reported an attempt to identify prognostic indicators. Based on mothers' reports on six areas of functioning at follow-up, each child was judged to be in a good outcome, intermediate outcome, or poor outcome group. The six areas were peer interactions, relationship to authority, degree of antisocial behavior, object relationships, number of present complaints, and sexual adjustment. The 28 children rated as satisfactory in five of six areas were assigned to the good outcome group, whereas the 18 children rated as unsatisfactory in four of six areas were assigned to the poor outcome group. Forty-one additional children were assigned to the intermediate group, and 4 children were not classified due to a lack of information. Good versus bad outcome was unrelated to either the duration of drug treatment or the use of psychotherapy or counseling. Two significant predictors of poor outcome at follow-up were high aggression ratings and high scores on the Psychopathic factor of the Peterson–Quay scale (Peterson & Quay, 1967) at referral. In comparison to the good outcome group, the poor outcome patients also tended to have had at referral: high ratings on most target symptoms; a positive history of brain damage; low IQ; low socioeconomic class; a poor mother–child relationship; and poor family environment. Although none of these measures individually discriminated between good versus poor outcome, their combined use in a discriminant analysis resulted in a significant discrimination between the two groups.

In a further effort to identify prognostic indicators, Weiss *et al.* (1975) examined the relationships between three initial referral measures (degree of hyperactivity, WISC full scale IQ, and family diagnosis ratings) and four measures of follow-up outcome (emotional adjustment, delinquency, mother's impression of improvement or deterioration, and academic performance). The family diagnosis score was the sum of six 5-point ratings, one each dealing with the parents' marital relationship, psychiatric illness of the parents, continuous presence of the mother or mother-substitute in the home, the emotional climate of the family, the number of moves made by the family, and the physical condition of the home.

Consistent with previous findings, WISC IQ at referral correlated significantly and positively with academic performance at follow-up. In addition, for the group of patients who had been treated with methylphenidate, a good family diagnosis was significantly correlated with three measures of good outcome (academic achievement, positive emotional adjustment, and absence of delinquency).

Mendelson *et al.* (1971) conducted a 2–5-year follow-up study of 75 male and 8 female hyperkinetic children. Subject selection criteria included symptoms of hyperactivity and/or distractibility for at least 2 years, and at least 4 of 35 additional hyperkinetic symptoms over a 2-year period (e.g., irritable, aggressive, daydreams). Also included in the sample were 8 children who met the hyperactivity–distractibility criteria and gave a "global impression of the syndrome" but did not meet the criterion of 4 additional symptoms. Unlike the Montreal group, the authors did not employ psychosis, major brain damage, low IQ, or absence of parent figures in the home as exclusion criteria, which suggests that the Mendelson *et al.* (1971) sample was a more loosely defined and heterogeneous group than the one studied by Weiss and her colleagues.

The Mendelson *et al.* study relied on structured interviews with the mothers of the patients. At follow-up, the patients were between 12 and 15 years of age and had received several forms of treatment, predominantly psychostimulant therapy. Improvement at follow-up was reported for 55% of the children. However, most of them were thought by their mothers still to be displaying core hyperkinetic symptoms, approximately 50% had had some contact with the law, and a comparable percentage were described as having low self-confidence. Additional salient concerns of the mothers were problems with rebelliousness and poor schoolwork.

The authors then selected subgroups of the sample based on two separate dimensions. Patients who were described as globally improved in all areas of functioning were compared with those who were unchanged or worse; in addition, those with six or more antisocial symptoms at follow-up were compared with those displaying three or fewer antisocial symptoms. Whereas no predictors of global improvement were identified, the patients with six or more antisocial symptoms were signficantly more likely to have had fathers with a childhood history of learning, behavior problems, or several police arrests.

A few additional investigators have reported the results of follow-up studies of hyperkinetic children (Denhoff, 1973; Dykman & Ackerman, 1975; Dykman, Peters, & Ackerman, 1973; Huessy, Metoyer, & Townsend, 1974; Laufer, 1971; Stewart *et al.*, 1973). However, none of these authors has reported systematic attempts to identify specific environmental correlates of symptomatology or indicators of prognosis.

In summary, it is difficult to draw conclusions regarding the relationships between environmental influences and hyperkinesis. Very few efforts have been directed either toward classifying the symptoms of hyperkinetic children or toward assessing specific environmental influences and their relationships to symptoms. The primary focus of follow-up investigations has been on general description of the adolescent outcome of heterogeneous patient groups. The attempts to identify specific prognostic indicators have been generally described incompletely and nonsystematically; it is thus difficult to draw conclusions about the usefulness of the identified indicators.

Several advocates of empirically based measurement of the environment have pointed out that it is inappropriate to conceptualize the environment as a unitary, single entity. Such investigators as Sells (1963), Frederiksen (1972), Insel and Moos (1974), and Mischel (1977) suggest that the environment should be viewed as the combination of a number of subenvironments, which may be related differently to various person characteristics. Much of the limited work in the general area of environmental measurement has reflected this emphasis on the study of specific subenvironments, for example, college and university settings, industrial settings, penal and psychiatric settings, and home environments (Insel & Moos, 1974; Moos, 1973; Walberg & Marjoribanks, 1973). Sells (1963) has argued that a satisfactory conceptualization of any set of subenvironmental influences can be based only on a taxonomic, dimensional analysis of the relevant environmental variables, rather than on "piecemeal" and nonempirical approaches. In a review of the systematic approaches that can be utilized in the construction of environmental taxonomies (e.g., factor analysis, disciminant analysis, inverse factor analysis, cluster analysis), Frederiksen (1972) noted that all approaches are grounded in a concern for objectivity and empirical feasibility of the resulting factors or clusters.

Unfortunately, existing examinations of environmental influences on hyperkinesis still reflect the nonempirical approach that Sells (1963) admonished against. Although most investigators have focused on home environments of hyperkinetic children, across studies these environments have been defined and measured very differently, reflecting quite arbitrary, nonempirical views of important variables and measurement indices.

A SYSTEMATIC STUDY OF CHILDHOOD HYPERKINESIS AND HOME ENVIRONMENT

Recently, our research group has begun to examine the relationships between environmental influences and childhood hyperactivity. In the study reported here, the purpose was to examine the cross-sectional and longitudinal interrelationships among empirically derived dimensions of hyperkinetic symptomatology and the home environment.

Methodology

DATA ARCHIVE

The clinical sample was drawn from the data archive of a comprehensive cross-sectional and longitudinal investigation of the hyperkinetic–minimal brain dysfunction (MBD) syndrome presently being conducted by Loney and her colleagues (Langhorne & Loney, 1975; Langhorne, Loney, Paternite, & Bechtoldt, 1976; Loney, Langhorne, & Paternite, 1978; Loney, Langhorne, Paternite, Whaley-Klahn, Broeker, & Hacker, 1976; Loney & Ordoña, 1975; Paternite & Loney, 1975; Paternite *et al.*, 1976). Of all 4–12-year-old boys seen for outpatient diagnostic evaluation at the University of Iowa Child Psychiatry Service between January 1, 1967, and September 1, 1972, there were 482 who had not been treated with drugs within the previous 6 months. Senior psychiatrists recommended 62% of these (N = 300) for a trial of cerebral stimulants. Of these 300 boys, 59 were excluded from the investigation because their tested IQs were less than 70 or because they were suffering from peripheral sensory loss, psychosis, epilepsy, cerebral palsy, or unequivocal brain damage. Because the aim of the original investigation was to identify predictors of clinical response to Ritalin and Dexedrine, the sample was limited to outpatient boys whose treatment with these drugs was initiated and followed by staff psychiatrists or residents. It was further required that drug treatment be initiated within 6 weeks of the outpatient evaluation, and that at least one progress note be placed in the child's medical record before termination of drug treatment, addition of other drugs or therapies, or referral to a local physician for drug follow-up.

Application of these exclusionary criteria resulted in a total sample of 135 boys. The mean age at referral was 8.7 years, and IQs ranged from 71 to 133 with a mean of 99.5. The group included boys from rural and urban areas of Iowa and a few surrounding states, and was 98% white (as is the Iowa general population). A wide range of socioeconomic background was represented. At the time of initial referral, 35% of the sample were private or full-fee patients, 35% were clinic or reduced-fee patients, and 30% were indigent or no-fee patients. As defined by the Hollingshead (1957) scale, 21% of the children came from social classes I or II, 33% from class III, 26% from class IV, and 20% from class V. Based on information presented by the clinic staff at the time of the outpatient evaluations, 95 of the 135 boys were diagnosed Hyperkinetic Reaction of Childhood according to the

Diagnostic and Statistical Manual (DSM-II) of the American Psychiatric Association (1968). Sixteen boys received no diagnosis, or their diagnosis was deferred. Each of the remaining 24 boys was given one of the variety of diagnoses (e.g., adjustment reaction, unsocialized aggressive reaction, learning disability, nonpsychotic chronic brain syndrome, "other"), with no more than 5 boys receiving any one diagnosis.

As the initial part of the comprehensive investigation, Loney and her colleagues developed an extensive data archive concerning the 135 boys at referral. Pretreatment data were compiled on a multitude of family, perinatal, developmental, psychological, psychiatric, neurological, and educational variables. The medical records of children seen at the Child Psychiatry Service during the 1967–1972 period were unusually extensive, detailed, and orderly. In addition to information abstracted from the intake forms, ratings of clinic staff reports were made by research personnel.

Between September, 1973, and December, 1975, 92% of the original sample were reevaluated. The follow-up data were collected directly from parents as well as from the boys themselves. The sources of information included the following: revisions of the intake evaluation forms; extensive semistructured interviews with the mother, father, and child separately; ratings and checklists completed by parents, teachers, and research staff; and psychological testing of the child.

CLINICAL SAMPLE

From the total group of 135 boys, the main clinical sample for the present study was limited further to the 103 boys who at referral were 6–12 years old and were living in households with both a mother and father figure. All 103 boys were subsequently given a clinical trial of Ritalin. Four cases were excluded due to the absence of completed intake forms and sufficient record information at referral for assessing symptomatology and the environment, resulting in a final sample of 99 boys. Follow-up was completed for 95% (N = 94) of the sample of 99.

A replication sample, identified by Loney and her colleagues, consists of 65 additional hyperkinetic–MBD boys excluded from the initial sample only because drug treatment or progess notes describing drug response were delayed for more than 6 weeks, progress notes were incomplete, or drug treatment was started subsequent to the outpatient evaluation by a physician in the family's community, instead of by a physician at the University of Iowa. In all other respects the criteria for the initial and replication samples were identical. From the total of 65 subjects, the replication sample for the present study was limited to the 42 boys who were 6–12 years old and living with intact families at referral.

GENERAL PROCEDURE

The general steps followed were:

1. Empirical identification, using factor analysis, of dimensions of: (*a*) clinical symptomatology at referral; (*b*) home environment at referral; (*c*) change in home environment over time (referral to follow-up); and (*d*) clinical symptomatology at follow-up.
2. Examination, using stepwise multiple regression, of the relationships of: (*a*) environment at referral with symptomatology at referral; (*b*) symptomatology at referral with symptomatology at follow up; (*c*) environment at referral with symptomatology at follow-up; (*d*) change in environment over time with symptomatology at follow-up; and (*e*) symptomatology at follow-up with the combination of symptomatology and environment at referral and change in environment over time.
3. Replication for Step 2a. Since follow-up was not completed for the replication subjects, the replication analyses could only be completed for Step 2a.

A major purpose of the study was to examine several leads suggested by previous work, and the methodology was selected in an attempt to overcome several weaknesses of past studies. The choice of factor analysis as a means for defining dimensions of symptomatology and the environment was an attempt to avoid the pitfalls associated with arbitrarily assumed concomitance among measures. In an attempt to minimize the influence of information sources on the idenfication of symptom factors (Langhorne *et al.*, 1976), separate single-source analyses were conducted for information provided by mothers, by fathers, by parents together, and by research staff. We began with a lengthy list of variables which encompass a conceptually representative sample of the dimensions of interest, since the domain of factors that can result from factor analysis is limited by the variables entered (Frederiksen, 1972; Quay, 1979).

MEASURES OF SYMPTOMATOLOGY

An overview of the measures employed in the present study is provided in Table 4.1. The initial measures of behavioral symptomatology were selected to include indicators of frequently cited hyperkinetic symptoms, including core (or primary) and resultant (or secondary) behaviors.

The indicators of child symptomatology, as reported by the parents at referral and follow-up, consisted of dichotomous checklist responses from the intake evaluation forms, in which the presence or absence of each of 20 child descriptors was noted. This checklist was usually completed by the mother, in collaboration with the father. The 20 descriptors were as follows: impulsive, sensitive, resentful, resents authority, awkward, does not

TABLE 4.1
Overview of Measures

Referral data: main sample	*Referral data: replication sample*[a]
Child symptomatology	Child symptomatology
As reported by parents	As reported by parents
As rated by research staff	As rated by research staff
Home environment	Home environment
Follow-up data: main sample	
Child symptomatology	
As reported by parents[b]	
As rated by mother	
As rated by father	
As rated by psychologist examining the patient	
Change in home environment	
(Referral to follow-up)	

[a]The referral measures for the replication sample are the same as those for the main sample.
[b]The follow-up measures of child symptomatology as reported by the parents are the same as those for both samples at referral.

care, inconsiderate, impertinent, untruthful, quick-tempered, seclusive, cruel, will not mind, obedient, emotional, stubborn, inadequate, affectionate, spoiled, and considerate. This checklist is an early version of the Conners Parent Rating Scale (Conners, 1970, 1973c).

The indicators of child symptomatology at referral rated by the research staff consisted of the ratings of each child on the severity of nine hyperkinetic–MBD symptoms. The primary symptoms were hyperactivity, fidgetiness, inattention, judgment deficits, negative affect (excitability–irritability), and uncoordination. The secondary symptoms were aggressive interpersonal behavior, control deficits, and self-esteem deficits. For each of the six primary symptoms and for the secondary symptom, aggressive interpersonal behavior, the research staff ratings were made on 6-point scales. The rating for each of these seven symptoms was based on the presence in the clinic staff reports of specific child descriptors which had been judged to fit conceptually under the heading of the particular symptom. For the two additional secondary symptoms (control deficits and self-esteem deficits), the ratings were made on 5-point symptom severity scales used in a previous study (Loney, 1974). The nine symptom ratings for the main sample were completed independently by each of two judges. The values used as indicators of each symptom were the sum of the two judges' ratings. The effective rater reliabilities for the summed symptom ratings were estimated by applying the Spearman–Brown formula as described by Rosenthal (1973); their magnitude ranged from .72 to .80. For the replication sample, the ratings were completed by one of the two original judges; no reliability figures could be calculated, and no checks were made for possible rater drift. The indicators of child symptomatology at follow-up as rated by the psychologist examining the patient were similar in form and content to the ratings by the research staff at referral.

The indicators of child symptomatology at follow-up, rated separately by the mother and father, were derived from a dichotomous checklist constructed by our research group for the follow-up study (Loney *et al.*, 1976). Each parent noted the presence or absence of numerous child descriptors which fit conceptually under the headings of the primary and secondary symptoms. All of the child descriptors were presented to each parent in one alphabetized list and were not subdivided according to the general symptom headings. The measures of symptomatology based on these descriptors consisted of the sum of items checked as present, under each of the eight general symptom headings.

MEASURES OF HOME ENVIRONMENT

Selection of home environment indicators was based not only on past attempts to measure this environment for hyperactive children, but also on current conceptualizations in the general area of environmental assessment. Specifically, measures of a number of "distal" or macroenvironmental and more "proximal" or specific variables were included (Walberg & Marjoribanks, 1973). The "distal" variables included multiple measures of SES, family size and stability, home circumstances and resources, and quality of life in the home. The "proximal" variables included multiple measures of the mother–father relationship, parent–child relationship, parental discipline practices and styles, parental social competence and mental illness, structure and routine provided in the home, and parental aspirations for the child (Bronfenbrenner, 1974a; Cantwell, 1975c; Conrad & Insel, 1967; Garbarino, 1976; Paternite *et al.*, 1976; Sells, 1963; Werner *et al.*, 1968). A list of the 57 environment variables is provided in Table 4.2

Results and Discussion

Prior to the factor analyses, statistical transformations were performed on all variables in order to normalize and standardize the distributions, thereby rendering the data more tractible and appropriate for multivariate analysis (Harris, 1975; Langhorne, Loney, & Hacker, 1978). Then principal axis (factor) analyses, with iterations and varimax rotation, were performed (Nie, Hull, Jenkins, Stenbrenner, & Bent, 1975). Factors with eigenvalues exceeding 1.00 after initial factoring and exceeding .75 after iterations were retained. Two criteria were used for including variables on a given factor: a minimum loading of .40, and a significant correlation with each of the other variables included on the factor.[2] After determining the factor-defining variables for a particular factor, factor scores for each subject were computed by summing the normalized standard scores of each variable (Horn, 1965; Schweiker, 1967). All multiple regression analyses followed the stepwise techniques documented by Nie *et al.* (1975).

For ease in communicating the following results, labels are provided for each of the symptom and environment factors. The choice of labels was based on what appears primarily to be reflected by the variables comprising the factor. If the content of a factor could not readily be classified as reflecting a particular dimension, the factor was labeled "unclassified."

CHILD SYMPTOMS AT REFERRAL

From the 20 parent-reported indicators of child symptomatology at referral, four factors were obtained, accounting for 80.2% of the initial factor variance. One of these factors is apparently a cluster of Aggression indicators, one reflects Prosocial Behavior, one encompasses Internalizing symptomatology, and another represents Unclassified Behavior Problems. For the nine staff-rated indicators of child symptomatology at referral, one Aggression and one Hyperkinesis factor emerged, accounting for 82.7% of the initial factor variance. Labels and specific descriptors for each factor are listed in Table 4.3.

HOME ENVIRONMENT AT REFERRAL

The 57 indicators of the home environment were reduced to 18 factors, accounting for 96.5% of the initial factor variance (see Table 4.4). It was concluded that the Child Difficult to Raise factor reflects child symptomatology rather than home environment; thus this factor was excluded from the list of environmental predictors in the subsequent series of multiple regression analyses.

CHILD SYMPTOMS AT FOLLOW-UP

From the 20 parent-reported indicators of child symptomatology at follow-up, five factors resulted, accounting for 87.5% of the initial factor variance. Two factors emerged from mother's ratings of the eight indicators of child symptomatology at follow-up, accounting for 85.6% of the initial factor variance: one factor emerged from father's ratings, accounting for

[2]A complete set of tables for the varimax rotated factor matrices can be obtained upon request. Please write to: Carl E. Paternite, Ph.D., Department of Psychology, Miami University, Oxford, Ohio 45056.

TABLE 4.2
Indices of the Home Environment

Distal or Macroenvironmental Variables

SES INDICES

Father's Education: 1–7 scale based on Hollingshead (1957) and Lesser *et al.* (1965)
Father's Occupation: 1–7 scale based on Hollingshead (1957) and Lesser *et al.* (1965)
Mother's Education: 1–7 scale based on Hollingshead (1957) and Lesser *et al.* (1965)
Mother's Occupation: Dichotomous employed–not-employed rating
Family Income: Combined paternal and maternal income in dollars per year
Computed SES Index: Trichotomous rating based on Paternite *et al.* (1976)
Two-Factor Index of Social Position: Weighted sum of paternal occupation and education based on Hollingshead (1957)

FAMILY SIZE AND STABILITY, HOME CIRCUMSTANCES, AND RESOURCES

Number of Children in the Child's Sociological Family
Child's Sociological Birth-Order Position among Children Living in the Home (first, second, etc.)
Number of Previous Marriages of the Mother
Number of Previous Marriages of the Father
Child Ever Placed Outside the Home: yes–no dichotomy
Child Adopted: yes–no
Child from Rural Home: rural route versus city residence
Child Shares Bed: yes–no
Child Shares Room: yes–no
Population of City Nearest to the Family's Residence: according to the 1970 census
Child Born in Iowa: yes–no

Proximal Variables

MOTHER–FATHER RELATIONSHIP

Mother–Father Relationship According to Mother: trichotomous rating (more harmony than conflict, as much harmony as conflict, more conflict than harmony)
Mother–Father Relationship According to Father: trichotomous rating (more harmony than conflict, as much harmony as conflict, more conflict than harmony)

FAMILY INTERACTIONS AND RELATIONSHIPS

Maternal Shortcomings as a Parent
- *Too Busy According to Herself:* yes–no
- *Too Busy According to Her Spouse:* yes–no
- *Too Easygoing According to Herself:* yes–no
- *Too Easygoing According to Her Spouse:* yes–no
- *Too Strict According to Herself:* yes–no
- *Too Strict According to Her Spouse:* yes–no
- *Too Short-Tempered According to Herself:* yes–no
- *Too Short-Tempered According to Her Spouse:* yes–no
- *Too Demanding According to Herself:* yes–no
- *Too Demanding According to Her Spouse:* yes–no

Paternal Shortcomings as a Parent
- *Too Busy According to Himself:* yes–no
- *Too Busy According to His Spouse:* yes–no
- *Too Easygoing According to Himself:* yes–no
- *Too Easygoing According to His Spouse:* yes–no
- *Too Strict According to Himself:* yes–no

TABLE 4.2 *(continued)*

Too Strict According to His Spouse: yes–no
Too Short-Tempered According to Himself: yes–no
Too Short-Tempered According to His Spouse: yes–no
Too Demanding According to Himself: yes–no
Too Demanding According to His Spouse: yes–no

ADDITIONAL INDICES OF FAMILY INTERACTIONS AND RELATIONSHIPS

Sum for Research Staff Ratings of Maternal Gross Deviance (e.g., mental illness, severe retardation); Social Incompetence (e.g., heavy drinking, police contacts); and Poor Mother–Child Relationship (e.g., outright rejection, brutal punishment): dichotomous ratings based on Conrad and Insel (1967).
Sum for Research Staff Ratings of Paternal Gross Deviance (e.g., mental illness, severe retardation); Social Incompetence (e.g., heavy drinking, police contacts); and Poor Mother–Child Relationship (e.g., outright rejection, brutal punishment): dichotomous ratings based on Conrad and Insel (1967).
Mother–Child Relationship According to Mother: trichotomous rating (more harmony than conflict, as much harmony as conflict, more conflict than harmony)
Father–Child Relationship According to Father: trichotomous rating (more harmony than conflict, as much harmony as conflict, more conflict than harmony)
Child Difficult to Raise According to Mother: yes–no
Child Difficult to Raise According to Father: yes–no
Mother's Educational Aspirations for Child are Child-Centered (indicates choice is up to child versus stating own preference)
Mother's Occupational Aspirations for Child are Child-Centered (indicates choice is up to child versus stating own preference)
Father's Educational Aspirations for Child are Child-Centered (indicates choice is up to child versus stating own preference)
Father's Occupational Aspirations for Child are Child-Centered (indicates choice is up to child versus stating own preference)
Mother Talks to Relatives About Child's Problems: yes–no
Father Talks to Relatives About Child's Problems: yes–no
Mother Reads Books About Child's Problems: yes–no
Father Reads Books About Child's Problems: yes–no
Child Turns to Parents When He Is in a Jam: yes–no
Parents Help Child with Schoolwork: yes–no
Child Has Regular Bedtime: yes–no

82.1% of the initial factor variance. The nine staff-rated indicators of child symptomatology at follow-up yielded three factors, accounting for 85.9% of the initial factor variance. Labels and descriptors for each factor are provided in Table 4.5.

CHANGE IN THE ENVIRONMENT OVER TIME

Three exploratory measures of environmental changes from referral to follow-up were employed. The first two were based on factor-defining indicators from environment factors 1 and 2, which were selected primarily because they were available with very little missing data in the referral and

TABLE 4.3
Factors for Child Symptoms at Referral[a]

Parents' Report	Research Staff Ratings
1. *Aggression*	1. *Aggression*
Resents authority	Control deficits
Impertinent	Negative affect
Cruel	Aggressive interpersonal behavior
Inconsiderate	2. *Hyperkinesis*
2. *Prosocial behavior*	Judgment deficits
Obedient	Inattention
Considerate	Hyperactivity
3. *Internalizing behavior*	
Seclusive	
Inadequate	
4. *Unclassified behavior problems*	
Resentful	
Impulsive	

[a]The factor labels employed in this table are utilized for ease in communication of subsequent results. However, the reader is reminded that the specific descriptors listed below the factor labels constitute the operational definitions of the factors.

follow-up data sets: (*a*) change in the father's occupational level (Hollingshead, 1957); and (*b*) change in the mother's report that she and the father are too busy. The third change indicator is a trichotomous measure of whether the child's parent figures at referral and follow-up were the same people. (Specifically, the value of one was scored if both parents were the same, the value of two if the mother or father were different, and the value of three if both were different. These three measures were labeled Father's Occupational Change, Parents Still Too Busy, and Change of Parent Figures.

RELATIONSHIPS BETWEEN THE ENVIRONMENT AND CHILD SYMPTOMS AT REFERRAL

The results of the stepwise multiple regression analyses are summarized in Table 4.6. Reported in the table are the predictor variables that result in significant, independent contributions to the regression equations. The signs of the simple correlations and the beta weights reflect the direction of the relationships between each individual predictor variable and the criterion. For all multiple regression analyses, the direction of each factor scale is such that increasing numerical values indicate increased presence of child behavior pattern (e.g., high aggression, more prosocial behavior), or increased presence of a detrimental environmental condition (e.g., low SES, parents too busy).

The results of the multiple regression analyses for the environment and child symptoms at referral suggest that the relationships between symptomatology and the environment differ for different types or classes of symptoms. The magnitude of the multiple correlations for factors defined primarily by indicators of Aggression (.39 and .45) are consistently larger than those for factors defined primarily by indicators of Hyperkinesis and Internalizing symptomatology (NS and .26, respectively). Especially noteworthy is the failure to identify any environmental predictors for the symptom factor defined primarily by core indicators of Hyperkinesis.

For the Aggression factors, 4 of the possible 17 environment factors contribute significantly to the regression equations. None of these 4 environment factors contribute significantly to the regression equations for the Hyperkinetic and Internalizing symptom factors, thus providing futher evidence for a difference in the patterns of relationships between symptomatology and the environment.

In the present study the Parental Disturbance factor is related to staff-rated aggression. To the extent that parental disturbance (possibly including paternal alcoholism and sociopathy and maternal hysteria) is measured by this factor, the previously reported associations between parental psychopathology and childhood hyperkinesis (e.g., Morrison & Stewart, 1971; Cantwell, 1972) might be more accurately described as a link between parental disturbance and aggressive symptomatology.

The contribution of the Urban Residence factor suggests that, even for boys coming from primarily small-to-moderate-sized towns (population range from 175 to 201,404, with an average of 37,099), aggressive symptomatology is associated with a more urban type environment. There are a number of possible explanations for this relationship, including the increased pressures and opportunities for such aggression that are associated with any population center and population density, even within this restricted range. It may also be that similar aggressive behavior is considered less deviant in rural areas, because it is less likely to infringe upon the rights and/or standards of those outside of the immediate family.

The SES factor does not contribute significantly to any regression analyses for symptomatology at referral. This lack of contribution of SES is consistent with the suggestion offered by Paternite *et al.* (1976) that SES should be viewed as a multidimensional concept defined by a wide variety of SES-related influences, some of which are represented by the other environment factors in the present study. In fact, the SES factor is correlated with three of the five environment factors (r from .26 to .36, $p < .01$) that contribute significantly to the regression analyses for symtomatology at referral.

It is not possible to determine cause and effect in the relationships that have been identified. However, the present results are consistent with reports by previous investigators that relationships between symptomatology

TABLE 4.4
Factors for Home Environment at Referral[a]

1. *SES*
 Index of social position
 Father's occupation
 Father's education
 Computed SES index
 Mother's education
 Family income
2. *Parents too busy*
 Father too busy according to spouse
 Father too busy according to self
 Mother too busy according to self
 Mother too busy according to spouse
3. *Father too short-tempered*
 Father too short-tempered according to self
 Father too short-tempered according to spouse
 Father not too easygoing according to self
4. *Parental disturbance*
 Conrad & Insel (1967) social deviance rating of mother
 Number of previous marriages of mother
 Conrad & Insel (1967) social deviance rating of father
 Child placed outside home
5. *Child difficult to raise*
 Child difficult to raise, father's report
 Child difficult to raise, mother's report
6. *Mother too strict*
 Mother too strict according to self
 Mother too strict according to spouse
7. *Unclassified parent factor*
 Mother employed
 Father too strict according to spouse
8. *Talks to relatives*
 Father talks to relatives about child's problems
 Mother talks to relatives about child's problems
9. *Parental knowledgeability*
 Mother reads books about child's problems
 Father reads books about child's problems
10. *Mother too short-tempered* ●
 Mother too short-tempered according to self
 Mother too short-tempered according to spouse
11. *Mother–Father relationship*
 Mother–Father relationship, mother's report
 Mother–Father relationship, father's report
12. *Father too demanding*
 Father too demanding according to self
 Father too demanding according to spouse
13. *Child's birth order*
 Child's birth order

TABLE 4.4 *(continued)*

14. *Mother too easygoing*
Mother too easygoing according to self
Mother too easygoing according to spouse
15. *Urban residence*
Child from rural home
Population of city nearest to residence
16. *Child-centered educational aspirations*
Mother's educational aspirations for child are child-centered
17. *Parent–Child relationships*
Father–Child relationship, father's report
Mother–Child relationship, mother's report
18. *Child shares bed*
Child shares a bed

[a] The factor labels employed in this table are utilized for ease in communication of subsequent results. However, the reader is reminded that the specific descriptors listed below the factor labels constitute the operational definitions of the factors.

and the environment differ for different types of symptoms (Paternite *et al.*, 1976; Werner *et al.*, 1968). Support is provided also for the diagnostic utility of the frequently cited distinction between core hyperkinetic symptomatology and resultant aggressive symptomatology (Loney, 1974; Mendelson *et al.*, 1971; Palkes & Stewart, 1972; Paternite *et al.*, 1976; Stewart *et al.*, 1973; Wender, 1971).

REPLICATION ANALYSES: RELATIONSHIPS BETWEEN THE ENVIRONMENT AND CHILD SYMPTOMS AT REFERRAL FOR THE REPLICATION SAMPLE

The multiple regression analyses for the replication sample allow somewhat limited comparisons to the analyses for the main sample, because the following environment factor-defining indicators are not available for the 42 replication subjects: family income, computed SES index, Conrad and Insel (1967) Social Deviance rating of mother and father, and child's sociological birth order position among children living in the home. With these exceptions, the defining indicators for the environment and referral symptom factors are the same as those employed for the main sample.

For the replication sample, a series of stepwise multiple regression analyses was conducted to examine the relationships between the environment and child symptoms at referral (see Table 4.7). Despite the missing factor-defining environment indicators, the multiple regression pattern for the replication sample is generally consistent with the results for the main sample. The resulting multiple correlations for the two Aggression factors (.69 and .54) are notably larger than those for the Hyperkinetic and Internalizing symptom factors (.42 and NS, respectively).

TABLE 4.5
Factors for Child Symptoms at Follow-Up[a]

Parents' Report	Mother's Ratings	Staff Ratings
1. *Prosocial behavior*	1. *Aggression*	1. *Hyperkinesis*
Considerate	Aggressive interpersonal behavior	Hyperactivity
Sensitive	Negative affect	Fidgetiness
Affectionate	Judgment deficits	Inattention
Emotional	2. *Hyperkinesis*	Judgment deficits
2. *Unclassified behavior problems I*	Fidgetiness	2. *Aggression*
Stubborn	Hyperactivity	Control deficits
Impulsive	Uncoordination	Judgment deficits
3. *Unclassified behavior problems II*	Father's Ratings	Aggressive interpersonal behavior
Inadequate	1. *General behavior problems*	3. *Unclassified behavior problems*
Won't mind	Aggressive interpersonal behavior	Negative affect
4. *Unclassified behavior problems III*	Judgment deficits	Self-esteem deficits
Quick-tempered	Hyperactivity	
Impulsive	Negative affect	
5. *Aggression*	Fidgetiness	
Resentful		
Resents authority		
Untruthful		

[a]The factor labels employed in this table are utilized for ease in communication of subsequent results. However, the reader is reminded that the specific descriptors listed below the factor labels constitute the operational definitions of the factors.

TABLE 4.6
Stepwise Multiple Regression Analyses: The Relationships between the Environment and Child Symptoms at Referral

Step entered	*Predictor*	*Correlations* *Simple*	*Multiple*	*Beta*
	Criterion: referral symptoms by parents: aggression			
1	Environment: parent–child relationships	.33†††	.33	.34***
2	Environment: father too short-tempered	−.22†	.40	−.22*
3	Environment: urban residence[a]	.20†	.45	.19*
	Criterion: referral symptoms by parents: prosocial behavior[b]			
1	Environment: parent–child relationships	−.39†††	.39	−.39***
	Criterion: referral symptoms by parents: internalizing behavior			
1	Environment: parental knowledgeability	−.26††	.26	−.26**
	Criterion: referral symptoms by parents: unclassified behavior problems			
1	Environment: urban residence	.22†	.22	.22*
2	Environment: parent–child relationships	.21†	.30	.23*
3	Environment: parental knowledgeability	−.18	.36	−.19*
	Criterion: referral symptoms by staff: aggression			
1	Environment: parental disturbance	.39†††	.39	.39***
	Criterion: referral symptoms by staff: hyperkinesis			
—	—	—	—	—

[a] Increasing numerical values are associated with more urban residence.
[b] Increasing numerical values are associated with more prosocial behavior
†††Correlation significantly different from zero at $p < .001$ level.
††$p < .01$ level.
†$p < .05$ level.
*** Independent contribution of the factor significant at $p < .001$ level.
**$p < .01$ level.
*$p < .05$ level.

TABLE 4.7
Replication Stepwise Multiple Regression Analyses: The Relationships between the Environment and Child Symptoms at Referral

		Correlations		
Step entered	*Predictors*	*Simple*	*Multiple*	*Beta*
	Criterion: referral symptoms by parents: aggression			
1	Environment: parent–child relationships	.54†††	.54	.72***
2	Environment: parents too busy	−.16	.61	−.47*
3	Environment: SES	−.03	.69	−.37**
	Criterion: referral symptoms by parents: prosocial behavior			
1	Environment: parent–child relationships	−.38†	.38	−.38*
	Criterion: referral symptoms by parents: internalizing behavior			
—	—	—	—	—
	Criterion: referral symptoms by parents: unclassified behavior problems			
1	Environment: parent–child relationships	.33†	.33	.33*
	Criterion: referral symptoms by staff: aggression			
1	Environment: parent–child relationships	.47††	.47	.36**
2	Environment: mother–father relationships	.42††	.54	.29*
	Criterion: referral symptoms by staff: hyperkinesis			
1	Environment: mother–father relationship	.42††	.42	.42**

†††$p < .001$ level.
††$p < .01$ level.
†$p < .05$ level.
***$p < .001$ level.
**$p < .01$ level.
*$p < .05$ level.

Especially encouraging from a replication point of view is the fact that the most salient environment predictor for the main sample analyses is similarly important for the replication sample analyses. Specifically, for both samples the Parent–Child Relationships factor is the largest predictor for the analyses for referral Aggression by parents, and referral Prosocial Behavior by parents. In addition, this environment factor is the second largest predictor and the largest predictor, respectively, for the main and replication analyses for referral Unclassified Behavior Problems by parents; it is the largest predictor for the replication analysis for referral Aggression by staff. Thus, although there are some discrepancies between the main sample analyses and the admittedly limited replication analyses, the general patterns of relationships between symptomatology and the environment are consistent. Nevertheless, more extensive attempts to replicate clearly are indicated.

RELATIONSHIPS BETWEEN CHILD SYMPTOMS AT REFERRAL AND FOLLOW-UP

A third series of stepwise multiple regression analyses examined the relationships between child symptoms at referral and follow-up for the main sample (see Table 4.8). The magnitudes of the multiple correlations at follow-up do not differ markedly across types of symptomatology. However, there does appear to be a pattern to the relationships between symptomatology at referral and at follow-up. For the three Aggression factors, the two Hyperkinesis Factors, the General Behavior Problems factor, and one of the four Unclassified Behavior Problems factors at follow-up, the single largest predictor is a referral Aggression factor. Thus, there appears to be a predictable relationship not only between aggression at referral and aggression at follow-up, but also between aggression at referral and other symptomatology at follow-up. The referral Internalizing Behavior factor by parents contributes significantly to the regression analyses five times. It is a significant predictor, together with referral Aggression, in the analyses for two Aggression factors, the General Behavior Problems factor, one Hyperkinesis factor, and one Unclassified Behavior Problems factor at follow-up. Thus, when considered together with aggression at referral, internalizing symptomatology is useful in predicting a wide variety of follow-up symptoms. Also noteworthy is the fact that staff-rated Hyperkinesis at referral contributes significantly only to the regression analysis for the parent-reported Prosocial Behavior factor at follow-up, with the relationship being a negative one.

In light of the consistently small-to-moderate size of the multiple correlations for the referral-to-follow-up symptomatology regression analyses, it is important to consider additional classes of predictors (e.g., environment factors). Nevertheless, the pattern of the present findings is generally consis-

TABLE 4.8
Stepwise Multiple Regression Analyses: The Relationships between Child Symptoms at Referral and Symptomatology at Follow-Up

Step entered	Predictors	Correlations: Simple	Correlations: Multiple	Beta
	Criterion: follow-up symptoms by parents: prosocial behavior			
1	Referral symptoms by staff: hyperkinesis	−.30††	.30	−.25**
2	Referral symptoms by parents: prosocial behavior	.26††	.36	.21*
	Criterion: follow-up symptoms by parents: unclassified behavior problems I			
1	Referral symptoms by parents: unclassified behavior problems	.26††	.26	.26*
	Criterion: follow-up symptoms by parents: unclassified behavior problems II			
—	—	—	—	—
	Criterion: follow-up symptoms by parents: unclassified behavior problems III			
1	Referral symptoms by parents: aggression	.28††	.28	.28**
	Criterion: follow-up symptoms by parents: aggression			
1	Referral symptoms by parents: aggression	.39†††	.39	.28***
2	Referral symptoms by parents: internalizing behavior	.32†††	.47	.28**
3	Referral symptoms by parents: prosocial behavior	−.27††	.50	−.20*

	Criterion: follow-up symptoms by mother: aggression			
1	Referral symptoms by parents: aggression	.41†††	.41	.41***
	Criterion: follow-up symptoms by mother: hyperkinesis			
1	Referral symptoms by staff: aggression	.22†	.22	.22*
	Criterion: follow-up symptoms by father: general behavior problems			
1	Referral symptoms by staff: aggression	.31††	.31	.35**
2	Referral symptoms by parents: internalizing behavior	.23†	.41	.27*
	Criterion: follow-up symptoms by staff: hyperkinesis			
1	Referral symptoms by staff: aggression	.28††	.28	.32**
2	Referral symptoms by parents: internalizing behavior	.20†	.38	.26**
	Criterion: follow-up symptoms by staff: aggression			
1	Referral symptoms by staff: aggression	.27††	.27	.31**
2	Referral symptoms by parents: internalizing behavior	.18	.35	.23*
	Criterion: follow-up symptoms by staff: unclassified behavior problems			
1	Referral symptoms by parents: internalizing behavior	.24†	.24	.29*
2	Referral symptoms by staff: aggression	.19	.34	.24*

†††$p < .001$ level.
††$p < .01$ level.
†$p < .05$ level.
***$p < .001$ level.
**$p < .01$ level.
*$p < .05$ level.

tent with the results of other attempts to identify referral symptom predictors of follow-up outcome. Specifically, Weiss *et al.* (1971) and Minde *et al.* (1972) have reported that among the various referral symptom measures employed, only aggressive symptomatology was related to poor follow-up outcome.

RELATIONSHIPS BETWEEN ENVIRONMENT AT REFERRAL AND SYMPTOMATOLOGY AT FOLLOW-UP

A fourth series of stepwise multiple regression analyses examined the relationships between the environment at referral and child symptoms at follow-up (see Table 4.9). No referral environment factors contribute significantly to the regression analyses for two of the parent-reported follow-up factors (Prosocial Behavior and Unclassified Behavior Problems I) and for the staff-rated Unclassified Behavior Problems factor. For the remaining follow-up symptom factors, the magnitudes of the multiple correlations generally do not differ markedly from each other (range = .22–.39). One exception is the father-rated General Behavior Problems factor, which appears to be the best example, from the follow-up factors, of a comprehensive measure of general behavior problems. The multiple correlation of .49 for this factor indicates that almost twice as much symptom variance is accounted for by this analysis than by the regression analyses for more specific types of symptomatology (e.g., aggression and hyperkinesis).

We have noted that the relationships between referral symtomatology and the referral environment differ for different types of symptoms, with moderate relationships between aggression and the environment, and no relationship between hyperkinesis and the environment. In contrast, the multiple correlations for the follow-up Aggression factors are somewhat smaller (range = .29–.39), and an association emerges between the environment at referral and hyperkinesis at follow-up (multiple correlations of .37 for both of the Hyperkinesis factors).

For the 8 follow-up symptom factors related to the referral environment, 7 of 17 possible environment factors contribute to at least one regression equation, and the Parental Disturbance and Parent–Child Relationships each contribute to three. As noted before, both of these factors also contribute significantly to the analyses predicting referral symptoms from the environment at referral. Thus, a small number of environment factors is involved in predicting both referral and follow-up symptomatology. For the follow-up analyses, the contribution of the Parent–Child Relationship factor is primarily to the analyses for aggression. It is the largest predictor for 2 of the 3 Aggression factors and for 1 of the 4 Unclassified Behavior Problem factors. It is not possible to establish cause and effect in this relationship between poor parent–child relationships and aggressive symptomatology. However, the fact that this factor is a significant predictor at follow-up, as well as at referral, suggests a causal role for the environmental factor. With the exception of the Parent–Child Relationships factor, there is very little evidence for differential relationships between specific environment factors and types of follow-up symptomatology.

The SES factor contributes significantly to the regression analysis for one follow-up Hyperkinesis factor, a pattern that contrasts with previous reports of a lack of cross-sectional association between SES and hyperkinesis (Paternite *et al.*, 1976; Werner *et al.*, 1968). This discrepancy suggests that, over time, the detrimental effects of low SES may reach beyond an influence on aggressive symptomatology. Several possible factors may underlie this link between SES and hyperkinesis, including access to diagnostic and treatment resources, organicity, and the family's adaptability or resilience in dealing with the special needs of the hyperkinetic child.

In general, the results of the multiple regression analyses predicting follow-up symptomatology from the environment at referral do not suggest the presence of relationships that vary according to symptoms. Such limited specificity is consistent with the findings of previous investigators who have reported relationships between environmental influences and a wide variety of poor-outcome measures at follow-up (Minde *et al.*, 1972; Weiss *et al.*, 1971; Weiss *et al.*, 1975; Werner *et al.*, 1968). Considered together with these previous findings, the present results suggest the importance of careful environmental assessment, since the potential impact of adverse environmental conditions may be far-reaching. The small-to-moderate amount of variance in follow-up symptomatology accounted for by the present environmental factors also suggests that careful consideration be given to other potentially important mediating factors which undoubtedly influence the course of symptomatology over time.

RELATIONSHIPS BETWEEN CHANGE IN THE ENVIRONMENT OVER TIME AND SYMPTOMATOLOGY AT FOLLOW-UP

A fifth series of stepwise multiple regression analyses examined the relationships between the three measures of change in the environment and each of the 11 factors for symptomatology at follow-up. The only change to contribute significantly to any of the regression equations is Change of Parent Figures. For the General Behavior Problems by father factor, 20% of the variance ($r = .45$) is accounted for by the change score. For the Hyperkinesis by staff factor, 14% of the variance ($r = .37$) is accounted for by the change score, and for the aggression by staff factor, 8% of the variance ($r = .28$) is accounted for by the change score.

The relationship between Change of Parent Figures and follow-up symptomatology is not specific to symptom type. Rather, the change score con-

TABLE 4.9
Stepwise Multiple Regression Analyses: The Relationships between the Environment at Referral and Symptomatology at Follow-Up

		Correlations		
Step entered	*Predictors*	*Simple*	*Multiple*	*Beta*
	Criterion: follow-up symptoms by parents: prosocial behavior			
—	—	—	—	—
	Criterion: follow-up symptoms by parents: unclassified behavior problems I			
—	—	—	—	—
	Criterion: follow-up symptoms by parents: unclassified behavior problems II			
1	Environment: parent–child relationships	.32††	.32	.32**
	Criterion: follow-up symptoms by parents: unclassified behavior problems III			
1	Environment: child shares bed	.22†	.22	.22*
	Criterion: follow-up symptoms by parents: aggression			
1	Environment: parent–child relationships	.35†††	.35	.35***
	Criterion: follow-up symptoms by mother: aggression			
1	Environment: parent–child relationships	.29††	.29	.29**

	Criterion: follow-up symptoms by mother: hyperkinesis			
1	Environment: SES	.28††	.28	.26**
2	Environment: mother–father relationship	.27†	.37	.24*
	Criterion: follow-up symptoms by father: general behavior problems			
1	Environment: parental disturbance	.36†††	.36	.38***
2	Environment: mother too strict	.22†	.45	.29*
3	Environment: child shares bed	.18	.49	.20*
	Criterion: follow-up symptoms by staff: hyperkinesis			
1	Environment: parental disturbance	.30††	.30	.29**
2	Environment: parents too busy	−.23†	.37	−.22*
	Criterion: follow-up symptoms by staff: aggression			
1	Environment: parents too busy	−.32††	.32	−.30**
2	Environment: parental disturbance	.24†	.39	.28*
	Criterion: follow-up symptoms by staff: unclassified behavior problems			
—	—	—	—	—

†††$p < .001$ level.
††$p < .01$ level.
†$p < .05$ level.
***$p < .001$ level.
**$p < .01$ level.
*$p < .05$ level.

TABLE 4.10

Stepwise Multiple Regression Analyses: The Relationships of Symptomatology at Follow-Up with the Combination of Child Symptoms at Referral, the Environment at Referral, and Change in the Environment Over Time

Step entered	*Predictors*	*Correlations* *Simple*	*Multiple*	*Beta*
	Criterion: follow-up symptoms by parents: prosocial behavior			
1	Referral symptoms by staff: hyperkinesis	−.30††	.30	−.25**
2	Referral symptoms by parents: prosocial behavior	.26††	.36	.21*
	Criterion: follow-up symptoms by parents: unclassified behavior problems I			
1	Referral symptoms by parents: unclassified behavior problems	.26††	.26	.26*
	Criterion: follow-up symptoms by parents: unclassified behavior problems II			
1	Environment: parent–child relationships	.32††	.32	.32**
	Criterion: follow-up symptoms by parents: unclassified behavior problems III			
1	Referral symptoms by parents: aggression	.28††	.28	.30**
2	Environment: child's birth order[a]	.18	.35	.22*
	Criterion: follow-up symptoms by parents: aggression			
1	Referral symptoms by parents: aggression	.39†††	.39	.26***
2	Referral symptoms by parents: internalizing behavior	.32††	.47	.25**
3	Environment: parent–child relationships	.35†††	.52	.24*
	Criterion: follow-up symptoms by mother: aggression			
1	Referral symptoms by parents: aggression	.41†††	.41	.40***
2	Environment: mother too easygoing	−.20†	.45	−.19*

	Criterion: follow-up symptoms by mother: hyperkinesis			
1	Environment: SES	.28††	.28	.26**
2	Environment: mother–father relationship	.27††	.37	.24*
	Criterion: follow-up symptoms by father: general behavior problems			
1	Change in environment: change of parent figures	.45†††	.45	.45***
2	Environment: mother too strict	.22†	.52	.27**
3	Environment: child shares bed	.18	.59	.26**
4	Referral symptoms by parents: internalizing behavior	.23†	.63	.24*
5	Referral symptoms by staff: aggression	.31††	.65	.19*
	Criterion: follow-up symptoms by staff: hyperkinesis			
1	Change in environment: change of parent figures	.37†††	.37	.32***
2	Environment: parents too busy	−.23†	.45	−.26**
3	Referral symptoms by staff: aggression	.28††	.50	.26*
4	Referral symptoms by parents: internalizing behavior	.20†	.54	.23*
	Criterion: follow-up symptoms by staff: aggression			
1	Environment: parents too busy	−.32††	.32	−.34**
2	Change in environment: change of parent figures	.28††	.43	.23**
3	Referral symptoms by staff: aggression	.27††	.49	.27*
4	Referral symptoms by parents: internalizing behavior	.18	.53	.20*
	Criterion: follow-up symptoms by staff: unclassified behavior problems			
1	Referral symptoms by parents: internalizing behavior	.24†	.24	.29*
2	Referral symptoms by staff: aggression	.19	.34	.24

[a] Increasing numerical values are associated with ranks closer to first-born (oldest)
†††$p < .001$ level.
††$p < .01$ level.
†$p < .05$ level.
***$p < .001$ level.
**$p < .01$ level.
*$p < .05$ level.

tributes significantly to the General Behavior Problems factor, a Hyperkinesis factor, and an Aggression factor. For the General Behavior Problems factor, at least two possible explanations for the relationship to environmental change warrant consideration. The positive relationship may be due largely to the disruptive impact of such environmental change on child behavior. Alternatively, the relationship may be an artifact of change of father from referral to follow-up. That is, the new fathers at follow-up may take an overly critical or generally "hard" look at the child behavior at follow-up, relative to ratings made by fathers who have come to know and understand the child over time. However, evidence contradicting this latter explanation is provided by the fact that similar environment change–symptomatology relationships result not only for symptomatology as rated by father, but also for symptoms as rated by staff (Hyperkinesis and Aggression factors). It seems quite unlikely that the staff ratings would reflect the same kind and/or extent of bias that might be found in ratings by the new fathers. Careful examination of the pairwise correlations involving the Change of Parent Figures factor suggests that the change is correlated with follow-up symptom factors, and to a limited extent with referral symptom factors. Specifically, the correlation between environmental change and the parent-reported referral Aggression factor is .18 ($p < .10$), and the correlation for staff-rated referral Aggression is .23 ($p < .05$). Evidence is therefore provided for an association between environmental change and symptomatology at two points in time (referral and follow-up), thus suggesting that an explanation of the results based solely on rater bias is not well founded. However, a primarily causal link between environmental change and follow-up symptoms is also called to question by this evidence.

RELATIONSHIPS OF SYMPTOMATOLOGY AT FOLLOW-UP WITH THE COMBINATION OF CHILD SYMPTOMS AT REFERRAL, THE ENVIRONMENT AT REFERRAL, AND CHANGE IN THE ENVIRONMENT OVER TIME

A sixth series of stepwise multiple regression analyses examined the relationships of symptomatology at follow-up with the combination of child symptoms at referral, the environment at referral, and change in the environment over time (see Table 4.10). For 5 of the 11 follow-up symptom factors (3 of the 4 Unclassified Behavior Problems factors, 1 of the 2 Hyperkinesis factors, and the Prosocial Behavior factor), the combination of the three sets of predictors does not yield stronger associations than those resulting from the separate analyses. Even when the three sets of predictors are combined, for 3 follow-up symptom factors only referral symptomatology contributes significantly, and for 2 factors the only significant predictors are environment factors.

For the remaining 6 of the 11 follow-up symptom factors (the General Behavior Problems factor, 3 Aggression factors, 1 Hyperkinesis factor, and 1 Unclassified Behavior Problems factor), the multiple regression analyses combining the three sets of predictors produce results different from those obtained from separate analyses of each predictor set. In four of the analyses, the percentage of follow-up symptom factor variance accounted for is almost twice the amount explained by any of the three analyses in which the sets of predictors are treated separately. For Unclassified Behavior Problems III by parents and General Behavior Problems by father, the separate multiple correlations range between .22 and .28 and between .41 and .49, respectively. However, when the sets of predictors are combined, the multiple correlations increase to .35 and .65, respectively. For the follow-up staff-rated Hyperkinesis factor, the multiple correlations increase from .37 and .38 to .54. For the follow-up staff-rated Aggression factor, the increase is from multiple correlations ranging between .28 and .39 to a multiple correlation of .53. The marked increases in the magnitudes of the multiple correlations (and thus the percentage of variance explained) are not limited to a particular type of symptomatology. Rather, the effects are evident for factors reflecting General Behavior Problems, Hyperkinetic symptoms, and Aggression at follow-up. Thus, the prediction-enhancing effects of considering jointly the contributions of child symptomatology (person) and environmental (situation) influences are demonstrated.

SUMMARY AND CONCLUSIONS

Hyperkinesis is a designation for a heterogeneous group of children whose clinical symptomatology is variable not only when they are young, but also when they reach adolescence. Diagnosis and classification in the area is imprecise, and very little attention has been directed to the empirical derivation of clinically relevant components of hyperkinesis. Within the context of follow-up investigations, the cross-sectional and longitudinal correlates of symptomatology have been examined on a very limited basis. Specifically regarding the role of environmental influences, systematic efforts have not been directed toward examining the interrelationships among symptomatology of the child and familiar influences associated with the home environment. In an attempt to address simultaneously several of the preceding unanswered questions, the purpose of the present study was to examine systematically the cross-sectional and longitudinal interrelationships among empirically derived dimensions of hyperkinetic symptomatology and home environment. The clinical sample consisted of 99 Ritalin-treated hyperkinetic–MBD boys, 6–12 years old when first evaluated, and then reevaluated in a follow-up study an average of 5 years later. A wide range of multiple-source measures of child symptomatology and home environment was utilized.

Several independent patterns of symptomatology were identifed, with the two most prominent factors corresponding to primary (or core) hyperkinetic symptoms and secondary (or resultant) symptoms. These two patterns, which were labeled Hyperkinesis and Aggression, emerged for the analyses of both referral and follow-up data. In subsequent analyses, child symptoms at referral were found to correlate differentially with dimensions of the home environment at referral. Statistically and clinically significant associations were found for Aggression, whereas no such relationships were found for Hyperkinesis. In addition, it was found that Aggression at referral predicts the severity of symptomatology in general and Aggression at follow-up in particular, whereas other referral symptom patterns do not predict follow-up outcomes. Relationships also were identified between environment dimensions at referral and symptomatology at follow-up. The combined use of referral symptom and environment factors as predictors in regression analyses for follow-up symptoms enhanced predictability relative to the use of the predictors separately. A limited set of replication analyses for referral dimensions was completed, and it corroborates the previous findings.

Although the need for further replication and refinement of the present results is obvious, the findings do underscore the importance of comprehensive, broadly based evaluations of hyperkinetic–MBD children. It is especially encouraging that the relationships identified in the present study emerged despite the considerable amount of "measurement error" which is inevitable with a wide range of assessment dimensions, techniques, and circumstances. Even with these limitations, relationships were demonstrated that account for as much as 19% of variance in referral symptom factors and 42% of variance in follow-up symptom factors. It seems plausible that there would be clearer support for the present findings under better methodological circumstances. These results also confirm the inappropriateness of vague and monolithic diagnostic formulations. Syndrome definitions that uncritically mix primary and secondary symptomatology cloud diagnostic issues, and may preclude the precise study of etiology, course, prognosis, and treatment response. For example, only by making a clear distinction between primary and secondary symptoms in the present follow-up study was it possible to demonstrate that adolescent aggression is more validly linked to aggression at referral than to primary hyperkinetic symptoms. These findings indicate the significance of aggression at referral as a predictor of follow-up outcome among hyperkinetic–MBD boys and thus the importance of careful assessment of such symptomatology. In addition, the finding that hyperkinesis per se at referral has little usefulness in accounting for follow-up symptomatology is clearly inconsistent with the poorly substantiated, but often stressed, clinical impression that early hyperkinesis is implicated in the later development of aggressive problems. Based on the present findings, a more accurate rendering of this clinical impression is that among hyperkinetic children, early aggression predicts later aggression.

The findings also indicate the potentially significant influence over time of home or family factors on hyperkinetic children, and show the need for systematic measurement of such environmental variables. Due to the very limited replication data that are presently available, caution needs to be exercised in attributing importance to any of the specific environmental influences examined in the study. Nevertheless, the data provide clear support for the general conclusion that home environmental influences are related to the development and expression of symptomatology in hyperkinetic–MBD boys, not only when they are young but also when they reach adolescence. Additionally, based on the prediction-enhancing effects of jointly utilizing referral symptom and environment factors as predictors of follow-up symptomatology, evidence is provided for the interactive influences of person and situation variables on the behavior of hyperkinetic–MBD boys.

III

PATTERNS OF IDENTIFICATION AND TREATMENT: EPIDEMIOLOGICAL STUDIES

5

The Identification and Labeling of Hyperactivity in Children: An Interactive Model

JONATHAN SANDOVAL
NADINE M. LAMBERT
DANA SASSONE

INTRODUCTION: THE STUDY OF IDENTIFICATION AND LABELING

When studying the process by which children come to be identified and labeled as hyperactive, it is tempting to assume the existence of a single entity that may be operationally defined. If one is investigating the labeling and identification of a specific disease entity, the task is relatively simple. Using proper, reliable, exhaustive methods of diagnosis, the investigator follows the progress of subjects through the typical identification process. However, when one is investigating the identification of a problem defined by the absence of observable pathology and diagnosed by behavioral characteristics reported subjectively (Sandoval, Lambert, & Yandell, 1976), the task becomes much more complex.

A first problem in diagnosing hyperactivity arises from the lack of observable, objectively determined pathology. When the absence of something (e.g., assessable brain damage) becomes a criterion in the identification process, there is difficulty in deciding who does *not* meet the criterion. Nearly all children are free of assessable brain damage; therefore many would qualify on that criterion. Are overactive children without brain damage then "hyperactive?" Obviously not, but the absence of brain damage was specified as a criterion for the technical diagnosis of "hyperkinetic reaction of childhood" in the Diagnostic and Statistical Manual of Mental Disorders, Second Edition (DSM II), (American Psychiatric Association,

HYPERACTIVE CHILDREN
The Social Ecology of Identification and Treatment

ISBN 0-12-745950-2

Committee on Nomenclature and Statistics, 1968), which was in use during most of the current research on hyperactivity. The proposed revision of this manual (DSM III) does provide guidelines that rely on more observable behavior, and as such may eliminate some of these difficulties (American Psychiatric Association, Task Force on Nomenclature and Statistics, 1978).

A second problem is that the reports on a child's behavior are made by those who contribute to the child's environment. The attitudes and behaviors of the identifiers affect both the child's behavior and their perception of the child. Such subjective, potentially biased reports hardly can be comparable to laboratory methods used in the medical diagnosis of other disorders. Should an investigation of "hyperactivity" labeling address itself to the diagnosis of a syndrome by a physician, ratings of behavior by a variety of professionals, or the use of a report of hyperactive behavior by a parent or teacher as the criterion for identification? The answer is yes, all three. But it is important to identify the origin of the label and not to confuse the sources. Source confusion is natural when dealing with labels. When terms are conscientiously given to concrete, tangible objects, labeling is straightforward. But labels such as hyperactivity, hyperkinesis, and minimal brain dysfunction (MBD) are abstractions applied to children with widely varying combinations of observed behavior patterns. Studying the application of these labels is quite a different matter; even though there is agreement as to which children earn the labels, the reasons for calling a particular chid "hyperactive" may vary.

Many professionals understand that with hyperactivity they are using labels *descriptively,* to encompass a broad class of observable behaviors, rather than *diagnostically.* As Goodman (1977) points out, a descriptivist approach labels phenotypes, whereas a diagnostic approach labels genotypes. Both approaches are common. In medicine, the diagnostic use of a label occurs when there is a disease entity with a specific etiology, symptomatology, and prognosis; the label usually implies a biological basis for a condition. Some professionals, and most nonprofessionals, use "hyperactivity" in this diagnostic fashion, much as they would use labels such as hypothyroidism or anemia, to imply that the child has a known biological condition. In studying the labeling process, it is important to be aware that one individual's use of a label may be quite different from another's, and that individuals viewing the same child may be using a label strictly or loosely, descriptively or diagnostically.

AN INTERACTIVE SYSTEMS MODEL OF HYPERACTIVITY

To study the identification process, it is important to have a model of the origins of hyperactivity that encompasses major points of view. We have characterized our model as an interactive systems model, in contrast to a child deficit model or a pure social system model.

This model posits that individual differences in the organic and psychological makeup of the child, in his or her family, and in school environments all interact to determine whether or not a child is labeled "hyperactive." Rather than viewing the social structure as the sole arbiter of hyperactive behavior, or postulating that behavior is determined solely by a metabolic or organic deficit in the child, the multidimensional, interactive model posits complex interactions between the child's environment, and his or her physical and psychological status. Children's physical makeups may be placed on a number of continua of physical–neurological capacity, and children develop in social environments that may also be described by a number of continua or spectra. A child with a given physical constitution under certain environmental conditions may be considered hyperactive, yet a biologically identical child growing up in a different environment may not be considered hyperactive. For example, a child who is temperamentally difficult with a somewhat short attention span may, if placed in a classroom with a strict teacher who conducts many lessons with large groups of children, be more likely to be labeled hyperactive than if placed with a more lenient teacher who conducts most lessons in small groups.

By the same token, two children with different physical constitutions growing up in different environments both may be labeled hyperactive. The biological and environmental factors may either balance each other or combine in ways that affect the probability that the child will receive a label. The most extreme form of this view, one to which we are not quite willing to subscribe, would be that any given child placed in a particular environment will be labeled hyperactive. The same child can be placed in another environment and not receive the label. We are not quite willing to accept the extreme position because we believe there exists an unknown number of children (probably a small number) who will almost certainly be labeled hyperactive, regardless of the way they are treated at home and at school.

Bronfenbrenner (1974a) points out that psychological experimentation often is ecologically invalid because, in his view, applicable research must take place in a child's natural life setting. More investigators are turning their attention to the relationship of man to his environmert, and ecological psychology is becoming a recognized, important part of psychological inquiry. Mentioned in the 1940s by Lewin, the ecological perspective is now viewed as offering new insights into the problems of many children who are school failures; this perspective may provide a strategy for better understanding hyperactivity.

An examination of the environmental dimensions associated with hyperactivity must take into account those variables that potentially contribute to the problem, including possible etiological correlates and factors affecting the severity of the children's problems. We believe that studies of hyperactive children should include an investigation of classroom and home environments as well as attitudes of teachers and parents toward the children's behaviors and toward preferred treatments. As a first, limited step in model building, we propose the following factors as important in each of three critical systems influencing the identification and treatment process.

Factor One: Individual Differences in Children's Makeup

Stewart (1970) and Thomas and his coworkers (Thomas & Chess, 1977; Thomas, Chess, & Birch, 1968) have emphasized the fact that individual differences in children's temperaments are distinguishable at birth. Temperament characteristics such as activity level and distractibility in infants may be established early and continue to characterize individuals over a lifetime. Thomas *et al.* (1968) found that 10% of their upper-middle-class population could be classified as "difficult" children with symptoms of erratic behavior, overly intense reactions to new situations, resistance to change, and a tendency to withdraw from new stimuli. However, their observations of the group of difficult children who later developed behavior problems led Thomas *et al.* to conclude that objective, consistent treatment in an optimally malleable environment could prevent serious behavior problems. Individual differences most often manifest themselves in four observable behavioral domains: activity level, attentiveness–distractibility, impulsivity, and social intrusiveness–aggression. These characteristics are most commonly listed in clinical descriptions of hyperactive children (Lambert, Windmiller, Sandoval, & Moore, 1976) and are the most usual characteristics assessed in clinical trials of medication with hyperactive children.

Some investigators have suggested constitutional etiological factors other than temperament to account for individual differences in behavior. Wender (1971) proposes that hyperactive behavior patterns are due to a dysfunctional central nervous system. Feingold (1975) also suggests organic factors, proposing that hyperactive children react unfavorably to certain chemicals in food. Morrison and Stewart (1973) propose a polygenic inheritance model of the hyperactive child syndrome.

The extent to which child behaviors result from genetic–constitutional variables or from social learning is a question that will be debated for some time. If the interactive model is correct, such "either–or" questions are fruitless. The point here is that individual differences in constitutional factors need to be considered in research on the identification, course, and treatment of hyperactivity.

Factor Two: Individual Differences in Home Environments

The family environment into which a child is born is certainly important in determining if, when, and how a child is identified as hyperactive. Child rearing practices, parental beliefs about what is age-appropriate behavior, the parents' own temperaments and tolerance levels, and parents' skill in socializing children are all important in determining whether the family identifies a child as hyperactive and takes the child to a physician for a medical opinion. As Paternite and Loney (Chapter 4 of this volume) have outlined a number of relationships between symptomatology and family environments, we will not elaborate further except to mention Minuchin's notion that the identified child may well play an important role in the family social structure. Following this line of reasoning, the rest of the family may "need" the hyperactive child and his problems in order to avoid other conflicts that might flare up and destroy the family unit (Minuchin, Baker, Rosman, Liebman, Milman, & Todd, 1975). The emotional climate of the home is also influenced by less subtle factors such as death, divorce, mobility, poverty, and other events that create stress in individual family members and the family as a unit.

Factor Three: Individual Differences in School Environments

Educators have for years been of the opinion that a given classroom environment may facilitate some children's educational development and be detrimental to others. The currently popular movements toward individualized instruction and open classrooms are attempts to create environments in which a greater number of children may be successful than previously. Many children are not identified as hyperactive until they enter school, and some are not labeled until they have been in school for several years. Clearly the argument may be made that the educational environment is related both to the hyperactive behavior of children and to the process by which they come to be identified.

Only recently have investigators begun to consider the importance of classroom environment in behavior disorders of children. In a 1 year follow-up of a group of 6–12-year-old boys seen in a clinic for problems of persistent distractibility or motor restlessness and impulsivity, Flynn and Rapoport (1976) found that the children placed in what they term "open" classrooms were rated by their teachers as less different from their peers and less disruptive than were children placed in traditional classrooms. Direct classroom observations of activity by an outside observer contradicted teachers' judgments in that the boys in the open classroom functioned similarly to those in the traditional classrooms. As the authors point out, there are two possibilities. Either the children are less hyperactive in the open classroom, or their teachers are more tolerant of their behavior and do not preceive them as different from their peers. In either case, the hyperactive child may find the open classroom a more supportive environment. It should be mentioned that Flynn and Rapoport (1976) did not view their open classrooms as unstructured environments. Rather, they saw the open classrooms as being structured by the teacher and the pupils working together, whereas the traditional classrooms were structured by the teacher alone. The open classrooms were characterized by clear, explicit guidelines for acceptable behavior, teachers who were confortable in dealing with conflicts between individuals and capable of offering emotional support to children, and children who were task-oriented on individualized instructional projects.

In a related study, Koester and Farley (1977) analyzed changes in performance measures of visual discrimination, general information, concentration, motor steadiness, and stimulation-seeking in first grade children over 1 year. Those children they termed hyperkinetic on the basis of physiological measures of arousal level did not perform better in either an "open" or "traditional" classroom. However, children with high arousal levels (nonhyperkinetic, using their definition) showed decrements in their visual discrimination scores if they had spent the year in the open classroom. Although the results are quite tentative, they offer some credence to the notion that classroom environments may help or hinder children.

As part of a data collection effort aimed at determining the prevalence of labeling, to be described later, we asked almost 200 teachers what their advice would be to a new teacher about how to help a hyperactive child function well in the classroom (Sandoval & Sassone, 1977). We found the solutions they gave fit the same pattern of teacher behavioral strategies present in the open classrooms described by Flynn and Rapoport. The surveyed teachers indicated that children with hyperactive behaviors could be helped in a classroom where the teacher was accepting and supportive of the child but also made realistic achievement demands. The classroom environment should provide short and varied assignments with close individual monitoring of the child, and movement restrictions should be at a minimum.

Teachers' attitudes about children in general, and their views about what is age-appropriate and socially deviant behavior, are also critical in determining what the classroom behavior will be for a child. The manner in which limits on classroom behavior are enforced is one thing, but the nature of the limits and whether or not they are within the child's capabilities is quite another. If a teacher believes it is important for an 8-year-old boy to sit quietly in his seat for extended periods of time, the classroom environment for children will be quite different than if the teacher considers it important for the children to change activities often. Just as children vary in temperament so do teachers; and as teachers vary so do classroom environments.

Other more mundane factors also determine classroom environments. The number of children in the room, the number and variety of instructional materials, the availability of teacher aides, the educational orientations and readiness levels of the pupils in general, all contribute to the classroom milieu. These factors may support or handicap children at various levels of activity, ability to sustain attention, impulsivity, or social aggressiveness.

A structural model such as the one portrayed in Figure 5.1 displays the predicted causal relations among the number of domains of variables that we have hypothesized to be related to the behaviors labeled "hyperactivity." The model also allows us to clarify the multiplicity of factors that impinge on the labeling process.

The major independent factors accounting for hyperactive behavior in various settings are presented in the boxes: home environment, school environment, and the characteristics of the child. The constitutional makeup of the child, indicated in the hexagon, interacts with environments. Characteristics and attitudes of parents and teachers also influence the environments. The child's biological systems, in conjunction with family and school factors that appear in home and school environments, interact to determine

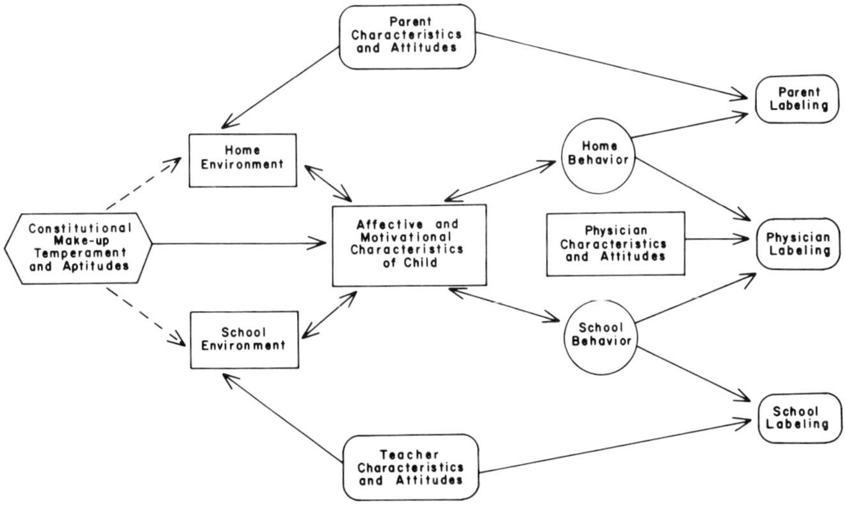

FIGURE 5.1. The structural model of interactive systems in the labeling of children is shown here.

whether the child eventually manifests observable hyperactive behavior patterns.

In this figure, we have indicated that the physician's labeling of hyperactivity is influenced by reports of the child's behavior rather than exclusively by identifiable factors in the child's constitutional makeup. These behavioral factors also are crucial in determining the type of treatment program to recommend. The child's behavior in conjunction with parent and teacher characteristics and attitudes likewise determine whether or not the child is considered hyperactive.

From the proposed structural model, it is apparent that we believe the labeling process is a result of: (*a*) home factors, including parent attitudes; (*b*) specific target home behaviors, which are influenced by home environments and constitutional makeup; (*c*) school behaviors, which are influenced by child attitudes, classroom environment and the child's constitutional makeup; and (*d*) physician training and attitudes. It should be noted that the arrows in the model are, in many cases, bidirectional; children both influence and are influenced by home and school environments. For example, even one child with an attention span shorter or less focused than his classmates can cause the teacher to make changes that affect the entire classroom.

AGENTS IN THE IDENTIFICATION PROCESS

As we have noted earlier, parents contribute greatly to the home environment of children in ways that may cause hyperactive behaviors to be expressed or, alternately, in ways that may cause the hyperactive behaviors to be unexpressed until the child enters the school classroom, or not at all. Somewhat independent of the magnitude of the behaviors are factors that determine whether the parent notes these behaviors, attributes these behaviors to an underlying condition, independently seeks help from a physician, accepts a suggestion of a referral from someone else such as a teacher, and accepts one treatment mode or another. No experimental data are available yet to shed light on what these attitudinal factors and environmental characteristics might be, although we are in the process of collecting such information from parent interviews and questionnaires.

Teachers and other school personnel are also important agents in the identification process. Many children are not identified as hyperactive until they enter school, leading many critics to feel that teachers often force parents, who would not ordinarily do so, to seek medical help for their children. Surely it is true that many teachers do contribute to the identification process, but it also is true that when the child enters school he or she is faced with demands on attention and self-control that are simply not present in most homes. The child is expected to work at lessons for extended periods of time, work cooperatively with a large number of other children, and solve problems in an orderly, systematic manner. But teachers also vary with respect to their tolerance of overt behaviors. They vary in whether or not they attribute the observable behavior to an underlying condition with a label and become involved in encouraging the parents to seek medical assistance for their child. As with parents, little experimental work has been done with teachers to explore which critical attitudinal, temperamental, or child competency variables might determine the teacher's behavior in the identification process.

Physicians are the third important agents in the identification process. In one paper we reported some findings on the differences in physician attitudes and training that may influence the sorts of labels they give to children and the treatments they recommend (Sandoval *et al.*, 1976). From our survey, we learned that physicians who had had psychiatric training placed more importance on the interpersonal attitudes and behaviors of the children in forming their diagnosis than did other physicians. Physicians with pediatric training reported relying less on "soft" neurological signs involving asymmetries and on focal or generalized electroencephalograph (EEG) abnormalities than physicians with a background in neurology or psychiatry. In general, there was a striking lack of consensus about what factors in a medical evaluation physicians judged to be important in arriving at a diagnosis of hyperactivity.

Physicians also expressed a wide variety of attitudes toward hyperactivity and the various treatment alternatives available. Most physicians reported publicly that they favored multiple treatment approaches. Our research has shown, however, that parents do not always follow recommendations of counseling or psychotherapy for themselves or their children, even though physicians often make such recommendations. The physician's own attitude toward these alternatives may be communicated explicitly to parents or may be more subtly conveyed through a tendency to focus on particular types of treatment recommendations, to the exclusion of others.

Figure 5.2 illustrates the times and ways in which a hyperactive child may be identified. For many children considered hyperactive by parents or teachers, a medical diagnosis may not be given. To be consistent with general medical practice and the research literature, we have used the criterion of medical confirmation or diagnosis for a child to be considered hyperactive in our illustration.

The diagram begins with the constitutional makeup of the child at birth. If the child manifests target behaviors in infancy, a physician may be con-

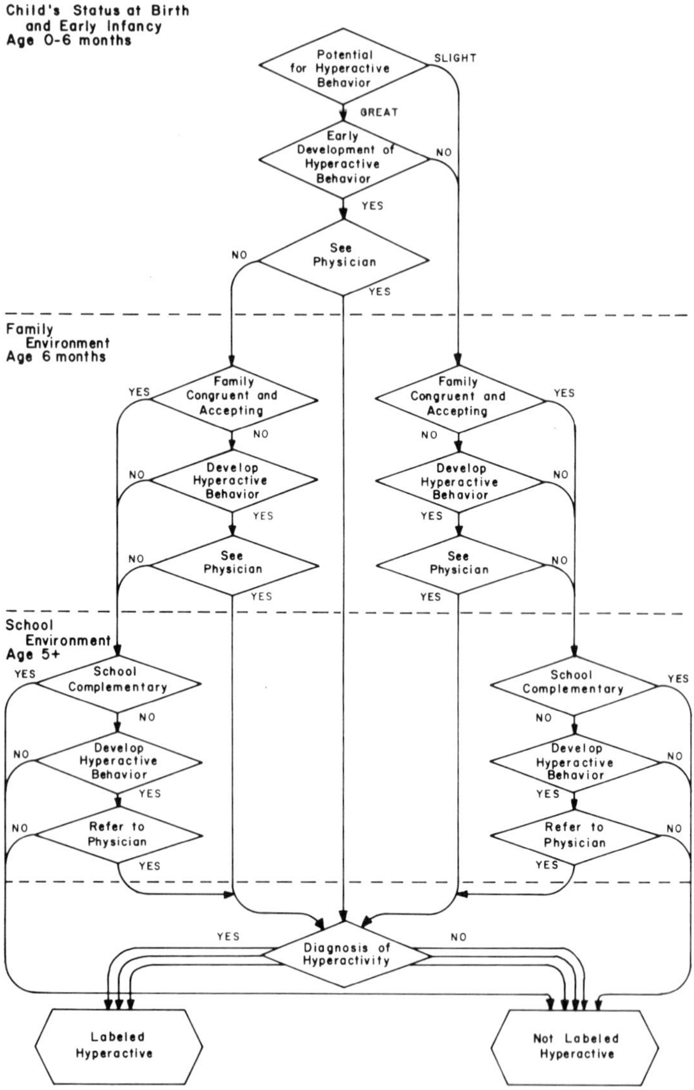

FIGURE 5.2. This figure presents a flow chart of the identification process.

sulted. If the environment is congruent and accepting, the child will be less likely to develop observable hyperactive behavior patterns during early childhood. We use the term "congruent" to mean a match between the home and child that reduces the probability of target behaviors. The term "accepting" refers to target behaviors that are manifest but neither labeled nor considered unusual. If the home and family environment are not complementary, the child will be more likely to develop overt behavior patterns that violate parental expectancies, and the family may seek the advice of a physician for diagnosis and treatment.

The child next enters school. If the school environment is able to accommodate to and accept the child and his behavior, the child will not be considered hyperactive. If not, overt behaviors associated with the hyperactive label may develop in the school setting, and school personnel will be likely to contact the parents and suggest that the child be taken to a physician. As with the home environment, there may exist no complementary school environment for some children.

Figure 5.2 illustrates that the point at which the child enters the identification process varies with respect to social system factors. At this point in the study of hyperactivity, we believe it inappropriate to speculate about the relative importance of individual differences in overt behavior patterns or social system factors in the labeling process. A major review of the labeling of deviance in alcoholism, mental illness, mental retardation, physical disability, criminal behavior, juvenile delinquency, heroin addiction, and sexual deviance (Gove, 1975) indicated that receiving these labels is primarily a consequence of individual behavior manifestations rather than of the person's social situation. Since the behavior labeled hyperactive is so much more subjectively determined than, say, a felony or even the presence of alcoholism, the child's social situation at home and at school may be relatively more important in labeling hyperactivity than it is in identifying other forms of deviance.

A PREVALENCE STUDY

Our first effort to test the interactive model has been to conduct a prevalence study; we used multiple definitions of hyperactivity and gathered relatively independent information from each of the different agents of identification. By attaching numbers and percentages to the different agents, and by carefully noting when the identification is made by each agent, it is possible to speculate about what may be happening in the environment to stimulate, hasten, or retard the identification process. Before describing the findings of this study (Lambert, Sandoval, & Sassone, 1978), we will briefly describe the methodology.

We drew a random sample of classrooms from the population of 180,000 public and private school children attending kindergarten through fifth grade in the 1467 square mile East Bay region of the San Francisco metropolitan area. Within this area live 1.7 million individuals from diverse ethnic groups, who follow a wide variety of lifestyles in rural, suburban, and urban settings.

After listing each of the public and private schools in the two county areas, we randomly selected six samples of 40 classrooms each, one sample for each grade level kindergarten through fifth. This sampling process produced a list of 240 classrooms. After negotiating with the selected schools for their participation, we obtained a total sample of over 5000 children in 191 (from the original 240) classrooms in 146 different schools.

To obtain information from *parents,* we contacted all of the parents of chidren in each sampled classroom and asked them to notify us by phone or mail if they or others considered their child to be hyperactive. This method provided a large sample of home-identified hyperactive subjects, but not necessarily all of the children in the representative sample considered hyperactive by the home. In order to consider other cases known to the school, we asked teachers, psychologists, principals, nurses, and special educators to compare names in the representative sample with children considered hyperactive in their school district. The additional cases that they noted were children known to be under treatment for hyperactivity and under the care of a physician, but who had not yet been referred to us.

We requested that the school district personnel contact the parent and ask the parents' permission for a member of the project staff to call the parent. If the parent agreed, the school district provided us with the parent's phone number. We then contacted and interviewed these parents in addition to those who had responded to our letter.

If parents, in response to questions on our home interview, indicated that they considered the child to be hyperactive, we considered the child to be identified as hyperactive by the home environmental system. Our home-identified sample is about equally divided between initial parental response to our letter and follow-up school referral.

To obtain information from the *school,* we asked the school personnel also to name the children in the representative sample they considered to be hyperactive and whose parents had agreed to participate in the study. We asked them also to tally by sex and age, but not name, those children whom they considered to be hyperactive, but whose parents had not responded to our requests to participate. These cases were added to those others identified by the school whose parents were willing to be interviewed, but who did not consider their children to be hyperactive, although the school did. If teachers, principals, and other concerned personnel indicated a child in the representative classrooms was hyperactive or would be considered hyperactive by a physician if the parents would consent to take the child for an evaluation, we considered the child to be identified as hyperactive in the school system.

Simultaneously with the parent and school identification phase, we asked all of the *physicians* in the two-county area to refer to us any children from the representative sample they had identified as hyperactive, and whose parents gave their written permission for the referral. To assist the physicians in this process, we listed all of the schools in which the representative sample was located, and offered to send them the lists of representative sample pupils in their area. In addition to working with private physicians, we asked the major pediatric clinics and hospitals to check their records.

When we were able to determine from the home, school, or physician that a child had seen a physician for hyperactive behavior or problems associated with hyperactive behavior, and we had obtained consent for information release from the parent, we asked the physician to complete a medical evaluation form. This form was developed in consultation with a group of neurologists, pediatricians, and child psychiatrists. The outcome of this pooling of expertise was a questionnaire that contained items under the following headings: child's medical history, physical examination results, laboratory findings, family history, general behavior, school performance, diagnostic summary, and treatment recommendations. All interviewed parents gave their consent for release of medical information. Approximately 85% of the 75 physicians involved returned the medical evaluation forms. If there were no competing medical explanation (e.g., epilepsy) of the problem behaviors and the physician's diagnosis was hyperactivity, hyperkinesis, minimal brain dysfunction (MBD) with hyperactivity, or if the physician prescribed a cerebral stimulant (such as Dexedrine or Ritalin), we reasoned that the physician considered the child to be hyperactive.

The described procedures provided us with a pool of children considered to be hyperactive who were identified to us by parents, physicians, and/or the school. All of these children were included in prevalence estimates, after assigning them to a classification based on the social systems that considered them to be hyperactive.

Many investigators do not consider a child to be hyperactive unless a physician has made this diagnosis. Other investigators, centering on the school behavior of children, accept the judgments of the classroom teacher, often formalized in ratings. Recognizing that the behavior of the child may not be the same at home as at school, still other investigators require evidence of hyperactive behaviors in both home and school settings before using the label of hyperactivity. We collected information on all children labeled hyperactive by at least one social system. There are six combinations here, and each group is of interest.

1. *HSP,* children whom all three definers, home (H), school (S), and physician (P), consider to be hyperactive.

2. *HP*, children whom parents and physicians but not educators consider to be hyperactive.
3. *SP*, children whom physicians and educators but not parents consider to be hyperactive.
4. *HS*, children whom parents and educators consider to be hyperactive.
5. *H*, children whom only parents consider to be hyperactive.
6. *S*, children whom only educators consider to be hyperactive.

Children in the last three groups have not been identified as hyperactive by their physician. Some of these children may not have seen a physician for the problems of hyperactive behavior. In other cases, the attending physician may not have offered hyperactivity as an explanation of the child's problems to either the parents or the school. Such children usually are excluded from studies of hyperactive children, especially drug studies.

In addition to prevalence estimates based on the home, school, and physician as definers, we produced a prevalence rate based on the children who were behavioral equivalents (BE) to those consensually identified as hyperactive (the HSP group). To accomplish this, we used teacher ratings from the Behavior and Temperament Survey, a questionnaire consisting of 31 behavioral descriptions that was obtained for all students in the representative classrooms. This rating form correlates highly (.89) with the widely used Abbreviated Symptom Questionnaire (Conners, 1973c) but contains a more comprehensive set of behavioral items (see the appendix to this chapter). We established a critical region by locating the lowest point on the score distribution that would include all the children identified as HSP hyperactive but who were not taking medication at the time of the teacher ratings. This region contained roughly the upper 10% of the total sample. Then, we identified children as members of the BE group if their ratings fell above the cutoff point and they were *not* considered hyperactive by any of the three defining agents. Inclusion of this BE group in an overall prevalence estimate produces a higher bound estimate, one that would be achieved only if all of these BE children were ultimately considered to be hyperactive by parents, school, and physician.

IDENTIFIERS AND THE PREVALENCE OF HYPERACTIVITY

We were surprised to find that the overall prevalence rate of children identified as hyperactive by the home, the school, and the physician (HSP subjects) was only 1.19% of an elementary school population. Table 5.1 displays all of the rates by grade level. The HSP group can be considered to

TABLE 5.1
Prevalence Rates (%) of Children Identified as Hyperactive by Defining System

	Grade						
Defining system	*K*	*1*	*2*	*3*	*4*	*5*	*Total*
Home–school–physician	1.28	1.38	1.17	.59	1.49	1.21	1.19
Home–physician	.26	—	—	.12	.11	.09	.10
School–physician	—	.12	—	.36	—	—	.08
Home–school	.38	—	.13	.47	.23	.09	.21
Home only	.13	—	.13	—	—	—	.04
School only	2.98	1.86	3.12	4.90	3.56	3.44	3.30
Total by school	4.64	3.36	4.42	6.32	5.28	4.74	4.78
Total by home	2.05	1.38	1.43	1.18	1.83	1.39	1.54
Total by physician	1.54	1.50	1.17	1.07	1.60	1.30	1.37
Total by one or more definers	5.03	3.36	4.55	6.44	5.39	4.83	4.92
Behavioral equivalent not otherwise defined	6.65	8.31	8.17	8.43	8.31	6.49	7.75
Maximum prevalence rate	11.68	11.67	12.72	14.87	13.70	11.32	12.67
Number of children in representative sample	781	869	769	843	873	1077	5212

be most like those who are the subjects of clinical drug studies. It is the most restrictive definition we have used. This rate is rather constant across grade levels, being lowest at second and third grade and highest at first and fourth grade.

The constancy of the prevalence rate of the HSP subjects contradicts the assumption that once a child is identified as hyperactive, he continues to be considered hyperactive throughout his school career. If it were the case that children remained hyperactive and that new cases continued to be identified, we would expect an increase in rates as grade level increases. The most reasonable explanation to us for the similar rates across grades seems to be that children are treated as hyperactive during only a particular period of their school lives. In subsequent years, their problems may become less severe because of changes in the home and school environments, or the child himself may change and the need for special treatment diminish. Whether or not the children are "cured" after they have been identified and treated cannot be answered by these data but can be evaluated by longitudinal studies.

The prevalence rates for the children defined by combinations of two of the H, S, and P definers indicate that there is not always concurrence in the identification of hyperactivity. For combinations with the home as a definer, we suspect that rates may be artifically low because some parents were reluctant to bring additional attention to their children, or did not wish to participate in a research study and, therefore, did not respond to our or the school's requests.

A child's entry into school at kindergarten is considered by many to represent a normal crisis period, followed by increasing demands for independent school learning and conformity with school behavior standards. Then too, at the third grade increasing demands are made on the child to work independently and use skills acquired in the lower primary grades (K–2). At the third grade, reading difficulties become more apparent and cause increasing concern. The peaks in the prevalence rates for any child identified by the school occur at kindergarten within the lower primary grades, and at third grade in the upper primary grades (3–5). Doubtlessly these peaks reflect children's reactions to these normal school crisis periods. The peaks in HSP prevalence rates at first and fourth grades may result from a 6-month to 1-year lag in physician diagnosis and treatment from the time of school identification. We discovered that it often takes about a year after a child is considered hyperactive by the school for him or her to be evaluated and diagnosed by a physician. The process seems to be somewhat more rapid for kindergarten children, who are normally more involved with pediatricians.

Table 5.1 shows the same pattern for physicians as for other identification agents. The rate of physician identification fluctuates slighly, being highest at kindergarten, first, and fourth grades, but does not show an increase over time. Because the physician "peaks" generally follow the school "peaks," it is likely that the school plays an important role in the physician's identification.

The prevalence rates across groups indicate the percentage of children identified by each defining system. The school group is by far the most prevalent. What happens to these children in the classroom and how parent–teacher relations affect them is of extreme interest because the numbers are large and the mental health ramifications of such a label are crucial to the child's well being.

PREVALENCE RATES AND SEX

How prevalence rates interact with sex is important both because of the presumed indication of sex-linked genetic causes of hyperactive behavior and because of the presumed "feminine" orientation of the school environment. As with other human individual differences that are presumed to be genetic in origin, there is no way to determine precisely the relative influence of environments and genotypes in the production of phenotypes. In addition, we are only beginning to learn how the home environments of female children may differ from those of male children.

The prevalence estimates presented in Table 5.2 indicate that boys are from six to eight times more frequently identified as hyperactive than girls. The estimated prevalence rates parallel one another across grades, with the exception of a peak rate for girls at kindergarten. This peak may reflect an early appearance of hyperactive behavior in girls or a generally better ability of girls to adapt to classroom demands over time. Such inferences need careful confirmation in longitudinal studies; they are offered here to en-

TABLE 5.2
Prevalence Rates of Males and Females Identified as Hyperactive by Defining Systems—Percentage of Representative Population by Sex

		Grade						
Defining system	*Sex*	*K*	*1*	*2*	*3*	*4*	*5*	*Total*
Home–school–physician	Male	1.83	2.39	1.91	0.86	2.68	2.13	1.97
	Female	.58	.24	.29	.26	.24	.19	.29
Home–physician	Male	.46	—	—	.22	.22	.18	.18
	Female	—	—	—	—	—	—	—
School–physician	Male	—	.22	—	.65	—	—	.14
	Female	—	—	—	—	—	—	—
Home–school	Male	.68	—	.24	.65	.45	—	.32
	Female	—	—	—	.26	—	.19	.08
Home only	Male	.23	—	.24	—	—	—	.07
	Female	—	—	—	—	—	—	—
School only	Male	4.50	3.01	5.19	8.19	7.06	5.72	5.21
	Female	1.15	.53	.65	.90	—	1.04	.77
Total by home	Male	3.22	2.61	2.39	1.73	3.35	2.31	2.54
	Female	.58	.24	.29	.52	.24	.38	.37
Total by school	Male	7.01	5.62	7.34	10.35	10.19	7.85	7.64
	Female	1.73	.77	.94	1.42	.24	1.42	1.14
Total by physician	Male	2.29	2.61	1.91	1.73	2.90	2.31	2.29
	Female	.58	.24	.29	.26	.24	.19	.29
Total identified by any one or more definers	Male	7.70	5.62	7.58	10.57	10.41	8.03	7.89
	Female	1.73	.77	.94	1.42	.24	1.42	1.14
Number of children in representative sample	Male	438	460	419	465	448	563	2793
	Female	343	409	350	378	425	514	2419

courage other investigators to learn more about the characteristics of girls who are defined as hyperactive, and to study factors associated with the life periods in which hyperactivity in girls and boys is first recognized and treated. Battle and Lacey (1972) also have presented provocative data concerning the interrelations among age, sex, and behavior of overactive children. We found that the highest prevalence of girls' hyperactivity is during kindergarten, which is interesting in light of Battle and Lacey's conclusion that "hyperactive" behavior in young (3–6-year-old) girls is more highly associated with positive variables, such as achievement, than it is for boys. Battle and Lacey also found far fewer correlations between maternal attitudes and behavior for hyperactive girls than for hyperactive boys.

TIMES OF CONCERN ABOUT HYPERACTIVITY—A LIFE HISTORY STUDY

The flow chart depicted in Figure 5.2 indicates that children are identified as hyperactive at different points in their life histories. Thus, it is of interest to analyze the patterns in children's ages both when parents report the first notice of the problem behaviors and when help is first sought. From our prevalence study, we were able to identify 65 of 71 children in the HSP, HP, and SP groups whose parents agreed to be interviewed twice over a 2-year period. The second interviews took place between 1 and 2 years after the initial study, when the children were in the first through seventh grade. These data are parents' recollections of what happened, and retrospective data are subject to errors of memory. Figure 5.3 presents the ages of children when the parents first noticed the symptoms and when they first sought help from a professional (usually a physician, although one family sought a psychologist's help).

Our data suggest that parents reported noticing the problem behaviors at three critical times: almost at birth, ages 3 to 4–11, and ages 5 to 6–11. The first period corresponds to the time when temperament is first manifested. The second (preschool) age level corresponds to a time after a period of interaction with parents, after the family environment has had a chance to influence the child, and after the child has gained some independence and opportunities to move about the environment (e.g., to wander away from home). The third age level corresponds to a period when the child becomes more autonomous from the family and enters the school environment.

It is generally the case (85%) that it is not until the child enters school (i.e., from age 5 to 6) that he or she begins taking medication, even though the child may have seen a physician earlier or the symptoms may have been noticed soon after birth. Both the identification as hyperactive and the

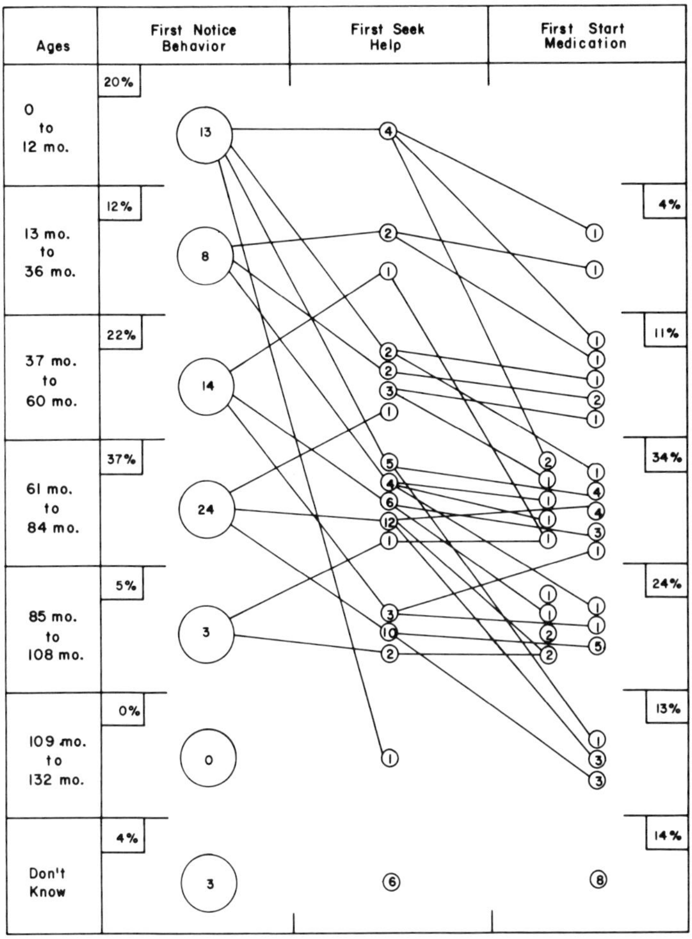

FIGURE 5.3. Physician identified sample (N = 65), which shows reported times of parental concern about behavior, first professional help, and first prescription of medication.

prescription and administration of medication are related to the child's entry into school or preschool.

A few parents reported seeking help *before* they noticed the typical pattern of behaviors. Although this discrepancy seems like an error in reporting, many parents indicated that they had sought help on the advice of others, such as friends, relatives, or teachers. At first they did not notice anything particularly unusual about their child, but after a year or so were able to observe the behavioral pattern pointed out by others. These parents would be an interesting subgroup for further study.

THE OUTCOMES OF IDENTIFICATION

The Prescription of Medication

The major focus of our work is learning what happens to children who are identified and labeled as hyperactive. The most common sequel to the identification by a physician is the prescription of medication, but this is not the only treatment intervention recommended. One study (Sandoval *et al.*, 1976) reported that physicians commonly considered multiple rather than single treatment recommendations. Whereas most indicated they prescribed Ritalin and other medications frequently, they also referred children to other specialists, suggested collaborating with school authorities on educational modifications, and recommended counseling or psychotherapy for parents, children, or both.

The prevalence study also provided us with information about how commonly medication is prescribed. Of the 224 children considered hyperactive by one or more sources, 39 (17.4%) were on medication the year the prevalence study was conducted. Of the HSP children, 58% were medicated, and of all children who saw a physician, 55% were taking various medications. Table 5.3 displays these data. This figure of 55% is not as large as one would expect, until one takes into account the fact that this figure represents the medication use at a particular time during 1 year. Of the 65 children followed for 2 years, 55 (84.6%) had taken medication at one time or another.

Ritalin was the medication most commonly prescribed for these children, as can be seen in Figure 5.4. The first line of the figure indicates that 49 children were first prescribed Ritalin (one was prescribed both Ritalin and Dilantin in combination, as indicated by the overlap in the circles), and 3 were prescribed Ritalin after a trial use of Dexedrine. One child received Dilantin as the first medication tried, changed to Tofranil as the second medication tried, and Ritalin as the third choice. The 2 children who had

TABLE 5.3
Medication Status of Hyperactive Subjects by Defining Systems

Hyperactive status	*Medicated*	*Not medicated*
Home–school–physician	36	26
Home–physician	2	3
School–physician	1	3
Home–school	—	11
Home only	—	2
School only	—	140
Total	39	185

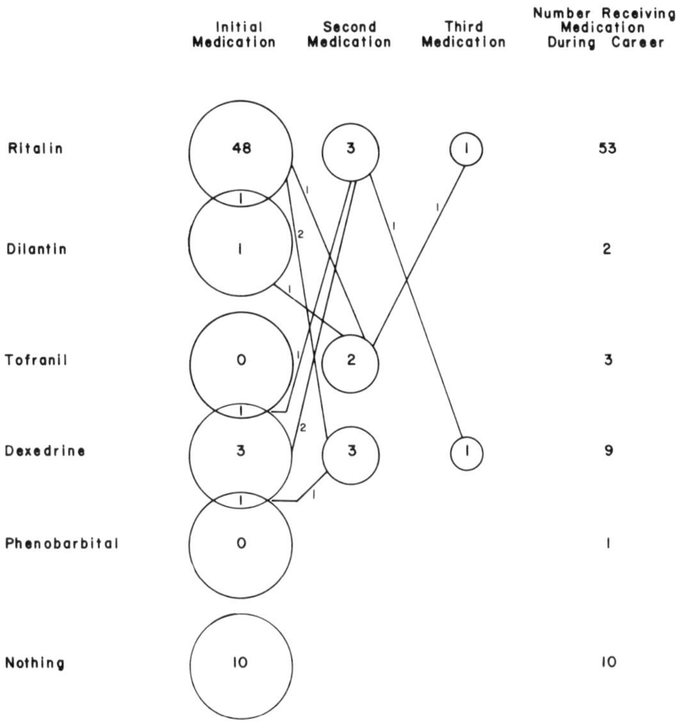

FIGURE 5.4. Physicians prescribe these medications for children considered hyperactive (N = 65).

taken three different medications were both older, 8 and 12, than many children in the study. The percentage of children who had been prescribed medication in this study closely approximates the percentage found by Krager and Safer (1974) in their study of children in the schools of Baltimore County, Maryland, although more of their subjects were prescribed Dexedrine than Ritalin.

Other Treatment Approaches

Medication was not the only treatment approach recommended for hyperactive children. Children in the study had also been in personal counseling or psychotherapy, family therapy, special education, and therapy to increase motor coordination. Other children had received various diet regimens or other nutritional interventions. In some cases the parents were in counseling and psychotherapy, and there were many instances where the physician, family, and school personnel were collaborating. Figure 5.5

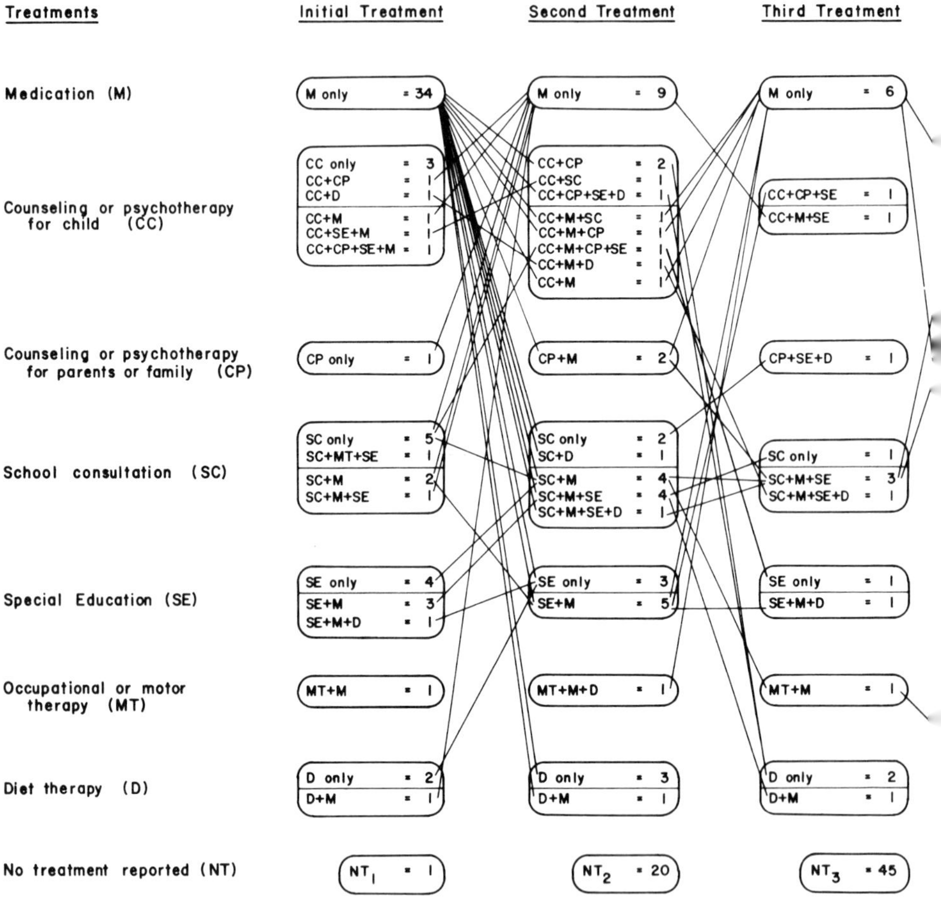

FIGURE 5.5. The course of treatment shown for 65 children identified as hyperactive.

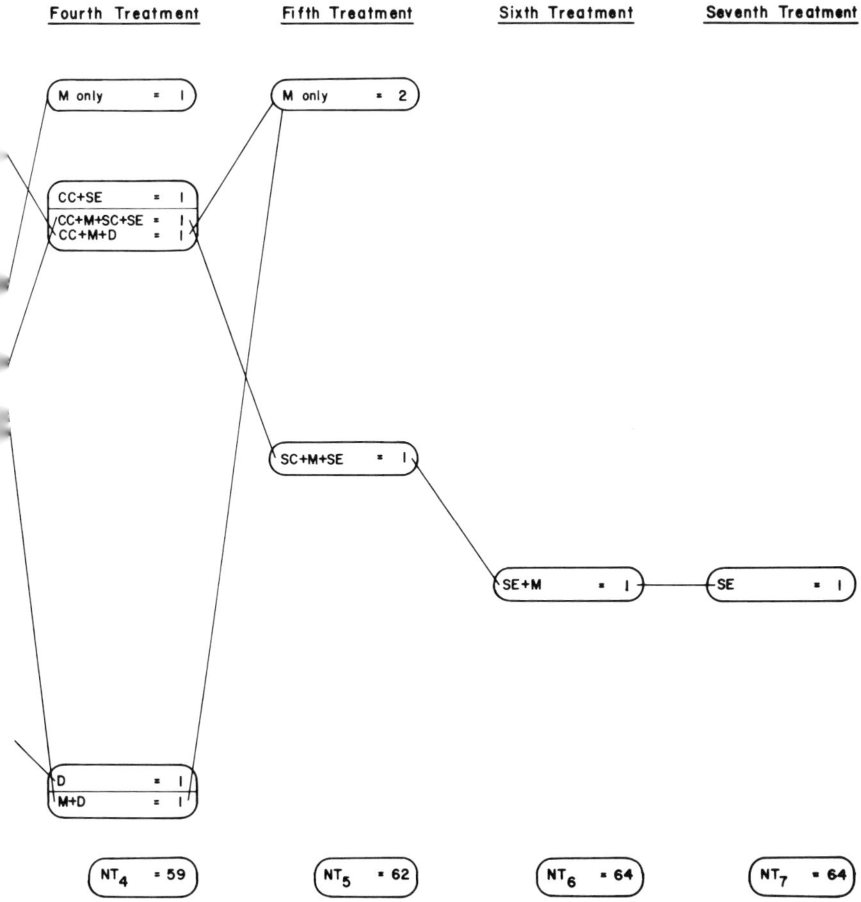
Fourth Treatment
Fifth Treatment
Sixth Treatment
Seventh Treatment
M only = 1
M only = 2
CC+SE = 1
CC+M+SC+SE = 1
CC+M+D = 1
SC+M+SE = 1
SE+M = 1
SE = 1
D = 1
M+D = 1
NT4 = 59
NT5 = 62
NT6 = 64
NT7 = 64

shows the number of children following different treatment recommendations. Only 1 of the 65 children had followed no treatment plan.

Figure 5.5 is a complicated chart at first glance. It depicts the multiple treatments undergone by the 65 children whose parents were interviewed twice. The children ranged in age from 6 to 13 and had been identified as hyperactive for different periods of time. Because these children were at various points in their "careers" as hyperactive children, they may not have yet undergone all of the treatments that might eventually be tried. In fact, at the time these data were collected, the Feingold (1975) diet was just beginning to be publicized widely, and the drug Cylert was about to be promoted vigorously to physicians. During the following year, many more children followed the diet and others shifted from Ritalin to Cylert. In any case, the figure does give an idea of the extensiveness of treatment regimens for many children. Parents are willing and do seek several solutions to their children's problems.

In the chart the treatments are laid out sequentially. A treatment was defined as all the interventions undertaken concurrently during 1 year. If one element was added to or dropped from the treatment, a change was reflected in the next year. Some of the treatments continued unaltered for years. Each line represents a child moving from one treatment to another. When more than one child shares a treatment sequence, the number is indicated. The complexity of treatment patterns reflects the interaction of a multitude of parent, child, and environmental factors.

At the time these data were collected, 1 child had had seven different treatment approaches, three approaches had been tried in 20 cases, 46 children had been involved with two, and 64, at least briefly, had been treated with one intervention or another. The parents of only 8 children on medication sought no other form of assistance. It is clear that physicians as well as parents seek many different kinds of help for children. Evidently no one form of assistance is entirely satisfactory or effective.

The most common interventions other than medication for these children are school-oriented: special education and school consultation. School consultation involves conferences between the parents, physicians, teachers, principals, and school psychologists, during which the concerned parties attempt to find ways to adjust to the child's special needs in the classroom. From the chart it is clear that school consultation often is associated with special education, suggesting that large numbers of these children cannot be accommodated in regular classrooms. Here again there is evidence that hyperactive behavior interferes with the child's schooling. The importance of teachers and their classroom programs cannot be underestimated in the life of the child considered hyperactive.

If we succeed in following all of these children until they reach adolescence or later, we will be able to chart the complete course of treatment interventions for children labeled hyperactive. The 65 children who are the subjects of this report are only a subset of a larger group, whose life histories we are currently following. Many of the others have been studied from the time of physician identification. This group will provide a sample with which we will replicate the results we have presented.

CONCLUSIONS

Throughout this chapter we have presented our perspective on the processes by which children come to be identified and labeled as hyperactive. The reader has undoubtedly noted the discrepancy between the complexity of interactive system theory and the sophistication of the empirical data we have presented to support our structural model. One of the advantages of a theoretical viewpoint is to generate a cohesive set of questions, rather than to supply a set of presumed eternal truths. In our continuing research efforts, we hope to redefine and test our model further, making additions and deletions as we learn more about children considered hyperactive. The following questions are of most vital interest to us at the present time.

1. Do children who are identified at different times (e.g., very early in life, before entering school, after beginning school, and after completing the primary grades) differ in such domains of home environment as: (*a*) demographic factors; (*b*) parental concerns for the child's achievement; (*c*) quality of parent–child interactions; (*d*) family stability and compatability; and (*e*) parent attitudes toward illness and treatment?
2. Is the hyperactive behavior of children affected by such domains of classroom environment as: (*a*) large versus small group instruction; (*b*) teacher standards for child behavior in the classroom; (*c*) warm versus work orientation of the teacher; and (*d*) individualization of curricular goals for children?
3. Are there differences in the classroom environments of teachers who consider many children hyperactive and teachers who consider few children hyperactive at particular grade levels?
4. What characterizes the temperament patterns, health history, home behavior, peer relationships and self-concepts of children identified at various times in their life histories?

From the data presented here, it should be apparent that the frequency with which children are labeled hyperactive varies greatly, depending on the labeling agent. There are developmental stages during which children's observable behavior may or may not be perceived as unusual. There are also temporal patterns in the implementation of interventions to modify these behavior patterns. The course of treatment for children receiving the label "hyperactive" is not a simple one, and medication is used both singly and in conjunction with other treatment approaches. The multiple problems of labeled hyperactive children cause parents, the schools, and physicians to search for the optimum combination of treatment approaches, as well as to modify these approaches over time in an effort to assist the child. The results of our studies of hyperactive children cause us to view with great skepticism those reports that treat these children as a homogeneous group.

APPENDIX: BEHAVIOR AND TEMPERAMENT SURVEY

Name of Pupil______________________________ Birthdate__________________ Grade________________

School___________________________ Prepared by___________________________ Date________________

Please indicate the extent to which each and every statement is characteristic of the above-named pupil. Place a ✓ in the appropriate box opposite each statement.

	Not at all Characteristic	A little Characteristic	Quite a bit Characteristic	Very much Characteristic
1. Unable to sit still - fidgets				
2. Talks too much				
3. Destructive of toys, material and furniture				
4. Gets into things				
5. Accident prone				
6. Reckless				
7. Doesn't stay with games - plays nomadically				
8. Unable to delay gratification				
9. Doesn't complete projects				
10. Adapts slowly to changes in the environment				
11. Inattentive, distractible				
12. Unpredictable show of affection				
13. Constant demand for attention				
14. Can't accept correction				
15. Teases other children or interferes with their activities				
16. Unresponsive to discipline				
17. Defiant				
18. Doesn't follow directions				
19. Lies				
20. Unpopular with peers				
21. Unusually aggressive in behavior				
22. Plays so as to provoke adult intervention				
23. Withdraws from new objects or persons				
24. Sits fiddling with small objects				
25. Hums and makes other odd noises				
26. Excitable				
27. Overly anxious to please				
28. Clumsy, poor general coordination				
29. Personality is very changeable and unpredictable with great changes in mood				
30. Fights				
31. Difficulty in handling frustration				

6

Hyperkinesis: Prevalence and Treatment[1]

JAMES J. BOSCO
STANLEY S. ROBIN

INTRODUCTION

One who examines the literature on hyperkinesis and its treatment soon learns that there is a great deal we do not understand medically, socially, educationally, and pharmaceutically about this condition. Indeed, it may seem as if there is little, if any, knowledge about which we can be confident. Since hyperkinesis may be a chronic, life-blighting condition of children, it is easy to understand why many who are concerned about these children are frustrated and impatient with the slow progress made by scientists and practitioners in reducing this uncertainty. Before we succumb to an excess of self-deprecation, we should acknowledge that many of the problems associated with hyperkinesis and its treatment preclude easily won knowledge. Nevertheless, researchers have been slow to provide answers to certain questions that are answerable, given the current status of methodological sophistication.

One such question, and an important one, is, What is the prevalence of hyperkinesis? Related to this question is the frequency of various types of treatments for hyperkinesis. Since much controversy has involved allegations of promiscuous diagnosis of hyperkinesis (or related diagnoses) and treatment with stimulants, the nature and quality of the data about preva-

[1]The research reported in this chapter was jointly supported by the National Institute of Mental Health and the Bureau of Educationally Handicapped, Office of Education, under Public Health Service Grant No. 3 R 01 MH27608-01S1 CPP.

HYPERACTIVE CHILDREN
The Social Ecology of Identification and Treatment

ISBN 0-12-745950-2

lence are extremely important. Furthermore, reliable information on prevalence could be useful in addressing questions about the etiology, epidemiology, and the scope and nature of medical programs and educational programs and policies for the welfare of hyperkinetic children.

One of the first major public confrontations on the prevalence issue occurred 8 years ago before the House Subcommittee of the Committee on Government Operations (Gallagher, 1970). At that time, essential information was unavailable to expert witnesses. The transcript of the testimony before the House Subcommittee illustrates how inexact was the information on prevalence in 1970.

MR. ROSENTHAL:[2] *Could anyone tell us what is the professional estimate, as to the number of children in the United States that may be affected by MBD disorders?*[3]

DR. LIPMAN: *Based on the percentage figures that we have seen, which have ranged from roughly 3 to 10% of the school age population, we would estimate somewhere between about 1½ to 3 or 4 million children. Based on surveys.*

At another point in the hearing a related issue was considered: The extensiveness of the use of stimulant medications for the treatment of hyperactive children.

MR. GALLAGHER: *How many children would you say today are being treated—we have seen quoted a figure of some 200,000 to 300,000 children. Would that be correct? More? Less?*

DR. LIPMAN: *Well, if you restrict it to amphetamine and to Ritalin, I would say that figure is probably high. It would probably be closer to about 150,000 to 200,000. That is just a rough estimate, Mr. Gallagher.*

MR. GALLAGHER: *Now, further, the man who gives that figure, Dr. Lipman, who we are speaking to here, you said that perhaps 300,000 children are now on the. . .*

DR. LIPMAN: *This is incorrect. The figure I presented had 200,000 as an upper limit.*

MR. GALLAGHER: *Then further you state, "I think the results of the last few years of research will soon reach the Nation's doctors. The pediatricians will begin using them." In effect, what will happen is it will zoom as word of its success spreads throughout the Nation's medical community.*

Where do you think it will zoom to 5 years from now?

[2]Mr. Rosenthal was a congressman from New York. Others were Dr. Ronald Lipman, chief clinical studies section, NIMH; Mr. Gallagher, congressman from New Jersey; Dr. Thomas Points, deputy assistant secretary for health and scientific offices, Department of Health, Education and Welfare.

[3]The term *MBD disorders* was used during the testimony synonymously with hyperkinesis.

DR. LIPMAN: *I didn't use the term "zoom." I said it would probably increase.*

MR. GALLAGHER: *I think your enthusiasm led to the word "zoom."*

DR. LIPMAN: *I guess really some evidence that we have indicates that child psychiatrists tend to be using more of the stimulant drugs than pediatricians. I think the more recent studies that are well controlled and meet scientific standards have strengthened the earlier clinical reports and I think as the scientific validity of the treatment of children with hyperkinesis with the stimulant drugs as part of their total treatment program becomes better known and better accepted by the medical community, that there probably will be some increase. Now, where it will go, I don't know.*

MR. GALLAGHER: *Do you think that it should be allowed to increase or zoom or whatever word we want to use, on the basis of the follow-up studies which involve, as I recall, some 250 children out of 200,000 or 150,000 or 300,000, whatever is the correct figure? Are we justified at this point in further funding the use of amphetamines for children?*

DR. LIPMAN: *Well, I think there are many gaps in our present knowledge* [Gallagher, 1970, p. 16].

PREVIOUS RESEARCH

An examination of the research literature on the prevalence of hyperkinesis reveals why the expert witnesses had difficulty testifying in 1970. Unfortunately, the research conducted subsequently provides no firmer basis for our understanding of prevalence.

Huessy (1967, 1974), Huessy and Gendron (1970), and Heussy, Marshall, and Gendron (1973), in research using teachers' ratings, found the rate to be between 10 and 20%. Werner, Bierman, French, Simonian, Conner, Smith, and Campbell (1968) reported 8–9% of the boys and 2–3% of the girls manifested "hyperkinetic symptoms," whereas Miller, Palkes, and Stewart (1973) concluded that 9.3% of the boys and 1.5% of the girls were hyperkinetic, on the basis of a study of teachers in St. Louis. Cantwell (1975c) and Wender (1971), generalizing from a series of studies, placed the rate between 5 and 20%, Stewart, Pitts, Craig, and Dieruf (1966) placed the rate at 4%, Renshaw (1974) at 7%, Office of Child Development (1971) at 3%, and the Staff Report of the Education Committee of the California State Senate (1974) at 15%.

The lowest reported prevalence of which we are aware comes from Lambert, Sandoval, and Sassone (1978), who conducted a study of 5000 school children, grades K–5, in 146 schools in two counties of California. The researchers gathered data from the home, physician, and school, and after a process of integrating these data sources concluded that the prevalence rate was 1.19%. (See Chapter 5 of this volume.)

Some of the confusion in estimates results from misinterpreting the literature. Even though Lapouse and Monk (1958), for example, do not draw a one-to-one relationship between maternal reports of the symptom of overactivity and the diagnosis of hyperkinesis, such misinterpretation occurs. Adding to this type of confusion are difficulties resulting from several methodological or conceptual problems.

METHODOLOGICAL PROBLEMS

One of the most critical problems in attempts to estimate prevalence is the population–sample problem. Lambert *et al.* (1978) used a two-county area from which to solicit cooperation from school districts. Other researchers have used counties or individual schools as samples or have relied upon convenience or ad hoc samples. In studies with such samples, the problem of determining what the prevalence estimate reveals is severe, since a discrete, meaningful population may not have been defined. Since there is reason to believe that differences in the prevalence of hyperkinesis may be associated with demographic characteristics, this shortcoming may be critical.

Other sampling problems center on the definition of population at risk. Almost all researchers gather data about school children, but some studies are confined to elementary schools while others stop at relatively arbitrary points, such as the fifth grade or age 11. It is essential, therefore, to define the population to which rates are being generalized. If the definition of the population is unrealistic in terms of the population at risk, then the limitations of the research are evident, and the risks of improper generalization clear.

In counting hyperkinetic children, we are engaged in an activity that differs from the calculation of other rates such as deaths, highway accidents, or even many other types of medical diagnoses (e.g., cancer and heart disease). In reality, there is not a single population of hyperkinetic children, but many populations. Each population is an artifact of the criteria used to consider a child within the category. There is no standard definition of the pathology, and various types of persons (physicians, teachers, social workers, psychologists) may categorize children as hyperactive, using a variety of procedures or approaches. Unfortunately, much of the previous research in this area has been conducted without explicit consideration of the alternatives involved in placing children in the category of "hyperkinetic." In counting hyperkinetic children, some researchers leave the impression that their approach is the only viable one, or that it accounts for the "real" hyperkinetic children.

Even if we are explicit in our definition of who is placed in the category, and recognize it as a stipulative rather than a real definition, there is another problem in counting hyperkinetic children. Should a 14-year-old, diagnosed as hyperkinetic at age 6, be counted as hyperkinetic? Should he or she be so categorized if treatment has been discontinued for 2–4 years? No single prevalence rate is sufficient, since medical procedures for pronouncing the child no longer hyperkinetic are often vague or nonexistent. Thus, what is required are several rates describing the different social and medical meanings of the condition.

Given decisions about the criteria for inclusion within the category, it is still necessary to determine which reporting source(s) should be used to calculate a prevalence rate. There is reason to believe that multiple-source reporting of hyperkinesis may be advantageous. In a situation in which we suspect that the prevalence rate is an artifact of the source of the data, independent sources, using common criteria for hyperkinesis, provide a more complete description of the prevalence.

PREVIOUS RESEARCH ON THE PREVALENCE OF STIMULANT TREATMENT

Although the controversy about hyperkinesis turns on the use of stimulant medication, little is known about the prevalence of stimulant treatment among school children diagnosed as hyperkinetic. A summary of this literature is found in Sprague and Gadow (1976). Much of the information is indirect. In the preceding testimony, Lipman speculated that between 150,000 and 200,000 children were receiving medication for hyperkinesis (Gallagher, 1970). Greenberg and Lipman (1971) reported 91% of the physicians surveyed in the Washington, D.C. area prescribed psychotropic medication for hyperkinesis. One-third of a sample of teachers in a midwestern urban area reported having one or more children in their classes, past or present, taking Ritalin (Robin & Bosco, 1973; Bosco & Robin, 1976). Scoville (1974), on the basis of 671,000 prescriptions written, estimated that 56,000 children were being treated (in 1973) with stimulant medication.

More directly, Sprague and Sleator (1973) calculated that 2–4% of the children in the Chicago School System received drug therapy for hyperactivity during the 1970–1971 school year. Conway (1976) reports the percentage of children on medication for the treatment of hyperkinesis ranged from .03 to 6.5% in 43 schools in seven counties of New York. Data from Krager and Safer (1974) indicated a prevalence rate of 1.07% of children in

Baltimore County, Maryland being treated with drugs for hyperkinesis in 1971, and 1.73% in 1973. These data are not confined to stimulant medication. To our knowledge, the only research that provides information on alternate treatments and untreated diagnosed children is that done by Lambert and her associates (Chapter 5 of this volume; see also Lambert *et al.*, 1978). Clearly, such data are needed to address questions about and charges of the misuse of medical diagnoses and medical treatments (particularly stimulant medication) and of inappropriate treatment and pressures from teachers and school systems.

A PREVALENCE STUDY IN GRAND RAPIDS, MICHIGAN

Methods

The research reported in this chapter is an attempt to develop prevalence rates of diagnosed hyperkinesis and treatment methods, using a school system as the unit of analysis. The use of random sampling within a public school system provides a basis for generalizing to the population. This population is the unit within which policies are created, to which procedures and directives are applied, and which is realistic in terms of the population at risk. This known population provides a basis for comparison with other populations of children. Such is not the case with the more casual sampling of undefined populations, which has been the typical situation in prior research.

Our research was conducted in Grand Rapids, Michigan.[4] One-half of the elementary, middle, and junior high schools was selected at random, and questionnaires were sent to the parents of 100% of the children attending these schools. These questionnaires solicited information about the structure and socioeconomic background of the student's family, the diagnosis of hyperkinesis of the student, and any treatment of that condition that the student has undergone or is undergoing. In developing the questionnaire, we were concerned with the ability of parents to provide valid information about the diagnosis and treatment of their children. As has been discussed, there are numerous conceptual and practical problems that confront investigators trying to find out if the child has been diagnosed and, if diagnosis has occurred, how the condition is being treated. We wanted to have clear information about whether a physician's diagnosis had occurred and, given

[4] It is of interest to note that we were informed by a CIBA detail man that California and Michigan were the states with highest sales of Ritalin.

a diagnosis, what type of treatment (if any) had been used. For purposes of developing prevalence rates, our criterion for inclusion was diagnosis of hyperkinesis by a physician.

A three-stage process was employed in order to provide an opportunity for an internal validation, as well as to increase specification on the part of the reporting parent. The first step in the process consisted of questioning the parents about the presence or absence of a medical diagnosis of a learning or behavior problem. If the parents responded affirmatively, they were asked to indicate the nature of the diagnosis and who made the diagnosis (i.e., physician, teacher, or counselor). The questionnaire was structured so that the second stage of the process would be visible only after the first question was answered and the page was turned. At the second stage, the parent was asked to check any of the 11 diagnostic terms most frequently used for hyperkinetic children.[5] The responses to the two items could be contrasted in order to provide for internal verification. Also, the second question, which provided the more structured response, could provide a stimulus that might "ring a bell" to a greater extent than the open-ended question. The third stage consisted of a description of the most common treatment approaches for hyperkinetic children. The parent was asked to indicate whether or not treatment such as "megavitamin therapy, counseling, special diet, behavior modification, psychiatric treatment, or one of several medications (Dexedrine, Mellaril, Dilantin, Cylert, Phenobarbital, Ritalin, Benadryl, Valium, Tofranil, coffee, or tea)" was being used. The final step in this process consisted of asking parents who were not certain about which medication the child was taking to look at the label on the medication and to copy the name of the medication onto the questionnaire. Since these questionnaires were to be used for other research purposes, not reported here, we had the opportunity to telephone the parents of each of the children identified as hyperkinetic by us, in order to verify the information on the questionnaires.

A parallel instrument for teachers was devised. This questionnaire was sent to the teachers in the schools from which the parent sample was drawn. All teachers in the same 50% sample of schools received this questionnaire. Since ethical and legal constraints prohibited the identification of specific children, the questionnaire to teachers elicited summary-type information. The teachers were first asked to provide the number of children in their classes they believed exhibited symptoms of hyperkinesis. The teachers were then asked to report the number of children in their classes who had been

[5]Since a variety of diagnostic terms was used interchangeably, it was necessary to include the following diagnostic terms: *MBD, hyperkinesis, hyperkinetic, hyperactive, overactive, impulse disorder, learning disorder, learning disability, minimal cerebral dysfunction, minimal brain dysfunction, hyperkinetic child behavior syndrome.*

diagnosed *by a physician* as hyperactive (using the same set of terms in the parent questionnaire). This sequence of questions enabled the teachers to distinguish between their perception of each child's behavior and their knowledge of a physician's diagnosis. Teachers were also asked to identify the types of treatments that were being used for children in their classrooms. Although the teacher questionnaires were anonymous, the school and grade taught by the respondents were identified. The data from the teachers provided a second independent estimate of diagnosis and treatment rates.

In order to insure the maximum return, a five-step mailing process was used for both samples. Both teachers and parents received an introductory letter describing the nature of the research and promising that a questionnaire would follow. This letter (and all others) was signed by the two principal investigators, a school administrator, and a prominent physician in the Grand Rapids area. Three days later, another mailing was sent, consisting of a second letter describing the study and a questionnaire, along with a stamped, self-addressed envelope. One week following the mailing of the questionnaires, a third letter was sent thanking those who had returned the questionnaires and encouraging those who had not to do so. After the returns had been deleted from the mailing list, a fourth mailing was sent out that contained another questionnaire and another stamped, self-addressed envelope to those parents who had not returned the questionnaire. The fifth step was a final request that the questionnaires be returned. The teachers had self-addressed postcards included with their questionnaires, which they signed and returned separately to indicate that they had returned the questionnaires. these postcards were used as a basis for culling teachers from the fourth and fifth follow-ups. (For further explanation of these techniques, see Glock & Stark, 1966; Robin, 1965.) This process yielded a 67% return from parents and a 75% return from teachers. It should be noted that the response rate for parents was considerably higher than in previous research with parents in this population.

Results

The data from parents and teachers constitute a report on the same population of children. The 8% difference in response rate, however, results in a larger number (9293) of children reported by the teachers than by the parents (7248). Table 6.1 contains information on the prevalence of physician-diagnosed and treated children.

For reasons previously discussed, no single prevalence rate is adequate. Our first estimate of "ever diagnosed (unverified)" is calculated from information in the parent and teacher questionnaires. The estimate from teachers is .2% higher than that from parents. This estimate refers to all children

TABLE 6.1
Various Estimates of Prevalence of Physician-Diagnosed and Treated Children in the Grand Rapids School System

	Parent source (N = 7248)		*Teacher source (N = 9293)*	
Group	f	*Percentage*	f	*Percentage*
Ever diagnosed				
Unverified	229	3.16	314	3.38
Verified	212	2.92	—	—
Treated within past 5 years	130	1.79	—	—
Currently being treated with stimulants	52	.72	75	.81
Ritalin	46	.63	70	.75
Dexedrine	1	.01	1	.01
Cylert	5	.07	4	.04

who have ever been diagnosed by a physician as hyperkinetic: children recently diagnosed and currently treated; children diagnosed many years prior to the collection of data and no longer being treated; and children with long-standing diagnoses and still being treated. The rates of 3.16% and 3.38% represent the highest possible prevalence rates obtainable from our data, and we feel they are overestimates of the functional prevalence of diagnosed hyperkinesis in school systems.

As a result of our telephone calls to the parents of 229 children, 17 were found not to have been diagnosed by a physician. The verified prevalence, therefore, is based on 212 children (2.92%). We were unable to produce the same type of estimate for teachers because of ethical restrictions.

Parent and teacher estimates of "ever diagnosed" prevalence were similar. Initially we were concerned about parental underreporting and teacher overreporting and, thus, the need to rectify disparate rates. Given the data, these concerns appear to have been unwarranted.

Table 6.1 also contains data about the number of children who were treated for hyperkinesis sometime within the last 5 years. This rate was calculated to provide an estimate of a functional prevalence—a somewhat more useful picture of the number of children in the school system who could be considered hyperkinetic. One might reasonably propose that a child who has not been treated in 5 years might no longer be considered part of the hyperkinetic child population. We found that 130 children, or 1.79% of the school population, had been treated within the last 5 years.

Since treatment with stimulant medication has been of special concern, Table 6.1 concludes with the prevalence of school system children being treated with stimulants for hyperkinesis. Teacher and parent estimates were virtually identical. Based on these figures, between .7 and .8% of the children in the school system are being treated with stimulant medication. Ritalin accounts for almost all of the stimulants prescribed. Of interest is the fact that the newest stimulant medication, Cylert, has not been used as the treatment of choice to any appreciable extent.

In addition to the estimates presented in Table 6.1, we estimated the number of children in school, up to age 11, who were medically diagnosed as hyperkinetic. The number of children so identified is 94, which is 1.29% of the parent source sample. It is of interest to note that this number compares quite closely with the 1.19% rate produced by Lambert *et al.* (1978) for grades K–5.

In response to the question that asked teachers how many children they believed displayed the symptoms of hyperkinesis, 340 children (3.65%) were indicated. These children were exclusive of the 212 identified as physician-diagnosed. In order to produce a comparable estimate from parents, we examined data from the Conners (1973c) Parent–Teacher Questionnaire (10-item symptom checklist) completed by parents in the sample. Two hundred eighty-seven children (4.96%), excluding those diagnosed as hyperkinetic, were rated two or more standard deviations above the mean (mean = 15.55; standard deviation = 5.40; score values 1–4; possible range 10–40). Thus, there is a tendency for both parents and teachers to identify a larger proportion of children manifesting the symptoms of hyperkinesis than have actually been diagnosed medically.

Table 6.2 is a summary of the treatments for the physician-diagnosed children as reported by parents in our sample. This table shows that the most common treatment for hyperkinesis was Ritalin. Almost 75% of the physician-diagnosed hyperkinetic children were treated with Ritalin at some time. About 32% of the hyperkinetic children received counseling. Other treatments were comparatively infrequent; behavior modification was used for about 10% of the children, and over 8% had Phenobarbital prescribed at some time. From another perspective, however, these figures show how few children in the school population have ever been treated for hyperkinesis by any of the methods: No more than 2.5% have ever been treated with any stimulant medication, which is 3.5 times the proportion of those currently being treated (see Table 6.1). With the exception of counseling (.94%), no other treatment had been experienced by more than .5% of the total school population.

Table 6.3 shows the comparison of the hyperkinetic and nonhyperkinetic children with regard to personal and family characteristics. This table supports findings in other research that the preponderance of hyperkinetic children are male. Males outnumber females by almost 4–1 for our sample. This table reveals that there were significantly more hyperkinetic children

TABLE 6.2
Summary of the Frequency and Percentage of Children Ever Treated (Verified) for Hyperkinesis[a]

Treatment	f	*Percentage of hyperkinetic children (N = 212)*	*Percentage of total school population (N = 7248)*
Megavitamin therapy	4	1.89	.06
Counseling	68	32.08	.94
Special diet	14	6.60	.19
Behavior modification	22	10.38	.30
Psychiatric treatment	9	4.25	.12
Dextroamphetamine	17	8.02	.23
Mellaril	14	6.60	.19
Dilantin	7	3.30	.10
Cylert	8	3.77	.11
Phenobarbital	18	8.49	.25
Ritalin	158	74.53	2.18
Benadryl	10	4.72	.14
Valium	5	2.36	.07
Imipramine	7	3.30	.10
Coffee or tea	19	8.96	.26
Other	9	4.25	.12

[a] Since some children received more than one treatment, the totals and percentages for this table will not sum to the number of diagnosed hyperactive children or 100%.

(48%) than nonhyperkinetic children (36%) who were oldest or only children in their families, $\chi^2 = 12.03$, $p < .001$. However, if we compare the proportions of only children who were hyperkinetic and nonhyperkinetic, we see that they are very similar. Within the multichild families, the proportion of oldest children who were hyperkinetic (36%) is significantly greater than the proportion of oldest children who were not hyperkinetic (27%), $\chi^2 = 8.82$, $p = .003$. A significant difference was also observed between the 15% of the hyperkinetic children who were fourth or later in their families and the 24% of the nonhyperkinetic who were also fourth or later, $\chi^2 = 9.74$, $p = .002$. We conclude that the best family predictor of hyperkinesis in our data is the child's place within a multichild family; being the first-born child is associated with higher rates of diagnosed hyperkinesis, and being born fourth or later is associated with lower prevalence.

One of the issues that has surrounded the question of hyperkinesis has been the extent to which the diagnosis has been used as a means of suppressing lower socioeconomic children. These children, the argument goes, display culturally differing patterns of behavior, which become interpreted as deviant behavior and then as "sick" behavior to be diagnosed and treated medically (Conrad, 1975). There is additional support for the relationship between socioeconomic status (SES) and the diagnosis and treatment of hyperkinesis from an extensive collection of theoretical and empirical papers in the medical literature. Various conditions (e.g., malnutrition, inferior prenatal care, premature births, etc.) have been linked to the presence of hyperkinesis. (See Ross & Ross, 1976, for an excellent summary.) Thus, there are several reasons to consider whether there is a relationship between hyperkinesis and socioeconomic status.

TABLE 6.3
Comparison of Personal and Family Characteristics of Physician-Diagnosed Hyperkinetic and Nonhyperkinetic Children

	Hyperkinetic children (N = 212)		*Nonhyperkinetic children (N = 7036)*	
Characteristics	f	*Percentage*	f	*Percentage*
Sex				
Male	167	78.77	3513	49.93
Female	45	21.23	3518	50.00
Missing data	—	—	5	.07
Family size				
One child	25	11.79	641	9.11
Two children	51	24.06	1642	23.34
Three children	66	31.13	1762	25.04
Four–six children	62	29.25	2454	34.88
Seven or more children	5	2.36	529	7.52
Missing data	3	1.42	8	.11
Mean family size	3.17		3.59	
Oldest and youngest children				
Oldest child	102	48.11	2553	36.28
Youngest child[a]	56	26.42	2203	31.32
Place of object child in multiple-child families[b]				
Oldest child	77	36.32	1911	27.16
Second child	54	25.47	1705	24.23
Third child	25	11.79	1109	15.76
Fourth or later child	31	14.62	1669	23.72
Youngest child[b]	56	26.42	2203	31.30

[a] Youngest children are reported separately since this category is not exclusive of second child, third child, and so on.

[b] Since "only children" are excluded, the total and percents for this table will not sum to the number of children in the sample or 100%.

TABLE 6.4
Means and Standard Deviations for Socioeconomic Status (SES) Scores by Treatment of Hyperkinetic Children

	Fathers' mean			*Mothers' mean*		
Group of children	n[a]	*SES*	(SD)	n[a]	*SES*	(SD)
Hyperkinetic ($N = 212$)	162	35.03	(22.94)	198	20.56	(22.47)
Stimulant treated ($N = 168$)	131	35.85	(22.53)	159	21.83	(23.04)
Diagnosed–never treated ($N = 9$)	3	19.67	(2.08)	6	13.83	(9.24)
Nonhyperkinetic ($N = 7036$)	5462	37.74	(25.35)	6508	20.13	(23.54)

[a] The number used for calculation (n) reduced from the number in group (N) due to single parent families and missing data.

Using the Duncan (1961) measure of SES, we compared various subsamples of children.[6] Table 6.4 presents these comparisons. Both mothers' and fathers' SES scores are shown. As Table 6.4 reveals, there are only very small SES differences among hyperkinetic children, nonhyperkinetic children, and hyperkinetic children treated with stimulant medication. Although additional indicators of social status are not used here, occupation, the single strongest social indicator, does not reflect SES differences in the diagnosis and treatment of hyperkinesis.

Table 6.5 contains a frequency distribution for the prevalence of the currently treated children by school. Table 6.5 shows, for example, that six schools in the sample fell within the 0–.29% range. Table 6.5 indicates that there is an appreciable amount of variability with regard to the extent of stimulant treatment. Four schools have a rate of treatment with stimulant medication roughly double that of the school system prevalence rate for treatment with stimulants. It can be seen that information about a school system in general may obscure substantial variations among schools within the system. An individual who insists on a finding of "a lot" or "very little" hyperkinesis and stimulant drug treatment may be quite correct for *that part of a school system to which the individual has access.* However, that person may be quite wrong for the system as a whole and may reach a different conclusion than an individual viewing another part of the same school system. Although we cannot explain the reason for the variation among the school rates of prevalence of currently treated children, one factor, the mean SES of all children's fathers by school, is not significantly associated with the variation in prevalence rates. In other words, schools

[6]The Duncan scale ranges from a high score of 96 to a low of 2. For example, plumbers and pipefitters rate 34, lawyers and judges 93, and roofers 15.

TABLE 6.5
Frequency Distribution of Physician-Stimulant-Treated Hyperactive Children

Prevalence of currently treated children (in percentages)	*Number of schools*
.00– .29	6
.30– .59	5
.60– .89	5
.90–1.19	5
1.20–1.49	5
1.50–1.79	3
1.80–2.09	0
2.10–2.39	0
2.40–2.69	1

with low SES levels do not have greater prevalence than schools with higher SES levels.

DISCUSSION AND CONCLUSIONS

The data just reviewed contained some surprises for us. We were not prepared to find the low prevalence rate for the medical diagnosis of hyperkinesis or for treatment with stimulants. Our findings for diagnosis and treatment were substantially lower than almost any comparable figures in the literature. Given the comparability of parent and teacher estimates, however, it seems that these findings are accurate.

We really do not know why the estimate is so much lower than previous estimates made by others. One possibility is that the previous beliefs about the prevalence of the diagnosis and treatment of hyperkinesis were accurate, but that there has been a turning away from the propensity to diagnose and treat. We have seen some indication of this in our study, but it is impossible to document the magnitude of this phenomenon. It is also possible, for the reasons advanced earlier, that the prior estimates for the prevalence of hyperkinesis were simply incorrect. Nevertheless, it might be well to advise authors and newspaper columnists that the time is over for scare stories about the increasing number of children diagnosed as hyperkinetic and the massive number treated with stimulant medication.

These data, however, indicate a problem. If stimulant medications are intended as adjunctive to other therapies (as the manufacturers state), such medications are not being used in that fashion. Our data indicate a mean of

1.3 types of treatments for hyperkinetic children. Few children receive more than one treatment, and many potential treatments for hyperkinesis are rarely applied.

There seems to be little reason to conclude that hyperkinesis and its treatment have been used to suppress lower SES children. Birth order and sex are associated with diagnosis and treatment, but SES is not.

As we saw, the proportion of children in the school system diagnosed as hyperkinetic was small, and the proportion of currently treated children was even smaller. If, however, we were to use information about diagnosed or treated children as an index of the amount of concern about this problem within the school system, we would probably underestimate the amount of concern. Based on the data from the teachers and the parents, the pool of candidates within the school system for possible diagnosis as hyperkinetic was estimated at between 3.65 and 4.96%—in spite of the relatively small proportion of children diagnosed by a physician as hyperactive and the smaller proportion of currently treated children. For some policy or procedural considerations, it is reasonable to expect that parents and teachers of children in this undiagnosed pool, in addition to parents and teachers of diagnosed and treated children, may be concerned. This underscores our previous discussion of the need for several prevalence rates.

In a second stage of this study, we will see what has happened to those children who have been diagnosed as hyperkinetic. We plan to examine our data about those children reported to have behavior problems. In this second stage, we also hope to have a clearer picture of the natural history of diagnosis and treatment and the ways in which the three most relevant social systems (medical, family, and educational) interact.

We have no reason to assume that the data gathered from Grand Rapids, Michigan are very different from other similar communities. More studies of prevalence, however, are needed in order to assess the size of the problem, to plan policy, prevention, and treatment, and finally to free ourselves from the tyranny of myths about the nature of hyperkinesis and its treatment.

IV

NONPHARMACOLOGIC TREATMENT APPROACHES: ADJUNCTS AND ALTERNATIVES

7

Two Psychoeducational Treatment Programs for Young Aggressive Boys[1]

BONNIE W. CAMP

Characteristic patterns of cognitive deficit, measured in terms of academic achievement or verbal intelligence, have been demonstrated repeatedly in aggressive and delinquent adolescent and adult males (Eron, Walder, & Lefkowitz, 1971; Feldhusen, Thursten, & Benning, 1973; Giora, 1975; Glueck & Glueck, 1972; Kohlberg, LaCrosse, & Ricks, 1972; Lefkowitz, Eron, Walder,& Huesman, 1977). For example, descriptions of aggressive males have noted a significant reduction in verbal intelligence as opposed to nonverbal intelligence (Camp, 1966; Prentice & Kelly, 1963; Wechsler, 1944), and significant deficiencies in acquisition of academic skills, especially reading (Graham & Kamano, 1958). Behavior has been characterized by impulsivity, lack of self-control, poor ego development, and lack of logical thought (Megargee, 1971; Staub, 1971).

Though cognitive deficits are well recognized in these groups, treatment and preventive programs have seldom been designed to improve cognitive functioning. Early efforts in delinquency prevention concentrated primarily on psychotherapy and casework (Powers & Witmer, 1951; Tait & Hodges, 1962). More recently, remedial reading has been added to the list of services

[1]These investigations, from the Departments of Pediatrics and Psychiatry, University of Colorado Medical School, were supported in part by a Research Scientist Development Award No. MK2-47356 from the National Institute of Mental Health, by Grant No. NEG 00-3-002 from the National Institute of Education (NIE) and by Grant No. R03-MH-29333 from the National Institute of Mental Health. Opinions expressed herein do not necessarily reflect the position or policy of NIE, and no official endorsement by the NIE should be inferred.

ISBN 0-12-745950-2

provided to predelinquents. Results of these approaches have been equally disappointing. However, a few reports have suggested that improving cognitive competence may lead to a decrease in maladaptive socioemotional behavior (Bandura, 1973; Staats & Butterfield, 1965), but this approach has received limited attention.

We were interested in exploring the possibility that cognitive training might benefit both cognitive functioning and socioemotional behavior in aggressive boys; the dismal results of treatment efforts with older youth suggested that more success might be expected from work with younger children. Identifying a group of young children at risk for developing aggressive behavior problems in adolescence and adulthood was no problem. Aggressive behavior in early childhood is a powerful predictor of later aggressive behavior and adult mental health problems in general (Kohlberg *et al.*, 1972; Lefkowitz *et al.*, 1977). The predictive relationship between aggressive behavior and later delinquency appears as early as kindergarten and first grade (Conger & Miller, 1966; Glick, 1972). There remains, however, some question of whether cognitive functioning in young aggressive boys shows deficits similar to those seen in older boys.

Kohn and Rosman (1972a, 1972b), for example, found that aggressive preschoolers tended to become aggressive second graders, but aggressive behavior in preschool was neither related to cognitive competence in preschool nor predictive of achievement in second grade. Conger and Miller (1966) found that aggressive behavior in kindergarten was predictive of delinquency in adolescence, but poor academic achievement did not begin to predict later delinquency until grades 3–6. Farrington and West (1971) found that patterns of cognitive functioning in young aggressive boys were similar to older delinquent youth, but their youngest subjects were already 8 years old.

We thought it curious that aggressive behavior and cognitive competence should be so poorly related in the early school years and become so highly correlated later. Both the cognitive and behavior problems of aggressive and delinquent youth seemed to reflect failure in developing inhibitory processes, especially those dependent upon use of language as an internal regulator or mediator. Whether it occurs below the level of awareness, as in performing coding tasks (Estes, 1974), or overtly when talking to oneself to guide problem solving or block impulsive action, verbal mediation activity appears to be an essential element in a variety of mature human behaviors. White (1965, 1970) and Jensen (1966) have summarized a considerable body of literature supporting the idea that use of verbal mediation strategies is essential for school learning and abstract thought. Others studying impulsive behavior have concluded that verbal mediation is necessary for developing self-control over socially undesirable behavior (Meichenbaum, 1975), or for cognitive controls in general (Razran, 1961).

Language as a regulator does not appear to become well established until late in the preschool period, and internalization of this function does not occur until 5–7 years of age. We thought the disparity between early and later correlations might be explained by the fact that deficiencies in development of verbal mediation are revealed very early in social behavior, whereas school learning does not require verbal mediation until later. In other words, academic demands in early years might not expose delay in this developmental stage; in contrast, failure to inhibit aggressive impulses might be readily evident in social situations from an early age.

These considerations led us to hypothesize first that young aggressive boys would differ from normal boys in aspects of cognitive development reflecting use of verbal mediation strategies; secondly, we hypothesized that significant improvement in both cognitive and social behavior would result from training in verbal mediation activities for problem solving. Although we were not specifically addressing the problem of impulsivity in other types of deviant children, such as those with hyperactive behavior or learning disorders, we expected that our findings with aggressive boys would generalize to these other groups. This was particularly likely since aggressive and hyperactive behavior often occur in the same children and, as mentioned previously, learning disorders characterize a sizeable proportion of older aggressive boys.

Our first studies necessarily addressed the question of whether young aggressive boys differed from normal boys on a battery of cognitive tests that emphasized verbal functioning and language development. As Jensen (1966) has noted, a certain amount of verbal development is necessary before language can be used in verbal mediation. If young aggressive boys showed delays in verbal intelligence similar to the pattern seen in older delinquents, it might be reasonable to pursue the problem as a general delay in language development.

In our first study (Camp, Zimet, van Doorninck, & Dahlem, 1977), we screened 995 kindergarten through second-grade boys in the Denver Public Schools for aggressive behavior problems. We asked teachers to complete Miller's (1972) School Behavior Checklist (SBCL) on all boys in their classes. This measure was selected because of the extensive research on reliability and validity that had gone into development of the final scales. In our aggressive group, we included all boys who obtained scores equal to or higher than two standard deviations above the mean on the Aggressive scale of the SBCL. As each of these boys was identified, we selected a boy of the same age and residential census tract whose SBCL scores were within the normal range. In this sample, we had 71 pairs of boys whose parents agreed to participate.

A battery of cognitive tests was administered to all boys selected. This battery was heavily weighted with verbal tests, including subtests from the Illinois Test of Psycholinguistic Abilities (ITPA) and the verbal scale of the Wechsler Intelligence Scale for Children (WISC). However, we also included the three tests comprising Cohen's (1959) perceptual–organization factor from the WISC.

We used discriminant function analysis to determine whether the aggressive and normal boys differed in their pattern of performance on this battery, and we performed univariate analyses of variance to determine whether the two groups differed on individual tests. Our findings were somewhat surprising. Discriminant function analysis did show significant differences between the two groups; correct group membership could be identified from the cognitive battery alone in 79% of the cases. Most surprisingly, the major differences were on the nonverbal tests, with normal boys obtaining significantly higher scores than aggressive boys.

This finding was puzzling because we expected to find deficits on tasks that others described as measuring verbal mediation activity. However, on reflection, it seemed likely that we had actually shown that aggressive boys have a verbal mediation deficiency without a deficit in language development or overt verbal skills. Verbal mediation has been described as talking to oneself to guide problem solving (Jensen, 1966) or to guide other behavior (Meichenbaum, 1975). The process is usually automatic and becomes overt only when problems become difficult. Jensen (1966) suggested that deficiency in mediational activity may be most evident in dealing with problems that require verbal mediation but are ostensibly nonverbal. He explains this apparent paradox by suggesting that for some individuals, verbal behavior is not aroused by the task unless the problem is posed verbally. In such instances, he says, "The subject tries to solve the problem on the perceptual level, and for more difficult problems this approach is totally ineffective [Jensen, 1966, p. 104]." A possible interpretation of our findings is that the aggressive boys had developed adequate verbal abilities but failed to use them in guiding problem solving on the nonverbal tasks. It seemed that more direct assessment of such mediational activity might reveal this deficit more clearly, particularly on tasks where linguistic controls might be useful in curbing impulsivity.

Consequently, we redesigned our test battery to include the Matching Familiar Figures Test (MFFT), several tasks comparing effectiveness of overt and covert self-guiding speech in controlling motor behavior, and direct measures of verbal mediation activity during nonverbal problem solving. This new battery was administered to a second sample of aggressive and normal boys (Camp, 1977a). This time we screened 832 boys in first and second grades, and the test battery was administered to 49 aggressive and 46 normal boys selected in the same manner described previously.

Results were again subjected to both univariate analyses of variance and a stepwise discriminant function analysis. When results were confined to the subgroups with nonverbal IQ equal to or greater than 90, we achieved the best discrimination. This time, 88% of the boys were classified correctly using the combination of test scores. When children with lower IQ levels were included in this analysis, 79% were classified correctly.[2] Ten of the 14 scores contributing to the discriminant function represented new measures added to assess verbal mediation activity and impulsivity. Six of these also showed differences significant at the .10 level or better on the univariate analysis. The most powerful variables in the discriminant analysis showed that aggressive boys tended to have shorter latencies on the MFFT, to use more immature, irrelevant and social forms of private speech, and to tap more slowly on a motor regulation task, when self-commands were overt.

In general, these results confirmed our expectation that aggressive boys tended to have a rapid response style,with some failure to use verbal mediational activity unless specifically requested. Since they had good vocabularies, did use self-guiding speech in some circumstances, and showed the ability to inhibit responding by overt self-verbalization, we thought this represented a "production" deficiency rather than a mediational deficiency. Production deficiency is a term introduced by Flavell, Beech, and Chinsky (1966) to describe the situation in which children fail to use a skill that is in their possession.

DEVELOPMENT OF THE COGNITIVE BEHAVIOR MODIFICATION PROGRAM: THINK ALOUD

These findings confirmed our expectation that cognitive functioning in aggressive and normal boys differed at least as early as 6–8 years of age, particularly in the use of verbal mediation activities. We were encouraged to explore the hypothesis that cognitive functioning might be improved or "normalized" through training in use of verbal mediation strategies. In addition, we hypothesized that improved social behavior would accompany improved cognitive functioning.

[2]To avoid unnecessary repetition, details of this analysis are not being presented at this point. The reader is, however, referred to Footnote 5 and Table 1.1 for a general idea of what this first analysis provided.

Others had shown previously that training in use of self-guiding verbalizations could be effective in improving the cognitive performance of impulsive or hyperactive children (Bem, 1967; Douglas, Parry, Marton,& Garson, 1976; Meichenbaum, 1975). Early studies in this area selected children on the basis of test behavior. Few attempts had been made to work with children selected because of clinically significant behavioral deviance.

In a few instances where the response of deviant children in a self-instructional program was studied, effects were variable. Meichenbaum and Goodman (1971), for example, found changes on cognitive tests but not in classroom behavior. However, their training program was brief and children were not selected in a homogeneous fashion. Also, their program did not address social behavior directly. Other programs, focused more explicitly on social behavior, did yield improvements in this domain (Goodwin & Mahoney, 1975; Pitkanen, 1974; Sarason, 1968). We felt that a program for aggressive boys should address both cognitive and social problems in order to have an impact on both areas.

To this end, we developed a program entitled Think Aloud (TA). The procedures were very similar to those described by Meichenbaum and Goodman (1971) in that heavy emphasis was placed on modeling of cognitive strategies and on developing answers to four basic questions:

1. What is my problem?
2. How shall I do it?
3. Am I following my plan?
4. How did I do?

The "copycat" game was used to engage the child in imitating both speech and action. The imitation component was later faded and the child encouraged to verbalize his own strategy. Eventually all problem analysis and planning were faded to a covert level (cf. Camp & Bash, 1977).

We used visual materials similar to those described by Meichenbaum and Goodman, but we also added auditory verbal tasks that would require blocking the first impulsive association and reasoning to a solution—for example, a complex version of the Simon Says game. We also adapted the interpersonal problem-solving games developed by Shure and Spivack (1974) for use in the TA format. These carefully sequenced games focused on identifying emotions, thinking about likes and dislikes, and considering outcomes and fairness of actions. In addition to formal games and dialogues, Shure and Spivack presented a general problem-solving approach that was easily incorporated into the cognitive problem-solving portion of our program.

In the initial trial with this program, 24 second-grade aggressive boys were randomly assigned to the experimental group or to the untreated control group. There were also 12 normal, untreated controls. Prior to the program, boys in the two "aggressive" groups had achieved scores more than two standard deviations above average on the Aggressive scale of the SBCL. All boys, aggressive and normal, had also received the test battery used in the second study of normal and aggressive boys.

Boys in the aggressive–experimental group received daily, individual, half-hour sessions in TA for 6 weeks. At the end of the 6-week training program, portions of the test battery were repeated. Teachers were asked to complete the Low Need Achievement (LNA)[3] and the Aggressive scales of the SBCL, with the addition of judgments regarding whether each item had shown "no change," "worsening," or "improvement."

To provide a basis for summarizing test data, test scores on first- and second-grade subjects who participated in the study of normal and aggressive boys ($N = 93$) were reanalyzed, using only those test variables on which both pre- and posttest measures were available on the boys participating in the TA trial.[4] The mean discriminant function for the normal group on this reanalysis was $-.49$ and that for the aggressive reference group was .49. Weights derived from this discriminant function analysis were used to calculate a discriminant function score (*d*-score) for both pre- and posttest data of subjects in the TA trial.

It was hypothesized that training in TA would bring the scores of the aggressive–experimental group closer to those of the normals as reflected in a significant interaction between the time of testing (pre versus post) and treatment group. Thus, aggressive–experimental and aggressive–control groups should be similar, and different from normals on pretest. On posttest, however, aggressive–experimental and normal–control groups should be similar to each other and different from aggressive–controls. The results, presented in Figure 7.1, confirmed these expectations. The pre- and posttest means were .60 and $-.69$ for the aggressive–experimental group, .42 and $-.03$ for the aggressive–control group, and $-.58$ and $-.73$ for the normal–control group.

A repeated measures analysis of variance showed significant differences for pre- versus postdiscriminant scores, $F(1, 30) = 14.47$, $p < .001$; for treatment group, $F(2, 30) = 3.80$, $p < .05$; and the Time (pre- versus posttreatment) × Treatment group interaction, $F(2, 30) = 4.29$, $p < .05$. Specific contrasts showed a significant difference at pretest between normal–control and the aggressive groups combined, $F(1, 30) = 21.74$, $p < .001$, and non-

[3]Items in the LNA scale were prosocial in form. However, Miller reversed the scoring and renamed the scale, in order that high scores would reflect deviance.

[4]The tests comprising this revised battery are listed in the note to Table 7.1. The reader is cautioned that the data in Table 7.1 refer to the comparison study, which is described on pages 205–211 in the present chapter.

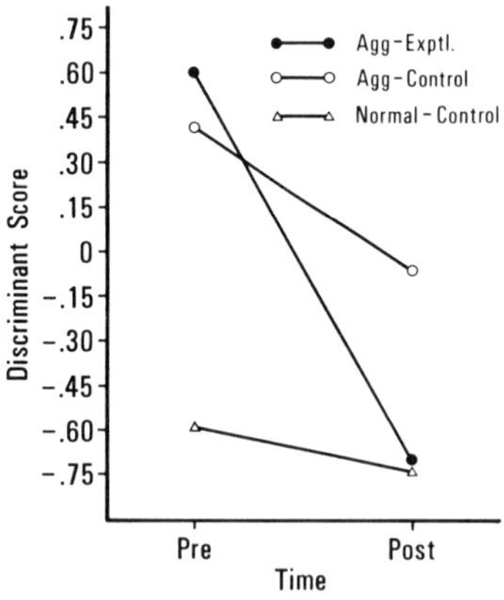

FIGURE 7.1. Pre and post discriminant scores shown for aggressive—experimental, aggressive—control, and normal—control groups. [From Camp, B. W., Blom, G. E., Hebert, F. W., & van Doorninck, W. J. "Think Aloud": A program for developing self-control in young aggressive boys. **Journal of Abnormal Child Psychology**, 1977, **5**, 157–169. Copyright 1977, Plenum Publishing. Reprinted by permission.]

significant differences between the two aggressive groups. On posttest, significant differences were observed between aggressive–controls and aggressive–experimentals, $F(1, 30) = 5.32$, $p < .05$, whereas differences between aggressive–experimental and normal–controls were nonsignificant.

Analysis of teacher ratings showed that scores on both the LNA and Aggressive scales of the SBCL did not change significantly for any of the three groups. Groups were also compared on the average number of items teachers indicated as improved on the two scales. On the Aggressive scale, the average number of items improved was 9.7 for the aggressive–experimental group, 10.9 for the aggressive–control group, and .75 for the normal–control group. Differences between the two aggressive groups were not significant. On the LNA scale, however, the two aggressive groups did differ significantly. The aggressive–experimental group showed an average of 10.3 items improved, whereas the aggressive–control and normal–control groups showed an average of 3.9 and 1.7 items improved, respectively. On the Tukey test, used to evaluate differences between all pairs of means, a difference of 4.87 was necessary to reject the null hypothesis at $p < .05$.

From these findings, we concluded that the TA program was powerful enough to produce significant improvement in both test performance and classroom social behavior in aggressive boys. At the same time, the program failed to produce significantly more improvement in aggressive behavior (as rated by teachers) in the experimental than in the control group. Furthermore, results of the teacher ratings were potentially contaminated by the fact that teachers knew who was in the program and who was not. Analysis of behavior recorded during the program also suggested that inadequate attention had been given to curbing silliness and improving the quality of verbal output. Our next efforts were therefore oriented toward improving program content as well as designing a trial that would compare TA with another program providing adult attention.

Changes in program content were guided in part by the impracticality of field-testing an individual program in public schools. Consequently, when we made revisions in several tasks to improve quality of performance, we also redesigned the entire program for use with pairs of children. This revised program was tested with 10 children, somewhat heterogeneous for presenting problem. Results were of the same magnitude as those obtained in the original program, although statistical significance was not achieved (Camp, 1977b).

ISSUES IN APPLIED RESEARCH DESIGN

There were four issues that greatly influenced the direction our research took at this point: (*a*) choice of a treatment comparison; (*b*) decreasing within-program sources of variability and increasing power of the program; (*c*) generalizability of treatment to different settings with different change agents; and (*d*) choice of dependent measures.

Choice of a Treatment Comparison

In treatment research there are basically two forms of comparison to be made. One involves comparing Treatment A with no treatment and the other involves comparing Treatment A with one or more alternative treatments. Our initial project utilized the first type of design. This may help to establish whether the treatment has an impact, but differences between Treatment A and no treatment may result from differences in so many dimensions that this comparison seldom yields completely satisfying answers. More definitive answers can be obtained if Treatment A is compared with an alternative treatment that resembles Treatment A except in a few well-specified ways.

If one is concerned with having a beneficial impact on an individual child, rather than merely studying functional relationships among variables, careful thought must be given to ethical issues in designing alternative treatments. Control groups receiving benign attention from an adult may be justifiable in brief encounters. However, programs that extend over several weeks or months and consume significant amounts of a child's valuable educational time may not be justifiable, unless there is good reason to believe that participating children may actually benefit.

To satisfy these considerations, we developed an alternative program entitled Great Expectations (Camp & Simmons, 1977). Great Expectations

(GE) included three basic activities in each 30-min "lesson." The first 5 min were devoted to relaxation training to decrease tension. The second 5 min consisted of Fry's (1975) method of inducing a happy mood, which had been found to increase resistance to temptation. The final 20 min were devoted to an activity judged to be challenging and satisfying for each child. During this time, teachers were instructed to make at least one "great expectations" comment modeled on those used by Rappaport and Rappaport (1975) in order to increase achievement by raising children's expectations of success. These included comments to praise superior performance, to build a feeling of exceptional talent ("Have you always been so good at ________?"), to predict doing very well in school ("I bet you'll be one of the best kids in [subject] in your room"), and to show that the adult will follow the child's progress. Both TA and GE provided benign adult attention to pairs of children, but GE did not use modeling or an emphasis on self-verbalization.

Enhancing Program Power

It is generally recognized that treatment research in the mental health field suffers from the problem of "weak effects" (Bergin & Strupp, 1972; Hersen & Barlow, 1976): There are so many variables increasing the within-treatment variability that treatments usually have to be very powerful to demonstrate statistically significant change. In planning treatment research, it is obviously desirable to decrease these within-treatment sources of variability and increase the power of the treatment as much as possible. Several discussions regarding procedures for decreasing within-treatment variability (Hersen & Barlow, 1976) and statistical sources of invalidity (Cook & Campbell, 1976) are available and will not be reviewed here. The power of a potentially good treatment program may be attenuated in at least four ways:

1. Design of the program (length, content, schedule) may be inadequate.
2. Program delivery may be inadequate.
3. Impact on the child may be attenuated by nonprogram factors.
4. Individual differences in magnitude of response may result in averaging out of effects.

PROGRAM DESIGN

Aside from program content, one of the first questions to be addressed in planning a treatment program is how long it should be applied for a fair trial. In drug research this may be gauged partially by answers to questions about avenue of introduction, rate of absorption, blood and tissue concentrations, excretion, etc. In behavioral programs, especially those that require learning or change over time, this question is much more difficult to answer. Our experience in a tutoring program suggests that daily evidence of learning may occur, but unless a child has at least 40 lessons or 2 months of concentrated lessons, learning in this program will not be reflected in test results (Camp, 1976a). Meichenbaum and Goodman (1971) offered six sessions over 2 weeks and found changes in impulsivity on tests close to the program, but not on classroom variables. Others (Bugental, Whalen, & Henker, 1977) report similar experiences.

Brief programs that do not substantially influence a child's life may produce only trace effects. If one plans longer programs that do engage significant portions of a child's time and are expected to have a significant prolonged effect, one should address the question of whether long-term changes are sufficient to justify the program. Campbell and Stanley (1966), for example, have commented on the need to evaluate long-term effects in educational programs irrespective of short-term effects. When this has been done, short-term gains have often not been sustained (Bronfenbrenner, 1974b).

This washout effect has been disappointing in that many have expected intervention programs to, in effect, immunize children against later problems. Yet, early intervention programs have seldom been designed as "immunization" programs. In medicine, for example, a well-established approach to immunization is to give an initial challenge followed by boosters at periodic intervals. This model has seldom been adapted for mental health programs, yet would seem to have great promise. In the young child, immunological competency cannot be relied upon to produce an effective recall response without systematic rechallenge. A conceptually similar problem is seen in preventive mental health programs when a good initial "take" is often followed by loss of the acquired competency—perhaps with disuse or failure to challenge. In the terminology of psychological learning theory, the analog of a booster may be reinstatement—a partial repetition of the learning experience to maintain its effect through time (see Campbell & Jaynes, 1966).

To evaluate long-term effects and to test an application of the immunization model, we decided to include a refresher course 6–12 months after the original programs. Since our main interest remained in the development of training for cognitive and social problem solving, we used the same TA-based refresher program for both the GE and TA graduates.

PROGRAM DELIVERY

How can one be sure that the program one thinks is being delivered is actually being delivered? In recent years, educators have answered this question by at least insisting that teachers complete a course of training and achieve a minimum proficiency (Camp, 1976a; Engelman & Bruner, 1969). Others have included on-site monitoring to assess continued fidelity to the program (Castner, Della-Piana, Hogben, & Allen, 1968; Miller & Dyer, 1975). We incorporated both procedures in the present program. The first two assistants were trained together and role-played various lessons. Their individual sessions with children were tape recorded, reviewed by the author, and discussed for modifications. Subsequently, these two assistants trained additional teachers using role-playing, weekly in-service group meetings, and on-site visitations. Midway through the program, supervisor and trainee completed questionnaires assessing important aspects of program delivery.

For the follow-up program, one of the original assistants designed and carried out refresher courses with all boys. The author supervised by periodically reviewing and discussing this assistant's report of activities. We encountered a few situations where program delivery was somewhat attenuated in our clinical judgment, but where our objective assessments did not reflect enough difference for us to feel justified in eliminating data.

IMPACT ON THE CHILD

In working with any child, an instructor or therapist forms definite opinions about how the child is being affected by the program. In our early trials we did not consider this issue sufficiently. Initially, most of our assessment of immediate impact was concerned with evaluating and modifying the program content. In the follow-up study, however, we did address the issue directly by obtaining a global assessment of progress in the program from the refresher program instructor at the conclusion of each child's program.

INDIVIDUAL DIFFERENCES

The fact that individuals respond differently to treatment poses several well-known problems for research using group comparisons (Hersen & Barlow, 1976; Jensen, 1967). The variables predicting individual response are difficult to identify. Usually, any treatment group is composed of some who clearly change and some who clearly do not or who get worse. In this situation, treatment effects may average out so that group means fail to reflect any effect or show an effect determined by the proportion of one type of individual in a particular sample.

We used two approaches to examine individual × treatment interactions. One consisted of using groupings based on response within the refresher program. Another was to find a laboratory measure that could be used to characterize the individual child's standing in relationship to a reference group, and then determine the type of child who improved the most on this measure.

For this latter purpose, we returned to the discriminant function analysis of cognitive tests in our second study comparing aggressive and normal boys (Camp, 1977a). In that investigation each boy received a discriminant function score, or *d*-score, based on weights derived from the discriminant function analysis.

Such weights could be used to calculate a *d*-score on boys in any new study and determine how close the cognitive pattern of each new boy was to the earlier group of 46 aggressive boys or the earlier group of 49 normal boys. A boy in a new sample could then be classified as *d*-score aggressive if his *d*-score had a higher probability of coming from the aggressive reference group, or *d*-score normal if his *d*-score had a higher probability of coming from the reference group of normal boys.

Generalizability

As Hersen and Barlow (1976) note, a major question regarding effectiveness is whether a treatment shown to be effective with one therapist in one setting can be generalized to other therapists and other settings. In a project such as ours, this became a question of whether a program delivered to a small number of boys working with two closely supervised teachers, who helped develop the program, could be taught to a heterogeneous group of teachers. This group would be less familiar with the background of the program, would have less supervision, and would be working in a wider variety of schools. Even if program delivery could be successfully implemented under these circumstances, the power of the treatment program would undoubtedly be diluted by increasing these sources of within-treatment variability. Some estimation of this dilution effect could be obtained by comparing results from these new trials with earlier results from both treated and untreated groups.

Dependent Measures

In evaluating treatment programs, choice of dependent variables is obviously critical. Often goals of a program may be quite global, such as "impact on social behavior," with specification of "impact" and "social behavior" left until later. Even if one knows the system one wishes to influence, one may not know whether to expect a direct decrease of undesirable behavior, an increase in positive or incompatible behavior, or both. With respect to social behavior, we resolved this by assessing program effects on both undesirable (aggressive) and desirable (prosocial) behavior. Even if one happily selects the correct variables to examine, there is still the problem of finding measures of these variables appropriate to the treatment being undertaken, sufficiently stable not to change with the passage of time alone, yet sensitive enough to register actual treatment effects.

There are also questions as to whether one chooses dependent measures that reflect generalization or transfer of program effects to different contexts and settings, how soon such effects should be observed, and how the behavior to be measured relates to behavior observed, rehearsed, or taught in a program. In our project, the larger goal was to develop a program to deal with cognitive–emotional behavior in a setting with one adult and two children, a program that could also alter spontaneous social behavior in a classroom with one adult and 20–30 children. Thus, our goal was to develop a program that would alter behavior in a much different setting, as well as behavior very different from that dealt with directly in the program.

Our approach to this assessment question was to develop a logical progression of expected program effects and then select dependent measures that tapped these effects at various points. We expected the most direct effects of a verbal mediation training program to be on cognitive behavior in a setting with similar structure to the actual program, that is, individual testing with materials and activities similar to those used in the program. More distantly, we hoped to find effects transferring to classroom behavior, first by an increase in behavior similar to that developed in the program and later by a decrease in more indirectly related behavior, that is, aggression.

In addressing the issue of measuring direct effects on cognitive behavior, we had to decide what cognitive behavior we wanted to change and how individuals, rather than variables, should be characterized. Our decision was to design a program that targeted cognitive variables known to distinguish aggressive from normal boys in the age range of interest (Camp, 1977a; Camp *et al.,* 1977). We concentrated some of the program design on activities to decrease the particular characteristics of the cognitive pattern of aggressive boys, for example, impulsivity and use of associative thinking instead of logic. In our earlier study of the TA program, the aggressive boys had shown changes in cognitive pattern, indicated by *d*-score shifts toward the pattern shown by normal boys. We decided to use these *d*-score changes as dependent variables in the present study, indicating improvement or normalization of cognitive pattern.

We also made direct observations of classroom behaviors, using a scale we had previously adapted from Werry and Quay (1969), and for which we had some information about the relationship to teacher ratings (Camp & Zimet, 1974). For example, we found that teachers' ratings of prosocial behavior correlated significantly with daily observations of "off-task" behavior ($r = -.38$, $p < .01$). We selected reading and math periods for observation; these activities often require the most inhibition of impulsivity, concentration on a defined task, and presumably challenge the use of skills developed in the cognitive training program.

In addition to these objective tests and behavior observations, we continued to use teacher ratings. Although the SBCL was a good scale for selecting aggressive boys, we found that scores were so stable within a year ($r = .84$ fall to spring) and even across years ($r = .52$; Camp, 1976b) that the measure may not be sensitive to treatment effects. We also became concerned that the SBCL did not distinguish aggressive from distractible and hyperactive problems (as perceived by teachers). For these reasons, we added two additional scales to the assessment battery at the time of follow-up, the Schaefer and Aaronson (1966) Preschool and Primary Classroom Behavior Scale, and the Conners short form for rating hyperactivity (Werry, Sprague,& Cohen, 1975).

EVALUATING THE IMPACT OF THINK ALOUD AND GREAT EXPECTATIONS: DESIGN OF PROJECT

The preceding considerations were incorporated into the design of a project in order to evaluate the impact of the two training programs, TA and GE, on cognitive and social behavior of 6–8-year-old aggressive boys. First- and second-grade boys were selected for the study on the basis that teacher ratings of classroom behavior yielded a *T* score of at least 65 on the Aggressive scale of the SBCL. Thus, the entire sample showed significant amounts of aggressive behavior in the classroom. Boys meeting this criterion were randomly assigned to participate in one of the two experimental programs on a daily basis for 2 months during the spring of 1976.

The two programs were delivered by 19 resource teachers and 17 teacher aides who were trained concurrently with delivery of the program. Trials were conducted in schools where at least 4 boys meeting the criterion were identified. Within each school, the 4 boys were assigned randomly to either the TA or the GE program. Loss of subjects from family moves after the program began reduced the numbers to 31 TA boys and 32 GE boys, ranging in age from 74 to 99 months.

Prior to beginning the program, all boys were administered the battery of cognitive tests used to obtain *d*-scores. At the end of the 8-week training program, these tests were repeated and teachers were asked to complete the LNA and Aggressive scales from the SBCL, including analysis of each item in terms of "improved," "worse," and "no change."

Beginning in the fall of 1976, attempts were made to contact these 63 boys, along with a sample of 18 boys who had participated in a project staff-administered version of TA, to invite participation in a refresher course designed to emphasize social problem solving. For this long-term follow-up, we were able to locate 48 boys who had participated in the teacher-administered TA and GE programs and 14 boys who had participated in the staff-administered TA trial. When boys were located, teachers were asked to complete the Aggressive and LNA scales of the SBCL; the Schaefer and Aaronson Preschool and Primary Classroom Behavior Scale, and the Conners short form for rating hyperactivity. Boys were also retested with the cognitive battery used to derive *d*-scores, as well as experimental tests of reading and spelling (Camp & Dolcourt, 1977).

After the refresher course ended, the refresher course instructor rated the progress of boys in the program itself, and classroom teachers independently completed the Schaefer–Aaronson and the Conners scales on the basis of classroom behavior. Posttesting consisted of the MFFT, the Raven Progressive Matrices, and the experimental tests of reading and spelling.

The refresher course consisted of three lessons per week for 1 month. Irrespective of their initial program, boys received the same basic refresher course, though content of individual sessions was derived from a child's own circumstances. The total group was divided geographically. The refresher course was offered to different areas at 6, 9 or 12 months after the original program. Circumstances prevented six children from receiving more than the initial follow-up evaluation. There were no consistent differences among the geographical-time groups; data were collapsed across this variable.

For purposes of this discussion we addressed the following questions:

1. Did the training programs differ in short-term effect on cognitive pattern, teacher ratings of behavior, and observations of classroom behavior?
2. How did the programs differ in long-term effects on cognitive pattern, teacher ratings and academic test performance?
3. What effects did a brief refresher course have on test performance and teacher ratings?
4. What initial variables identified boys who would show good progress by the end of the refresher course?

Short-Term Program Effects

A modified version of the Preschool Interpersonal Problem-Solving Test (PIPS) (Shure & Spivack, 1975) was used to determine whether boys in the TA program actually learned the techniques taught by the program. The TA program emphasized developing alternative solutions to social problems and decreasing irrelevant and repetitious answers. The PIPS test presents social problems in a manner closely related to the way they were presented in TA, and thus provides a "take" measure for this training program. The TA boys showed significantly less repetitious and irrelevant talk than GE boys. They also showed a higher percentage of solutions to total verbalizations. These findings assured us that TA skills were learned and retained.

We then turned to assessing the impact of the two programs on cognitive pattern. Again we first reanalyzed data from our earlier reference population, utilizing only subjects in the age range represented by the sample of boys participating in the TA–GE comparison, eliminating IQ restrictions.[5] The mean discriminant function for the normal group in this analysis was −.89 and that for the aggressive group was .81. Because these variables and their weights were used in all subsequent analyses, the 13 variables with the largest weights are presented in Table 7.1, along with mean scores achieved by TA and GE boys on these variables. Weights derived from this analysis were then used to derive a *d*-score for each child and to classify each *d*-score as resembling the normal or the aggressive reference group. Children in each training program could then be described as "*d*-score normal" if their score had a higher probability of coming from the normal group, and as "*d*-score aggressive" if their *d*-score had a higher probability of being classified with the aggressive reference group. Although all boys were significantly aggressive in classroom behavior, approximately one-third of the boys in each training group obtained *d*-scores classified as "normal."

These data were analyzed using the North Carolina multivariate general linear model program to perform a one-way multivariate analysis of variance on four groups (TA *d*-score aggressive, TA *d*-score normal, GE *d*-score aggressive, and GE *d*-score normal) with two measures (pre and

[5]This reference population actually contained data on 115 boys from kindergarten through second grade. The first reported discriminant function analysis (Camp, 1977a) concentrated on finding the optimal pattern that distinguished between aggressive and normal boys on the basis of test pattern alone. The second discriminant analysis on the same data was restricted to the subset of variables on which both pre- and posttest measures were available in the first trial with TA. This third discriminant function analysis was performed on the same data, but used data from all children whose age was comparable to that of boys in the TA–GE comparison irrespective of IQ. In this last analysis, the discriminant function had an associated F (23, 77) = 2.47, $p < .002$, and achieved 82% correct classification of normal and aggressive boys in the reference population, χ^2 (1) = 42.71, $p < .001$. The actual variables that were weighted most heavily in each of these analyses changed in only minor ways. Errors in classification of subjects also changed very little over the different analyses. However, the size and sign of the standardized discriminant coefficients changed considerably. Weights derived from the third analysis were used for calculating *d*-scores on tests performed at each time period in the TA–GE comparison and the follow-up project.

TABLE 7.1
Means and Standard Deviations for Pre- and Posttest Scores and Standardized Discriminant Function Coefficients Used to Derive **d**-scores

	Program								
	Think aloud				*Great expectations*				
	Pre		*Post*		*Pre*		*Post*		
Variable	*Mean*	SD	*Mean*	SD	*Mean*	SD	*Mean*	SD	*Standardized discriminant coefficient*[a]
MFFT–INN	1.3	1.4	2.6	3.9	1.2	1.8	1.6	2.3	−.99
MFFT–IRR	1.0	1.2	1.7	1.9	.8	.9	.9	1.2	.83
MFFT–REL	4.3	4.2	4.9	4.3	3.4	3.3	3.1	3.4	.62
VOCAB	10.0	2.6	9.8	1.9	10.0	2.2	9.5	2.4	.55
MFFT–RT	10.5	5.1	12.0	4.9	9.6	4.2	9.0	3.9	−.54
FT–OVT	23.1	8.3	22.7	8.4	23.7	7.2	23.7	10.3	−.53
DIGIT	8.5	2.8	8.8	1.9	7.9	3.1	8.4	2.4	−.46
FT–BASE	38.9	11.6	46.9	16.5	40.8	11.6	46.0	10.9	.39
AGE	80.9	9.1	—	—	85.4	6.1	—	—	.34
MAZES	10.6	2.7	12.2	2.9	10.6	2.4	11.2	2.3	.31
WRAT	1.9	.8	2.2	.9	1.8	.8	2.0	1.0	−.30
AUD REC	35.4	5.7	38.0	6.1	35.2	6.5	34.1	5.7	−.28
SS–NON	1.9	1.6	.9	1.1	2.1	1.7	1.5	1.4	.27

Note: Abbreviations: MFFT–INN = inner-directed speech on Matching Familiar Figures Test; MFFT–IRR = irrelevant speech on Matching Familiar Figures Test; MFFT–REL = relevant speech on Matching Familiar Figures Test; VOCAB = WISC-R vocabulary subtest; MFFT–RT = average reaction time on Matching Familiar Figures Test; FT–OVT = finger tapping-overt command *slow;* DIGIT = WISC-R digit span subtest; FT–BASE = finger tapping–baseline speed; AGE = age in months; MAZES = WISC-R mazes subtest; WRAT = reading achievement; AUD REC = ITPA auditory reception subtest; SS–NON = Simon-Says errors, not facing examiner.
[a] Derived from discriminant function analysis of reference population of normal and aggressive boys.

post) on each subject. By varying the dependent variable matrix and/or the design contrast matrix, the same error matrix could be used to make the following comparisons: TA versus GE on pre- and posttests; TA *d*-score aggressive versus GE *d*-score aggressive on pre- and posttests; TA *d*-score normal versus GE *d*-score normal on pre- and posttests; TA *d*-score aggressive pre versus post; TA *d*-score normal pre versus post; GE *d*-score aggressive pre versus post; and GE *d*-score normal pre versus post.

The resulting analysis accomplished much the same as a repeated measures analysis of variance for Treatment (2) × *d*-score groups (2) × pre–post (2) in which preplanned contrasts examined hypotheses regarding main effects attributable to treatment, two-way interactions between treatment and *d*-score group, and three-way interactions between treatment, *d*-score group and change from pre- to posttest. Advantages of using a program based on the general linear model include the fact that it can handle unequal cell sizes and, when appropriate, take account of the correlation between pre- and posttest scores in calculating test statistics.[6]

There were no significant differences between the two training groups on either pre- or posttest *d*-scores. The two programs did, however, have different effects depending on the pretest *d*-score classification. Table 7.2 shows the means for groups based on pretest *d*-score classification. On pretest, TA and GE "*d*-score aggressives" have equivalent scores, and TA and GE "*d*-score normals" have equivalent scores. On posttest, however, TA "*d*-score normals" did not change significantly from pretest, whereas GE "*d*-score normals" became significantly more like the original aggressive group, $F(1, 58) = 15.94$, $p < .001$. As a result there were significant posttest differences between TA and GE "*d*-score normals," $F(1, 58) = 6.22$, $p < .01$. Seemingly, for "*d*-score normals" the TA program helped stabilize the cognitive pattern, whereas the GE program led to deterioration. Both TA, $F(1, 58) = 3.27$, $p < .07$, and GE, $F(1, 58) = 6.97$, $p < .01$, boys with aggressive *d*-scores showed changes toward classification as normal, and differences between TA and GE were not significant.

To assess more "distant" effects of the program, we compared the two groups on teacher ratings and classroom behavior observations. On the Aggressive scale of the SBCL, both groups had scores more than two standard deviations above the mean after the program (TA: $\bar{X} = 73.6$, GE: $\bar{X} = 73.2$). Scores on the LNA scale were also comparable (TA: $\bar{X} = 57.9$, GE: $\bar{X} = 55.1$). However, GE boys ($\bar{X} = 13.5$) had significantly more items on the Aggressive scale rated as improved than TA boys ($\bar{X} = 8.4$), $F(1, 59) = 4.95$, $p < .05$, and a trend toward fewer items rated as worse, $F(1, 59) = 3.55$, $< .10$. Improvement on the LNA scale was comparable for the two groups (TA: $\bar{X} = 9.0$, GE: $\bar{X} = 9.8$).

Comparisons with previous findings from earlier trials with TA and with pooled findings on untreated controls led to the conclusion that boys in the present TA program improved less in aggressive behavior than those in previous trials. Both TA and GE boys showed about the same amount of improvement in prosocial behavior as those in previous TA studies. Grouping boys within each program according to *d*-score classification did not change the picture substantially.

[6]Only results of the univariate analyses are reported. Multivariate *F* values were calculated where groups were compared on pre- and posttest measures. These *F* values had 2 *df* corresponding to the number of contrasts being performed simultaneously (1), plus the number of dependent variables minus 1 (2 − 1). In this analysis, the multivariate *F* was significant at $p < .05$ or better in each case where one or more univariate analyses were significant. Hence the multivariate *F* values are not being reported.

TABLE 7.2
Means and Standard Deviations of Pre and Post Program **d**-scores for TA and GE Blocked on the Basis of Pre-**d**-score Classification

d-score group	N	*Pre* $\bar{X}$	*Pre* SD	*Post* $\bar{X}$	*Post* SD
TA–agg	20	1.29	.94	.78[a]	1.29
TA–normal	11	−.98	.55	−.77	1.17
GE–agg	22	1.15	1.02	.45	1.22
GE–normal	10	−.97	.67	.59	1.31

Note: Reference group aggressive centroid = .809, normal centroid = −.894
[a]N = 19.

Children in the two programs were also distinguishable on the basis of behavior observations. A stepwise discriminant function analysis was performed to obtain the optimal combination of the two programs. At the end of seven steps, this analysis correctly identified 22/31 boys from TA and 25/32 boys from GE, χ^2 (1) = 15.25, $p < .001$.

Although it would be of interest to be able to characterize differences in the classroom behavior of the two groups, the small sample sizes and the complexity of the relationship among the variables make this difficult with the present analysis. It is clear, however, that the groups are not distinguishable merely on the basis that one shows more desirable behaviors than the other. Physical contact (usually hitting), which had the greatest relative importance in distinguishing between the two groups, was higher among GE than TA graduates. But GE graduates also had higher means for being "on task" and for periods of "no deviant behavior," which were also weighted highly in the discriminant analysis. For purposes of the present discussion, these results are presented primarily to demonstrate that the two programs had different short-term effects on classroom behavior.

Overall short-term effects suggest that *d*-score aggressive boys showed improvement in both cognitive pattern and behavior following the GE program. In the TA program, *d*-score aggressive boys showed improvement in cognitive patterns, but this was not reflected in teacher ratings or observed behavior. Clearly, these results did not substantiate our predictions regarding the relationship between program effects on cognitive patterns and classroom behavior. Characterizing children in terms of cognitive patterns was, however, useful in sorting out the differential effects of the two programs. Some interesting questions and possibilities regarding interpretation were also raised for the long-term follow-up. Would the behavioral improvement and cognitive changes be sustained in *d*-score aggressives who were GE graduates? Would behavioral changes catch-up with cognitive pattern in TA graduates? How would *d*-score normals in the two programs differ on long-term evaluation?

Long-Term Program Effects

Of the 63 boys completing the TA and GE programs, 24 graduates from each program were available for study during the subsequent school year. An additional group of 14 boys, who had an earlier version of TA, was also available for study and is included for comparison. This group, referred to as TA-O, did not enter into analyses unless specifically noted.

Table 7.3 displays the *d*-scores obtained for TA and GE groups before and after the original program and before the refresher course. A priori planned contrasts revealed that the long-range linear trend toward normalization of *d*-scores noted in the two TA groups differs from the trend observed in the GE group, $F(1, 56) = 3.535$, $p < .06$. This difference suggests that prior to the refresher program, changes toward normalization of cognitive pattern were continuing in the TA groups, whereas GE graduates were drifting toward the aggressive pattern.

Nevertheless, 6–12 months after the original program, scores on the Aggressive scale of the SBCL remained at more than two standard deviations above the mean for all three groups, and scores on the Conners Hyperactivity scale were also more than two standard deviations above the mean for graduates of both programs (Normal: $\bar{X} = 4$, $SD = 5$). Table 7.4 presents mean scores for each group on Aggressive and LNA scales from the SBCL, Schaefer–Aaronson Classroom Behavior Inventory factors, and Conners Hyperactivity scale (Short Form).

Scores on LNA remained within the normal range. Although norms are not available for the Schaefer–Aaronson scale, mean scores on the three factors were in the direction of extraversion, hostility, and distractibility for

TABLE 7.3
Means and Standard Deviations of *d*-scores for TA-O, TA and GE Before and After the Original Program and Before the Refresher Course

	Preoriginal		*Postoriginal*		*Prerefresher*	
Group	$\bar{X}$	SD$\bar{X}$	SD$\bar{X}$	SD	$\bar{X}$	SD
TA–O	.504	1.70	.148	1.59	−.182	2.21
TA	.323	1.33	.075	1.33	−.074	1.86
GE	.243	1.26	.589	1.11	.636	1.61

Note: Centroids in reference groups: aggressive = .81; normal = −.89

TABLE 7.4
Means and Standard Deviations for Scores in Teacher Rating Scales for Children in Think Aloud and Great Expectations

Scale	N	*Preprogram* $\bar{X}$	*Preprogram* SD	*Postprogram* $\bar{X}$	*Postprogram* SD	*Prerefresher* $\bar{X}$	*Prerefresher* SD
SBCL–aggression[a]							
TA–O	14	—	—	71.0	9.0	67.7	14.3
TA	24	74.9	—	71.5	11.1	70.6	14.3
GE	24	76.1	8.3	72.6	10.4	74.0	14.3
SBCL–low need achievement[a]							
TA–O	14	—	—	56.4	9.6	56.7	10.2
TA	24	—	—	57.8	8.7	57.5	9.0
GE	24	—	—	53.4	8.1	55.0	6.5
Extraversion–introversion[b] (SA–I)							
TA–O	14	—	—	—	—	4.9	9.1
TA	24	—	—	—	—	12.7	9.4
GE	24	—	—	—	—	11.5	10.1
Friendly–hostile[b] (SA-II)							
TA–O	14	—	—	—	—	−5.2	10.4
TA	24	—	—	—	—	−7.0	11.2
GE	24	—	—	—	—	−9.0	12.5
Task-oriented–distractible[b] (SA-III)							
TA–O	14	—	—	—	—	−9.9	9.1
TA	24	—	—	—	—	−13.6	10.0
GE	24	—	—	—	—	−8.5	8.9
Conners Hyperactivity							
TA–O	14	—	—	—	—	16.1	7.7
TA	24	—	—	—	—	17.9	6.5
GE	24	—	—	—	—	17.9	5.1

[a] *T* scores.
[b] Negative scores refer to this pole.

all groups. Univariate analyses showed that TA graduates were significantly more distractible than GE graduates, $F(1, 34) = 5.29$, $p < .05$ (see Table 7.6). There were no other group differences based on either program or *d*-score classification.

It seemed that behavioral improvement noted previously was either not sustained or not sufficient to produce a significant change in global ratings. Failure to find a substantial change in overall ratings is consistent with previous results across school years for our general population (Camp, 1976b) and for pre–post program scores on the groups under consideration here. Trends in teacher ratings of aggression for the two TA groups appeared to be slightly downward in contrast to the GE boys, but this difference did not approach statistical significance.

Judging by teacher ratings, one would have to conclude that neither program had substantial long-term positive effects on behavior. Indeed, one could conclude that long-term effects of TA may have been negative because of the increased distractibility observed in this group. There was still the possibility that increasing normalization in cognitive pattern might be related to behavior in some way. Without any further work, the conclusion at this point could easily be that behavior is probably unrelated to cognitive pattern and that neither program produced significant long-range effects on behavior. Following our immunization model, however, we could also suggest that maybe program effects needed boosting. The refresher course was offered to study the effects of such a booster.

Effects of the Refresher Program

At the conclusion of the refresher course, children were grouped according to their progress in the refresher course itself. The refresher course instructor rated each child on a 3-point scale for overall progress. The "good progress" group all achieved ratings of good progress in the sessions. Those in the "poor progress" group received ratings of either "fair" or "poor." Independent teacher ratings of classroom behavior were also obtained following the refresher course.

The *d*-scores obtained prior to the refresher course were analyzed using a one-way analysis of variance, and preplanned contrasts were done as follows:

good progress versus poor progress
TA versus GE
TA good versus TA poor progress
GE good versus GE poor progress

There was a trend for the mean prerefresher *d*-score of the good progress group to be closer to normal than that of the poor progress group, $F(1, 37) = 3.86$, $p < .10$. Significant differences among the four groups were present on other variables, but these did not involve the preplanned contrasts.

Classroom teacher ratings on the SBCL were examined to assess differences between TA and GE graduates in the good progress and poor progress groups, beginning with ratings obtained prior to entrance into the original program. There was no distinction between children who eventually made progress in the refresher program and those who did not, on original teacher ratings or ratings of behavioral improvement following the first program.

There were, however, distinct differences in classroom teacher ratings of the good and poor progress groups, by the end of the refresher program. This was displayed in a multivariate analysis of variance performed on the Schaefer and Aaronson factors and the Conners scales obtained before and after the refresher program. Table 7.5 shows the mean scores for these ratings, and Table 7.6 shows the results of the multivariate analyses with preplanned contrasts. This analysis was performed in a similar way to the one reported on pages 208–209. (Also see Footnote 6 for explanation of multivariate *df*.)

Results clearly supported the equivalence of groups on hyperactivity and hostility prior to the refresher, with significantly greater improvement on both factors in good progress children following the refresher (Hyperactivity, $F(1, 34) = 6.01$, $p < .02$; Hostility, $F(1, 34) = 4.93$, $p < .05$). Indeed, on the Conners Hyperactivity scale, the good progress group obtained a mean score within the average range after the refresher course, whereas those in the poor progress group remained more than 2 *SD's* above the mean. Likewise, the mean score on the hostility–friendliness factor shifted from

TABLE 7.5
Teacher Ratings on the Schaefer–Aaronson Classroom Behavior Inventory and the Conners (Short Form) Hyperactivity Scale for Groups Based on Refresher Course Progress

	Good progress			*Poor progress*		
	TA (N = *10*)	*GE* (N = *7*)	*Total* (N = *17*)	*TA* (N = *10*)	*GE* (N = *11*)	*Total* (N = *21*)
SA–Factor I						
Prerefresher	19.5	14.4	17.4	4.7	11.7	8.4
Postrefresher	19.8	18.8	15.7	2.3	10.7	6.7
SA–Factor II						
Prerefresher	−7.6	−7.1	−7.4	−9.0	−9.9	−9.5
Postrefresher	−.4	−2.3	−.95	−8.2	−11.4	−9.9
SA–Factor III						
Prerefresher	−14.5	−8.0	−11.8	−14.9	−7.1	−10.8
Postrefresher	−9.4	−7.0	−6.8	−12.3	−11.8	−12.0
Conners hyperactivity						
Prerefresher	18.0	18.1	18.0	19.0	18.9	18:9
Postrefresher	13.8	13.1	13.5	17.4	20.4	18.9

Note: SA Factor I = Extraversion (+) Introversion (−)
SA Factor II = Friendliness (+) Hostility (−)
SA Factor III = Task-Oriented (+) Distractible (−)

TABLE 7.6
Results of Multivariate and Univariate Analyses of Variance on Schaefer–Aaronson and Conners Scales for Good and Poor Progress Groups

	F values			
	Multivariate	*Univariate*		
Contrasts	*(2, 33)[a]*	*Pre (1, 34)[a]*	*Post (1, 34)[a]*	*Pre × post[b] (1, 34)[a]*
		Extraversion–introversion (S-A I)		
Good versus poor progress	16.25**	10.86**	33.46**	3.32
TA versus GE	ns	ns	2.85	—
TA good versus TA poor	14.52*	10.59**	29.89**	ns
GE good versus GE poor	3.58*	ns	5.99*	2.74
		Friendliness–hostility (S-A II)		
Good versus poor progress	4.05*	ns	5.82*	4.93*
TA versus GE	ns	ns	ns	—
TA good versus TA poor	2.01	ns	2.67	2.67
GE good versus GE poor	2.06	ns	3.15	ns
		Task-Oriented–distractible (S-A III)		
Good versus poor progress	ns	ns	ns	ns
TA versus GE	2.94	5.29*	ns	—
TA good versus TA poor	ns	ns	ns	ns
GE good versus GE poor	ns	ns	ns	ns
		Hyperactivity (Conners)		
Good versus poor	3.60*	ns	5.77*	6.01*
TA versus GE	ns	ns	ns	—
TA good versus TA poor	ns	ns	ns	ns
GE good versus GE poor	3.62*	ns	4.77*	6.82*

[a] Degrees of freedom.
[b] Change in scores from pre to post.
*$p < .05$
**$p < .01$

clear weighting of hostility more than friendliness to showing close to equivalent amounts of each. The good progress group also showed a trend toward pre–post increases in extraversion ratings, $F(1, 34) = 3.32$, $p < .10$, but they were more extraverted on prerefresher ratings as well, $F(1, 34) = 10.86$, $p < .01$. As previously noted, changes on the distractibility factor were obscured by the fact that TA boys were significantly more distractible than GE boys on prerefresher ratings. Nevertheless, there was a trend for TA good progress boys to become less distractible, $F(1, 34) = 3.18$, $p < .08$, and for GE poor progress boys to become more distractible, $F(1, 34) = 3.01$, $p < .08$.

Returning to the question of how cognitive pattern relates to behavior change, we also examined posttest scores and composition of groups in terms of *d*-scores at various points in time. There were no differences among the groups in WISC-R Vocabulary and estimated Performance IQ, in WRAT Reading and Arithmetic scores, or in MFFT private speech and errors prior to the refresher course. On the Raven, given as postrefresher only, there was a trend for the good progress group ($\bar{X} = 23.4$) to surpass the poor progress group ($\bar{X} = 20.5$), $F(1, 35) = 3.84$, $p < .10$.

Significant differences were observed between the good and poor progress groups on MFFT reaction time and on correct spelling performance. On posttests, the good progress group showed significantly slower reaction times on the MFFT ($\bar{X} = 11.6$ sec) than the poor progress group ($\bar{X} = 7.4$ sec), despite initial equivalence on pretest (multivariate $F(2, 33) = 4.42$, $p < .05$; univariate $F_{post}(1, 34) = 5.42$, $p < .05$; univariate $F_{pre \times post}(1, 34) = 7.95$, $p < .01$). The poor progress group also showed a significant decrease in correct spelling performance ($\bar{X}_{pre} = 60\%$; $\bar{X}_{post} = 42\%$), whereas the good progress group showed essentially no change in percentage of words spelled correctly ($\bar{X}_{pre} = 58\%$; $\bar{X}_{post} = 55\%$), multivariate $F(2, 33) = 2.63$, $p < .10$; univariate $F_{post}(1, 34) = 3.91$, $p < .05$; univariate $F_{pre \times post}(1, 34) = 4.89$, $p < .05$). Taken together, these results attest to somewhat better cognitive functioning and improved behavior in the good progress group.

For GE graduates there was no consistent relationship between *d*-score classification and progress in the refresher course. Among TA graduates, however, there was a consistent relationship between prerefresher *d*-score and progress in the refresher program. Fisher's exact test indicated that significantly more boys in the good progress group (7/10 had *d*-scores classified as normal prior to the refresher than did TA boys in the poor progress group (2/11; $p < .05$).

DISCUSSION

The overall pattern emerging from this follow-up study is that there were long-range differences attributable to the original programs, but these became blurred by effects of the refresher course. Furthermore, the most salient findings at the time of follow-up were that both TA and GE boys continued to have significant problems with aggression, hostility, distractibility, and hyperactivity. The cognitive pattern in TA-treated boys, however, continued to show a trend toward normalization, whereas that of GE-treated boys became more aggressive. Although apparently not reflected immediately in behavior, this cognitive pattern was important for predicting response to the refresher program, at least for TA boys. Thus TA boys with a normal cognitive pattern prior to the refresher program were significantly more likely to show good progress in the refresher program. In turn, good progress in the refresher was associated with teacher ratings showing a significant increase in friendliness and extraversion and a decrease in hyperactivity; slower reaction times on the MFFT; and trends toward higher scores on the Raven and improved performance on a spelling test, suggesting more thoughtful and accurate application to the task.

These results for boys in the TA program who showed normal *d*-scores are reminiscent of observations made by Kohlberg *et al.* (1972) regarding the long-term relationship between cognitive and social maturity. They noted that maturity of cognitive pattern may not always be reflected immediately in behavior, but cognitive maturity is often predictive of the level of emotional–behavioral maturity ultimately achieved. Since similar effects were not observed for *d*-score normals in the GE program, our findings suggest that a program such as TA with a refresher may be necessary for some aggressive boys to achieve the level of emotional–behavioral maturity that would be predicted from their cognitive maturity.

One might argue that results with the refresher program were merely a recapitulation of earlier, unsustained effects of the TA program on *d*-score normal boys. This argument is not reasonable, however, since the effect of the original TA program was to assist *d*-score normals in stabilizing their cognitive pattern; unlike GE graduates, most of these showed a persistence of the normal cognitive pattern at follow-up.

On the other hand, the refresher program was not particularly beneficial for TA-treated boys with an aggressive cognitive pattern. These boys had originally shown improvement in cognitive pattern but not enough to change cognitive classifications. This group also tended to be introverted before the program began, had less prosocial behavior in the classroom, and over the course of the refresher program remained hostile, distractible, and hyperactive. On postrefresher testing, spelling test performance decreased despite increases in reading achievement.

There were no consistent predictors of which GE boys would be in the good progress group. The findings across different measures do, however, point consistently to improvement in test and classroom behavior among both TA and GE boys who responded well to the refresher course. The findings are more striking for teacher ratings of behavior than for cognitive test performance. This is easily understandable, since the refresher program emphasized social problem solving.

We had thought that increasing the sample size might clarify the situation. However, results were equivocal. Control over within-group sources of variance may have been too limited in the present trial, and program power too weakened by using many, initially naive teachers. Likewise, there may have been a methodological problem in asking teachers to make a comparative judgment of improvement rather than an absolute judment of current status. However, in view of the refresher program results, it seems equally reasonable to suggest that short-term measures of behavior may not be the best gauge of the ultimate long-term effects of a refresher program.

Nevertheless, it is interesting to consider different approaches to achieving both short-term and long-term effects, especially with the aggressive boy whose cognitive pattern is also "aggressive." One approach is to examine possibilities for achieving better matches between program and child. At the conclusion of the original TA and GE programs, for example, we had the clinical impression that some children were not able to profit from the TA program because of limited emotional resources. These were children we viewed as being primarily interested in gratification and essentially uninterested in mastery. TA and GE differed greatly in the extent to which they demanded mastery motivation. GE involved concentration on the pleasurable aspects of the activities, whereas TA involved concentration on developing skill at achieving inhibition, a difficult and frustrating activity. In a few instances, our retrospective analysis suggested that a child was too needy to marshall his resources to meet the demands of the TA program and would, perhaps, have done better with GE. Typically these children had aggressive cognitive patterns. Likewise, we thought a few children in the GE program might have responded better to the type of challenge offered by the TA program. At the time, we had not addressed the issue of assessing the child's response to the training program per se. Perhaps an assessment such as that performed at the end of the refresher course could have been performed soon after initiating the original programs, in order to determine whether child and program were properly matched. Another thought was that some children, particularly *d*-score aggressive boys, might profit most from some combination of an initial GE-type program followed by TA.

In a different vein, our results were also probably attenuated to an unknown extent by our lack of systematic involvement with families or life events outside the classroom. Is family stability necessary for ultimate success of either program? How much effort should be directed toward assessing and modifying the family situations of aggressive boys? Few would doubt that improvement in both cognitive and social behavior will be most rapid, extensive, and durable when families can be involved. The grim reality for many children and educators is that often families (and teachers) cannot be moved to take the positive steps needed to promote growth in their children. The tough challenge to programs such as TA and GE is whether we can find a way to promote mental and emotional growth in aggressive boys whose families cannot provide adequate support.

Lefkowitz *et al.* (1977) noted that parental nurturance, rejection, and punishment were important as contemporaneous instigators to aggressive behavior in school. In the long run, however, cognitive competence, which includes intelligence and identification with parents, was the best predictor of which 8-year-old aggressive boys would be aggressive 10 years later. Kohlberg *et al.* (1972) also concluded that antisocial behavior in childhood is less likely to predict antisocial adult behavior in cognitively and socially competent children. These findings contribute to our contention that improving the ultimate outlook for aggressive boys may become possible when a way can be found to improve their cognitive functioning in the early years. We are still hopeful that approaches such as those described here will be successful even without family support.

If so, it will be necessary to implement much more powerful programs than the ones described. For despite successes reported here, approximately 50% of the boys in both programs failed to respond to the refresher course and continued to show evidence of serious behavior problems fully 1 year after being identified in first or second grade. We might guess that this unresponsive 50% have a much higher probability of showing persistent aggressive behavior into adolescence and adulthood than those who responded to the refresher course. We must continue striving to reach this unresponsive group.

8

A Controlled Trial of Behavior Modification and Methylphenidate in Hyperactive Children[1]

RACHEL GITTELMAN
HOWARD ABIKOFF
EDITH POLLACK
DONALD F. KLEIN
SIDNEY KATZ
JEFFREY MATTES

INTRODUCTION

No rational, knowledgeable individual can dispute the efficacy of short-term stimulant treatment in the management of hyperkinetic children. Of all therapies in child psychiatry, it is the best documented. At the same time, legitimate concern has been expressed about the possibility of deleterious side effects that may result from long-term stimulant administration (Safer & Allen, 1975a). Other nonmedical interventions, especially behavior modification techniques, have been suggested for the treatment of hyperactive children. The use of these techniques is not associated with physical side effects, and if these techniques prove to be equally effective, they would offer a valuable alternative to medication in the treatment of hyperactive children. Werry and Sprague (1970) have recommended that pharmacotherapy of hyperactivity be undertaken only when behavior modification techniques are not realistically feasible. Others have turned the problem of how to treat hyperactive children into a moral issue (Grinspoon & Singer, 1973; Sroufe & Stewart, 1973). As usual, the intensity of the views held and the heat generated by the debate are inversely related to the number of facts available on the point in question.

The early studies of the effectiveness of behavior modification for hyperactive children took place in special experimental classrooms (Doub-

[1]Research for this chapter was supported in part by Grant No. MH-18579.

HYPERACTIVE CHILDREN
The Social Ecology of Identification and Treatment

ISBN 0-12-745950-2

ros & Daniels, 1966; Patterson, 1965; Patterson, Jones, Whittier, & Wright, 1965; Pihl, 1967; Quay, Sprague, Werry, & McQueen, 1967). Unfortunately, results obtained in such settings cannot be generalized to the ordinary school environment.

More recently, operant principles have been applied in regular classrooms. In an uncontrolled study of a 4-week behavior therapy program, Rosenbaum, O'Leary, and Jacob (1975) found a significant improvement in teacher scale ratings of 10 hyperactive children. Since no control group was included, the specific therapeutic effect of the behavior modification techniques cannot be estimated. In a subsequent controlled study, O'Leary, Pelham, Rosenbaum, and Price (1976) treated children rated hyperactive by both parents and teachers for a 10-week period. After treatment, the teacher ratings for the 9 children receiving behavior therapy were significantly better than those for the 8 untreated children. These two studies of behavior therapy are unique in their use of scale measures which have been validated for both the identification of hyperactive children and the detection of drug effects. The authors indicate that the magnitude of treatment-induced improvement with behavior therapy, as measured by teachers' ratings, is equivalent to that reported in studies of stimulant effects in hyperactive children. By extension, the assumption is made that the two treatment approaches have the same degree of therapeutic efficacy.

Another approach, used by Allyon, Layman, and Kandel (1975), argues for the usefulness of reinforcing academic performance—behavior presumably incompatible with hyperactivity. Using a multiple-baseline design, three hyperactive children were observed in the classroom while receiving methylphenidate, while receiving no medication, and while off medication but receiving reinforcement for academic performance. During reinforcement periods, correct math and reading performance combined averaged 85%, compared to 12% average correct performance under methylphenidate. The level of disruption during behavior modification was indistinguishable from that while the children were receiving methylphenidate.

The effects of behavioral techniques have been reported recently in case studies of hyperactive children (Parks, 1975; Stableford, Butz, Hasaxi, Leitenberg, and Peyser, 1976). Parks (1975), in a single subject design, investigated the usefulness of reinforcing academic performance with two second-grade hyperactive boys. Token self-reinforcement during academic work is reported to have improved performance on word recognition in one case, and work completed in the other. No objective behavioral ratings were obtained and no follow-up was performed.

Single case reports can provide useful information. They may, for example, help isolate the effective components in a multiple treatment program. When employed in a multiple-baseline design, they allow for the assessment of individual drug responsiveness. However, the single case approach does not contribute information regarding general treatment efficacy. In view of the carefully executed group studies of O'Leary and his colleagues, there remains little point in conducting case studies of similar techniques with similar children.

A combination of behavior modification and medication has also been recommended as an alternative to medication alone in the treatment of hyperactive children. Arguments have been advanced that behavioral techniques and chemotherapy have discrete, independent actions; consequently a combination of both modalities should be the treatment of choice (Eysenck, 1971; Sprague & Werry, 1971). Eysenck claims that stimulants enhance conditionability and therefore, in behavior disorders indicative of early defective social conditioning, the combination of stimulants and conditioning should maximize behavioral amelioration.

Stimulants can be viewed as enhancing attentional processes and reducing restlessness, whereas social reinforcement may teach the child to internalize the value of appropriate behaviors. There is no direct evidence that stimulants facilitate operant conditioning in hyperactive children. Stimulants improve performance, but whether it is by reducing maladaptive behavior, increasing attentiveness, or actually making the child more responsive to positive reinforcement is unclear (Gittelman-Klein & Klein, 1975).

Until recently, little empirical data existed regarding the advantages of combining stimulants with behavior therapy. One study has reported that methylphenidate in combination with conditioning reduced in-seat motor activity, measured by a stabilimetric cushion in a laboratory setting (Sprague, Christensen, & Werry, 1974). Twelve hyperactive boys were assigned to either methylphenidate or placebo. Seat movements were measured over 13 sessions: 2 sessions of baseline, 3 sessions of drug or placebo alone, 5 sessions of drug or placebo with conditioning, and 3 sessions following conditioning. Although methylphenidate was superior to placebo in reducing motor restlessness, the drug effects are difficult to interpret because the children in the placebo group were significantly more active initially than those in the drug group. The placebo group showed marked fluctuations in activity after initiation of placebo. The only statistically significant change for the children receiving placebo was an increase in activity during the 3 placebo alone sessions, compared to baseline. The conditioning contingencies significantly reduced motor activity only when compared to placebo, not when compared to the baseline levels.

In the drug group, methylphenidate alone did not reduce motor activity; however, the combination of drug and conditioning significantly reduced motor activity. There was no significant difference between the drug alone condition and the combination of drug and conditioning. Thus, the results are unclear; they can only suggest that a combination of approaches may be optimal in the control of hyperkinesis.

Further data regarding the effects of combined behavioral treatments and methylphenidate have been presented by Christensen (1975) for a group of 13 hyperactive mental retardates in experimental classrooms. The children received 2 weeks of behavior therapy with methylphenidate (mean daily dose, 11.7 mg) and 2 weeks of behavior therapy with placebo in a crossover design. No difference was found between the two conditions on a variety of measures. The author concludes that "the additive use of stimulant medication produces few additional benefits [p. 274]." In view of the atypically low dosages used and the special nature of the clinical group, the study failed to test adequately the hypothesis of additive effects between the two treatment modalities in hyperactive children.

The authors (and others) have been conducting an experimental study to assess the relative efficacy of methylphenidate, methylphenidate in combination with behavior therapy, and behavior therapy with placebo among hyperactive children. Through random assignment of hyperactive children to concurrent treatment groups, the relative merits of medication versus behavior therapy, alone or combined, have been investigated.

The data from an interim report (Gittelman-Klein, Klein, Abikoff, Katz, Gloisten, & Kates, 1976) indicated significant clinical improvement at home and at school with all three interventions. However, converging evidence—from different sources on a variety of behavioral indices—indicated that medication, either alone or in combination with behavior therapy, was significantly more effective than behavior therapy alone. These findings, although highly significant, were viewed as tentative given the relatively small total sample size (N=34). Twenty-seven additional children have since completed treatment, increasing the sample by almost 80% to a total of 61 cases. This chapter presents the treatment results based on this expanded sample.

PROCEDURE

Subject Selection

The following criteria were used: The children had to (*a*) have been referred to a psychiatric clinic for treatment, (*b*) be between the ages of 6 and 12, (*c*) be attending elementary school, (*d*) be free of gross neurological disease and psychosis, and (*e*) obtain either a Verbal or a Performance IQ of at least 85 on the Wechsler Intelligence Scale for Children. The parents had to be willing to participate in the study after it was explained to them. No child was receiving psychostimulant treatment at the time of selection, although a few had received very brief medication trials in previous years.

TEACHER RATINGS

The Conners Teacher Rating Scale was obtained for each child. The 39 scale items yield five factors: Factor I, Conduct Disorder; Factor II, Inattention; Factor III, Anxiety; Factor IV, Hyperactivity; Factor V, Sociability (Conners, 1969). To be accepted a child had to be rated hyperactive by the teacher, as defined by a minimum mean Hyperactivity factor score of 1.8 out of a possible 3.0. This cutoff score was based on results obtained in a study by Sprague *et al.* (1974) comparing normal and hyperactive children.

PARENT REPORTS

In addition, parents had to report that the child was hyperactive or had behavior problems at home. Thus, children who were *not* reported as hyperactive or who had no reported difficulties at home were not considered for the study, regardless of other clinical considerations.

CLASSROOM OBSERVATIONS

The last requirement was the presence of observable behavior problems in the classrooms recorded on a modified version of an observation code (unpublished) devised by O'Leary's coworkers (Tonick, Friehling, & Warhit, 1973). The index child and a classmate of the same sex, identified by the teacher as average in comportment, were observed for 16-min periods during structured lessons. The entire code consisted of 14 categories, but 9 were rated very infrequently and not included in the analyses. The 5 remaining categories are the following: (*a*) Interference: calling out, interruptions of others during work periods; (*b*) Off-Task: failure to attend to classroom assignments; (*c*) Gross Motor Movement: out of seat motor activity when it violates the class rules; (*d*) Minor Motor Movement: in-seat rump activity; and (*e*) Solicitation: seeking the teacher's attention. The code and relevant procedures are detailed in Abikoff, Gittelman-Klein, and Klein (1977).

The children were observed at least three times before treatment initiation and weekly thereafter. The five behavioral categories were rated as present or absent for each 15-sec interval of the 16-min observation periods. Scores are the mean frequency of the behaviors over 16 min.

Four of the five classroom observers were blind to the purposes of observation and to the type of children selected for study. At all times, all observers were blind to the design of the study. Any possible confound stemming from lack of total blind in one observer is substantially reduced, if not eliminated, given that each child was rated by different observers, over the course of the study, on a code that has demonstrated resistance to observer bias (Kent, O'Leary, Diament, & Dietz, 1974).

Because empirical observation criteria for identifying hyperactive children were lacking when the study was initiated, clinical judgments were used to determine children's entry into the study. The observations on each child were perused by one of us (R.G.K) who decided whether the ratings of the child, compared to his normal control, were high enough to confirm clearly the presence of behavior problems. Decisions based on this clinical "eye ball" approach yielded only a 55% acceptance rate among the first 40 referrals who met all other acceptance criteria.

To objectify the selection process, the observation scores of these first 40 pairs of referred and comparison children were inspected, in order to obtain mean scores that maximized the identification of hyperactive children and minimized false positives. The minimum scores identified as criteria for consideration in the study were the following: Interference, 10; Off-task, 3; Gross Motor, 3; Minor Motor, 21; and Solicitation, 3. A child had to receive a score at or above these levels on two of the five categories to be considered for acceptance in the study. (The combination of Interference and Solicitation was not used because the two ratings are not always independent.) Of the next 36 children referred for treatment, 29 (80%) met the two category criterion and were accepted into the study. In comparison, only 5 (14%) of the 36 normal children were elevated on two behavioral categories. A more detailed discussion of the ability of the classroom observation code to distinguish between children referred for treatment and normal children appears in Abikoff *et al.* (1977).

During the preliminary stage of the study, four children not accepted into the study because the classroom observations did not reveal their disruptive behavior were placed on a trial of methylphenidate. All four children, on the basis of parents' reports and psychiatrists' clinical impressions, showed considerable improvement while receiving medication. The children's responsiveness to the drug suggested that although the classroom observations discriminated well between hyperactive and normal children, they were not unequivocally valid diagnostic criteria for treatment selection. As a result, observation scores were dropped as selection criteria. Four of the 13 subjects, who subsequently entered the study did not reach criterion observation scores but met all other selection criteria. Problems of validity in the diagnosis of hyperactivity are discussed more fully elsewhere (Abikoff *et al.*, 1977; Klein & Gittelman-Klein, 1975).

An overall index of disruptive classroom behavior was obtained by combining the categories of Interference, Off-Task, and Gross Motor Movement. The other two categories, Minor Motor Movement and Solicitation, were not included in the overall disruption estimate, since in-seat movement has not been shown to be related to performance (Douglas, 1975). Solicitation is scored whether or not the child's demands on the teacher are appropriate. Therefore, it cannot be inferred that Solicitation regularly reflects disruptive, maladaptive behavior.

Experimental Treatments

Children who met the study criteria were randomly assigned to one of three experimental treatments for an 8-week period: behavior therapy with methylphenidate, methylphenidate alone, or behavior therapy with placebo. Parents were informed about the conditions of the study, including the possibility that their child might receive a placebo.

BEHAVIOR THERAPY

Operant behavior therapy was implemented both in the home and school, following procedures described by O'Leary and O'Leary (1972). Studies by O'Leary, Becker, Evans, and Saudargas (1969) and O'Leary and Drabman (1971) indicate that an effective classroom management program can be introduced within a relatively short period of time, that a teacher with no previous experience can learn to implement a behavior modification program with regular professional consultation, and that tokens are the most effective form of reinforcement.

Similarly, the feasibility of using parents as agents of change has been demonstrated (O'Leary, O'Leary, & Becker, 1967; Salzinger, Feldman, & Portnoy, 1970; Wahler, Winkel, Peterson, & Morrison, 1965). Both mother and father were trained to participate in the present program, which invariably consisted of a contingency management program both at home and in school.

The behavior therapist met with the parents for at least two initial sessions. These sessions served several purposes. General principles of learning theory were introduced and related to specific parental practices. For example, the behavior therapist would point out that yelling, nagging, and excessive explanations often functioned as reinforcers and actually strengthened the behaviors parents tried to eliminate. Concepts such as reinforcers, punishment, time out, consequences, rewards, and behavior were discussed. Use was also made of specific texts to familiarize parents with behavioral approaches to child management, and reading assignments were given to increase the parents' involvement. The books *Living With Children* (Patterson & Guillion, 1971), *Families* (Patterson, 1975), and *Parents are Teachers* (Becker, 1971) were given to all parents. Throughout the program, parents were encouraged to voice questions and doubts. Parents often expressed concern about bribing the child and the effect of the program on other children in the family. The distinction was clarified between a bribe, which usually connotes payment for illegal behavior, and a reward as a strategy for teaching a child desirable behavior. Parents were helped to recognize that they were already using rewards and punishment but were doing so noncontingently. The behavioral intervention was recognized as a special program that would help both parents and the child learn new ways of responding. The program was explained to the child and his siblings in this fashion. Siblings were involved whenever their behavior affected that of the patient. Target behaviors often involved interactions with siblings, such as fighting. Sometimes contingencies were also worked out for siblings, and often parents spontaneously applied principles and strategies that they found helpful for the hyperactive child to other children in the family.

During the initial sessions, the parents also were taught to describe their children's behavior in concrete terms rather than through the use of global labels and attributions. Behavioral descriptions were elicited of what the child actually did and did not do, under what circumstances, how the parent reacted, and how the parent wanted the behavior to change. Behavior was explained as a chain of concrete events with antecedents and consequences. The parent was asked to bring in concrete descriptions of actual behavior; what happened before, how they handled it, etc. These descriptions and discussions of age-appropriate behaviors enabled the therapist and parents to identify appropriate goals for a particular child.

In summary, the therapist used the sessions to conduct a functional behavioral assessment to be used in planning an intervention program for that child. The therapist learned the specifics about the child's routine, the physical set-up in the home, interactions with friends, siblings and other family members, and current reinforcers; this information clarified which environmental conditions were associated with the emission of target behaviors, and what consequences ensued.

Concomitant with the parent sessions, two or three interviews were held with the teacher at the child's school. The behavioral intervention program was explained to the teacher, and the texts previously mentioned were also offered. The therapist elicited concrete behaviors that the teacher felt interfered with the child's functioning in the classroom. These behaviors often included not listening, calling out, and leaving the seat at inappropriate times. During these sessions, the therapist also was interested in ascertaining specifics about the target behaviors—the antecedent events, peer reactions, methods of control the teacher used, and whether classroom rules were made explicit to the children by the teacher.

Initially, parents and teachers were asked to do a frequency count of specific target behaviors. When the actual intervention program began, that is, the initiation of concrete reinforcement, the child was included in the weekly sessions held with the parents and with the teacher, whenever scheduling permitted.

For both school and home, contracts were used stipulating positive and negative behaviors and respective contingencies. Initially, the child's behavior was monitored every 30 min in the school and at home. When possible, the 30 min interval was increased. The parents provided the backup reinforcements at the end of the day. Negative target behaviors monitored at home typically included not listening to parents, fighting, having temper tantrums, annoying pets, and not completing chores. School target behaviors were of both an academic and a social nature; the child was rewarded for behaviors such as completing a stated amount of work, handing in work on time, not calling out, and not fighting with peers.

Backup reinforcements were chosen by the therapist together with the parents and child. Very often children worked for money and exchanged each check for a penny. Other reinforcements consisted of extra television time, time alone with a parent, being able to choose a favorite dessert, and participation in enjoyable activities such as bowling trips. Bonuses were earned for perfect days or for meeting a stipulated behavioral goal.

Along with positive reinforcement for good behavior, punishments were also used to decrease problematic behaviors. Most frequently this involved loss of privileges such as television time, playing outside after school, using a bike, phonograph, telephone, or a time out procedure. For the time out procedure, the child had to spend a short amount of time, most often 5 min, by himself in a place where the availability of reinforcers such as toys or other people was reduced. Often a bathroom was used for this purpose.

When punishing the child, the parents were encouraged to behave in a matter-of-fact manner. Conversely, they were trained to show greater response to desired behavior, and pairing concrete reinforcers with social reinforcers was stressed.

In the course of treatment, contracts were rewritten or amended to alter specific behavioral goals as well as reinforcements. Other behavioral techniques were employed in addition to contingency management. For example, the therapist would model and role-play alternative ways of coping with difficult social situations. Cognitive restructuring was also used with parents to change attitudes toward certain behaviors. Parents often thought that temper tantrums had to be avoided at all costs and held themselves responsible for setting off the tantrum. Often, the parents needed to be less afraid of a behavior before they could act effectively to decrease it.

For many children, weekly sessions needed to be augmented by phone contact between parents and therapist. This was necessitated by several factors. Parents frequently needed encouragement when they did not see rapid improvement. In addition, phone calls were used to help parents cope with a specific issue that had not been discussed and they were unable to handle. In such cases, parents were helped to deal with new situations on the basis of the general treatment principles and those extracted from discussions of previous incidents. On occasion, more than one weekly session was necessary. Phone contact was also used in especially severe behavior problems. The therapist might ask the child to call and review his progress every day, rather than wait until the weekly session.

The behavioral intervention program was always incorporated in the broader psychosocial approach, in order that many interpersonal familial problems were discussed. However, the ancillary supportive counseling aspects of the program were always in addition to, never in lieu of, an operant program for the child. The beginning of treatment was defined as the day on which systematic reinforcement began to be dispensed, and did not include the 2–3 week prereinforcement period used for functional assessment at home and in school.

MEDICATION

Pills (methylphenidate or placebo) were administered within days of tangible reinforcement initiation. All children were prescribed 10 mg of medication per day for the first week, with gradual weekly increments.

Teachers were called weekly to obtain a description of specific aspects of the child's functioning. Inquiry was made regarding the child's motor activity, attentiveness, academic performance, and peer interactions. Medication regulation was guided by the teacher's report and by parent's descriptions of any side effects, problems, and changes in the child's behavior. Dosage was increased only if problematic behavior was reported. All medication was administered twice daily, in the morning and at lunch. A maximum of 80 mg/day was set.

Posttreatment Evaluations

The individuals involved in assessment were blind to different aspects of the treatment and study design. The classroom observers were blind to all aspects of the study: the diagnostic composition of the sample and the nature of the treatments. The other evaluators knew when behavior therapy was provided. The psychiatrists were aware of the treatment for children receiving methylphenidate alone, but were blind to the type of medication (methylphenidate or placebo) prescribed to children receiving behavior therapy. To maintain the blind, placebo as well as medication dosages were incremented. Parents and teachers knew when children were receiving medication, but were blind to its type.

After the 8 weeks of treatment, a second Teacher Rating Scale was completed for the hyperactive but not for the control children. In addition, Global Improvement scores were obtained from teachers, mothers, and psychiatrists, who reported their overall impression of the child's status on an 8-point scale: 1 = completely well, 2 = much improved, 3 = improved, 4 = slightly improved, 5 = unchanged, 6 = slightly worse, 7 = worse, 8 = much worse. In all cases, the mother, rather than the father, spent more time with the child and was more familiar with the child's daily functioning. Thus, the global ratings of improvement were routinely collected from the mother.

RESULTS

Sample Description

Of 64 children who entered the study, 3 failed to complete it. One child on methylphenidate was extremely sensitive to the drug, developing hypertension and tachycardia on as little as 5 mg/day. Another child was on methylphenidate for 2 weeks when his absent father returned home and refused to have the child on medication. A third child, receiving behavior therapy and placebo, was dropped from the study because he moved out of the parental home during the course of the study. The final sample consisted of 61 children, 58 boys and 3 girls; 54 of the children were white, 6 black, and 1 Oriental. The mean age was 8 years, 3 months. Twenty-one children received behavior therapy with methylphenidate, 21 received methylphenidate alone, and 19 received behavior therapy with placebo.

After 8 weeks of treatment, methylphenidate dosage ranged from 10 to 60 mg/day, with an average daily dose of 38.2 mg. Since the emergence of side effects was a consideration in dosage regulation, the children did not, as a whole, experience marked side effects at the dosages used.

Teacher Rating Scale

On the Teacher Rating Scale, the factors that are most meaningful for the evaluation of hyperactive children are Factors I (Conduct Disorder), II (Inattention), and IV (Hyperactivity). The pretreatment scores on these factors are presented in Table 8.1. As anticipated, the teachers' ratings of the hyperactive children were markedly higher than those obtained by 143 normal boys, in another study, whose mean factor scores on this scale were as follows: Factor I = .21; Factor II = .60; Factor IV = .56 (Sprague *et al.*, 1974).

TABLE 8.1
Mean Teacher Rating Scale Factor Scores

Groups	N	Factor I conduct disorder		Factor II inattention		Factor IV hyperactivity	
		Pre	*Post*[a]	*Pre*	*Post*[a]	*Pre*	*Post*[a]
1. Behavior therapy + methylphenidate	21	1.24	.11	1.63	.73	2.30	.79
		(.53)[b]	(.29)	(.51)	(.49)	(.31)	(.41)
2. Methylphenidate	21	1.40	.33	1.89	.89	2.56	1.04
		(.67)	(.56)	(.51)	(.50)	(.36)	(.35)
3. Behavior therapy +placebo	19	1.18	.76	1.56	1.28	2.31	1.40
		(.75)	(.67)	(.58)	(.67)	(.38)	(.50)
Total	61	1.28	—	1.70	—	2.39	—
	—	(.65)	—	(.54)	—	(.37)	—
F, pre (2.58); post (2.57) *df*[c]	—	.61	9.54	2.37	8.21	3.67	11.35
$p <$	—	n.s.	.0003	n.s.	.0008	.04	.0001
Tukey HSD,[d] $p <$		1 versus 2 n.s.		1 versus 2 n.s.		1 versus 2 n.s.	
		1 versus 3 <.01		1 versus 3 <.01		1 versus 3 <.01	
		2 versus 3 <.05		2 versus 3 <.01		2 versus 3 <.05	

[a] Post scores adjusted for initial values.
[b] Numbers in parentheses are standard deviations.
[c] *F* Ratios for pretreatment differences computed by analyses of variance, *F* ratios for posttreatment differences computed by analyses of covariance. Two-tailed tests.
[d] Tukey Honestly Significant Differences. All *p* values are two-tailed.

WITHIN-TREATMENT EFFECTS

All three groups improved after 8 weeks of treatment. Within-group comparisons of the pre–post differences, using *t*-tests for correlated means, showed significant decreases in each of the three factor ratings for each of the three groups (p from $< .002$ to $< .0001$).

BETWEEN-TREATMENT DIFFERENCES

To compare the treatments with each other, analyses of covariance (with pretreatment scores as the covariate) were done separately for the three teacher rating factors. As shown in Table 8.1, significant group effects emerged on all three factors. Specific contrasts using the Tukey Honestly Significant Differences (HSD) tests revealed that the two drug-treated groups, that is, methylphenidate with behavior therapy and methylphenidate alone, were significantly more improved than the group receiving behavior therapy with placebo. This pattern of relative superiority for the methylphenidate groups held for all three factors—Inattention, Conduct Disorder, and Hyperactivity. When the two drug-treated groups were compared to each other, their posttreatment factor scores were statistically indistinguishable.

TREATED HYPERACTIVE VERSUS NORMAL CHILDREN

To determine the extent to which the treatments had normalized the children's behavior, the posttreatment scores obtained by the hyperactive children on the Teacher Rating Scale were compared, using standard *t* tests, to those obtained by Sprague *et al.* (1974). After the 8 weeks of treatment, the factor scores of the children receiving behavior therapy with methylphenidate were indistinguishable from those obtained for the 143 normal boys in the Sprague sample ($t = 1.24, -.69, -1.37$, 162 *df*, for factors of Conduct Disorder, Inattention, and Hyperactivity, respectively).

The children treated with methylphenidate alone did not differ from the normals on the Conduct Disorder factor ($t = 1.72$, 162 *df*). On the Inattention and Hyperactivity factors, however, this group received significantly higher scores than the normal children ($t = -3.07$ and -3.72, 162 *df*, $p < .003$ and $p < .001$, respectively).

The group receiving behavior therapy with placebo had posttreatment scores that were significantly higher than the normals on the factors of Conduct Disorder ($df = 160$; $t = -4.94$, $p < .0001$), Inattention ($t = -4.09$, $p < .0001$) and Hyperactivity ($t = -5.23$, $p < .0001$).

Classroom Observations

Interobserver reliability for occurrences was determined by computing the effective percentage agreement (Gelfand & Hartmann, 1975). One of the authors' (H.A.) observation data always served as the criterion for calculating interobserver agreement. The number of interobserver agreements for the occurrence of a behavior within a 15-sec interval was divided by the sum of the agreements and disagreements, and multiplied by 100 to yield a percentage of agreement. The agreement obtained for Disruptive Behavior was 71%, for Minor Motor Movement, 75%, and for Solicitation, 68%.

The classroom observation values obtained before treatment initiation were averaged to provide a baseline measure for each child. At baseline, the hyperactive group was more elevated than their comparison classmates on all three observational measures, using pairwise t tests (Disruptive Behavior, $t = 12.73$, 60 df, $p < .0001$; Minor Motor Movement, $t = 4.35$, 60 df, $p < .0001$; Solicitation, $t = 6.69$, 60 df, $p < .0001$).

WITHIN-TREATMENT EFFECTS

Posttreatment scores for the classroom observations were obtained by averaging the scores obtained during the seventh and eighth week of treatment. Within-group comparisons indicated that the level of Disruptive Behavior was significantly improved in the two groups receiving medication ($p < .0001$). Among the children receiving methylphenidate with behavior therapy, the 15-sec intervals in which the children engaged in disruptive behavior decreased from 44.5% pretreatment level to 16.7% at the end of treatment. In the methylphenidate alone group, the pretreatment disruptive level of 46.2% was also reduced significantly at posttreatment to a prevalence of 24.9%. In contrast, this measure was not significantly affected by behavior therapy alone, as the occurrence of disruptive behavior in this group continued at an average level of 45.5%, a reduction of only 1.5% from the group's pretreatment level.

A similar pattern was obtained for Minor Motor Movement; only the methylphenidate with behavior therapy and methylphenidate alone groups showed a significant reduction in in-seat activity levels ($p < .001$). The degree to which the child sought the teacher's attention was not reduced by any treatment, as reflected in the ratings obtained for Solicitation.

BETWEEN-TREATMENT DIFFERENCES

The posttreatment scores are presented in Table 8.2. Again, comparisons among the treatments used analyses of covariance, with pretreatment levels as the covariate, followed by the Tukey HSD tests for specific contrasts. After 8 weeks of treatment, the children receiving behavior therapy with methylphenidate and those receiving methylphenidate alone were observed to be significantly less disruptive than those treated with behavior therapy with placebo ($p < .01$). No significant difference in disruptive behavior was found between the two groups treated with methylphenidate.

TABLE 8.2
Classroom Observations

				Posttreatment[a]			
Measures	*Group*	N	*Pretreatment means*	*Means*	F (2.57 df)	p[b]	*HSD tests* (p)[b]
Disruptive behavior	1. BT+M	21	28.49	10.68			1 versus 2 n.s.
	2. M	21	29.54	15.94			1 versus 3 <.01
	3. BT+P	19	30.05	29.11	17.87	<.0001	2 versus 3 <.01
	Total	61	29.34				
	4. Comparison subjects	61	7.79	9.45			
Minor motor movement	1. BT+M	21	22.73	9.69			1 versus 2 <.05
	2. M	21	19.05	14.11			1 versus 3 <.01
	3. BT+P	19	19.00	17.48	10.62	<.0002	2 versus 3 n.s.
	Total	61	20.30				
	4. Comparison subjects	61	16.11	13.80			
Solicitation	1. BT+M	21	3.17	2.20			
	2. M	21	3.85	3.10			
	3. BT+P	19	2.92	2.67			
	Total	61	3.33		.69	n.s.	—
	4. Comparison subjects	61	1.03	1.21			

[a] Post scores adjusted for pretreatment values.
[b] Two-tailed tests.

A significant difference in treatment efficacy was found in amount of in-seat activity (Minor Motor Movement). The children treated with the combination of behavior therapy and methylphenidate were significantly less restless than those who received either behavior therapy with placebo ($p < .01$) or methylphenidate alone ($p < .05$). No significant difference in restless behavior was found between the methylphenidate alone and behavior therapy with placebo groups.

TREATED HYPERACTIVE CHILDREN VERSUS NORMAL CLASSMATES

Analyses comparing the posttreatment classroom observation scores of the hyperactive children and their normal classmates indicate that the children receiving the combined treatment of behavior therapy with methylphenidate were indistinguishable from their paired classmates. The group receiving methylphenidate alone continued to be significantly more disruptive ($p < .01$) and more solicitous of teacher attention ($p < .01$) than their normal comparisons. The children who received behavior therapy alone were significantly more elevated than normal children in the same classroom on all three observational measures (Disruptive Behavior, $p < .0001$; Minor Motor Movement, $p < .03$; Solicitation, $p < .02$).

Global Improvement Ratings

For purposes of analysis, the global ratings of improvement were dichotomized. Ratings of completely well, much improved, and improved made up the improved category. Ratings of slightly improved, unchanged, slightly worse, worse, and much worse were combined to make up the unimproved category. Chi-square analyses were applied to the Global Improvement ratings. If significant treatment differences were found across the three treatment groups, further chi-square tests, with Yates' correction, were done between specific groups. The improvement rating data are presented in Table 8.3.

TEACHERS' RATINGS

After 8 weeks of treatment, the teachers rated all of the children receiving combined behavioral and stimulant treatment as improved. Of the children receiving methylphenidate alone, 76% were evaluated as improved, whereas 63% of the children treated with behavior therapy with placebo were similarly rated (Table 8.3). The combination of behavior therapy with methylphenidate was significantly superior to behavior therapy with placebo (χ^2 = 7.00, 1 *df*, $p < .01$). No difference in teachers' global improvement ratings was found between the other groups (i.e., methylphenidate versus behavior

TABLE 8.3
Global Improvement Ratings

		Teachers [a]		*Mothers* [b]		*Psychiatrists* [c]	
Group	N	*Improved*	*Unimproved*	*Improved*	*Unimproved*	*Improved*	*Unimproved*
1. Behavior therapy and methylphenidate	21	21 (100)	0 (0)	19 (90)	2 (10)	21 (100)	0 (0)
2. Methylphenidate	21	16 (76)	5 (24)	17 (81)	4 (19)	17 (81)	4 (19)
3. Behavior therapy and placebo	19	12 (63)	7 (37)	13 (68)	6 (32)	11 (58)	8 (42)

Note: Numbers in parentheses are percentages.
[a] $X^2 = 8.92$, 2 *df*, $p < .02$
1 versus 2 $X^2 = 3.63$, corrected, 1 *df*, $p < .06$
1 versus 3 $X^2 = 7.00$, corrected, 1 *df*, $p < .01$
2 versus 3 $X^2 = .31$, 1 *df*, n.s.
[b] $X^2 = 3.08$, 2 *df*, n.s.
[c] $X^2 = 11.20$, 2 *df*, $p < .003$
1 versus 2 $X^2 = 2.49$, 1 *df*, n.s.
1 versus 3 $X^2 = 8.58$, corrected, 1 *df*, $p < .004$
2 versus 3 $X^2 = 1.55$, 1 *df*, n.s.

therapy with placebo, $\chi^2 = .31$, 1 *df*, n.s.; and methylphenidate with behavior therapy versus methylphenidate) although a trend was obtained for the superiority of methylphenidate with behavior therapy as compared to methylphenidate alone ($\chi^2 = 3.63$, 1 *df*, $p < .06$).

MOTHERS' RATINGS

The mothers' global ratings of improvement did not favor any single treatment group. Rates of improvement varied between 68 and 90% across treatments, indicating a relatively high level of perceived improvement by mothers for all the treatments.

PSYCHIATRISTS' RATINGS

The psychiatrists' evaluations, based on teacher and parent reports as well as their own clinical impressions, parallel those of the teachers more closely than those of the mothers. Like the teachers, psychiatrists rated all children (100%) receiving the combination treatment as improved. Of the youngsters treated with methylphenidate alone, 81% were rated improved; of those receiving behavior therapy with placebo, 58% were rated improved. A significant advantage was found for behavior therapy with methylphenidate over behavior therapy with placebo ($\chi^2 = 8.58$, 1 *df*, $p < .004$). No difference in global improvement was found between the groups on medication ($\chi^2 = 2.49$, 1 *df*, n.s.), or between methylphenidate alone and behavior therapy with placebo ($\chi^2 = 1.55$, 1 *df*, n.s.).

DISCUSSION

A consistent pattern of treatment effects was obtained. All treatments produced significant clinical improvement, but the combination of methylphenidate and behavior therapy was regularly the best treatment, methylphenidate alone was next, and behavior therapy with placebo was the least effective. There was no exception to the preceding order. In only one instance (observed in-seat activity level in the classroom) was the combination of medical and behavioral treatment significantly superior to medication alone; for all other comparisons, the differences between the two were negligible. In contrast, behavior therapy with placebo was significantly less effective than methylphenidate on several measures obtained from teachers and objective observers in the classroom.

No untreated control group of hyperactive children was included in this study. Consequently, it is not possible to evaluate the degree of improvement induced by the experimental treatments against the effects of time alone or to separate the interactions of repeated measures from the treatment effects. However, in a previous study done with hyperactive children in which a placebo group was included and the same measures were repeated, little if any improvement was observed with placebo treatment (Gittelman-Klein, Klein, Katz, Saraf, & Pollack, 1976). Similarly, O'Leary *et al.* (1976) found no marked change in a nontreated control group of hyperactive children. Therefore, it seems unlikely that the changes found with behavior therapy could be due to time effects, given the length of the study. However, one cannot rule out the possibility that the improvement reported with behavior therapy reflects nonspecific treatment effects or the expectations of the raters (teachers and mothers) who were not blind to this experimental condition.

Although behavior therapy seems to be a useful clinical intervention when applied in the child's natural environment, it is significantly less effective than stimulant treatment. However, it cannot be assumed that the therapeutic advantage of the medication is absolute. The results are generalizable only to hyperactive children who are relatively severely disruptive; in the present study, both mothers' and teachers' complaints were a prerequisite for treatment, and the scale criterion for admission was relatively high. The findings are limited also to children who receive comparable methylphenidate dosages. It cannot be assumed that the same pattern of treatment outcome applies to mild cases of hyperactivity or to children treated with lower dosages.

Caution is also necessary in generalizing about the merits of behavior therapy. In this study, the behavioral treatment was intensive, always involving both parents as well as the teachers, and often the child was seen by the therapist as well. No limit was set on the amount of direct contact between the therapist and parents or teachers during the study period. A less dedicated effort might not yield the same magnitude of improvement.

Though statistically significant therapeutic changes are valuable, their clinical meaningfulness is dramatized if it can be demonstrated that, with treatment, the patients' behavior not only improves, but becomes indistinguishable from that of normals. Utilizing this criterion, the combination of the two treatment modalities seems optimal. On all key measures, the children who received behavior therapy with methylphenidate were not significantly different after treatment from normals. The hyperactive children treated with methylphenidate alone continued to be rated as more inattentive and hyperactive by teachers, and as more disruptive and solicitous of teacher attention by the observers. The greatest contrasts between treated and normal children were found for the group receiving behavior therapy with placebo. Children in this group continued to be significantly different from normal children on crucial aspects of functioning; they received higher scores on teacher ratings of conduct disorder, inattention, and hyperactivity, as well as on classroom observations of disruptive behavior, in-seat activity, and solicitation of the teacher. These findings further accentuate the lesser efficacy of behavioral treatment compared to methylphenidate.

As compared to the other treatments, the lesser efficacy of behavior therapy with placebo is more marked in the observational data. Within-group analyses of the classroom observation measures indicated that the group receiving behavior therapy with placebo failed to show significant reduction in disruptive behavior and in-seat activity. It is unlikely that this lack of observed improvement is due to the observation code's insensitivity to treatment effects in general, since the same measure detected the effects of the drug treatments. It might be felt that, in some way, the content of the code was selected to give undue focus to behavior known to be affected by drug treatment, thereby implicitly neglecting aspects of functioning typically altered by behavioral treatments. It is difficult to maintain such an argument, since the observation code used in this study was not developed for studying drug treatment. Rather, it is a version of a classroom code that was developed specifically to assess the effects of behavioral interventions (Kent & O'Leary, 1976).

Teacher evaluations of academic performance were also obtained and will be discussed in a subsequent publication. It is noteworthy that these teacher evaluations are consistent with the classroom observation results, showing no improvement for the behavior therapy alone group. Of 19 children treated with behavior therapy alone, only 4 (21%) were rated as improved by their teachers, whereas 16 (76%) of the 21 children in the methylphenidate with behavior therapy group were seen as improved ($\chi^2 = 10.03$), 1 *df*, $p < .002$). The academic performance of 11 (52%) of the 21 children treated with methylphenidate alone was rated as improved, a level of reported improvement not significantly different from the other two treatment groups.

Difficulties arise in attempting to compare observational data obtained in this study with those obtained by other investigators. O'Leary *et al.* (1976) reported classroom observations of hyperactive and normal children only for the pretreatment period; unfortunately, no observational measures following behavioral treatment for the hyperactive children were obtained. Allyon *et al.* (1975) reported marked reductions in observed classroom hyperactivity using contingency management techniques with three hyperactive children. The small number of cases and the absence of observational measures of attentiveness make comparisons with our findings difficult.

It is noteworthy that the children who received behavior therapy with placebo were seen as improved by their mothers and teachers. Since parents and teachers were agents of change in the behavioral treatment program, their own efforts and expectancies may have biased their evaluation of the child and led to perceptions of improvement even without objective evidence of change.

The mothers reported somewhat more improvement with behavior therapy than the teachers and psychiatrists, and the advantage of drug treatment was least salient in the global ratings of mothers. This finding is felt to reflect a real clinical phenomenon. By the time the parents come for treatment, they typically feel helpless and demoralized regarding their ability to deal effectively with their child. The implementation of a behavioral treatment approach probably gives them a sense of mastery. In turn, their attitude toward the child may be more positive and accepting, even if the child changes little. This shift in parental attitude is inferred from clinical observations; no empirical data were collected to measure it since it was not foreseen.

Different rates of global improvement reported by mothers and teachers may also reflect differences in the child's behavior at home and at school. Stimulant treatment has proved especially effective on tasks demanding sustained attention (Douglas 1972; Sprague, Barnes, & Werry, 1970; Sykes, Douglas, & Morgenstern, 1972). It is possible that there is greater opportunity for the child to show improvement in situations that require sustained attention, such as the classroom, than at home (Sprague & Sleator, 1973). In addition, parents' reports of drug effectiveness may be less elevated than teachers' if the stimulant effects have worn off by the time the child returns home from school (Katz, Saraf, Gittelman-Klein, & Klein, 1975).

It may be argued that behavior therapy was administered over an 8-week period only, and that given more time, results might have been quite different. True; however, behavior therapy is being compared to a treatment that produces marked amelioration in a very brief time span, and the time factor itself can be considered a criterion of effectiveness. Further, as noted in a previous presentation (Gittelman-Klein, 1975), children receiving behavior modification alone reached a plateau in behavioral improvement after 4 weeks of treatment.

Behavior therapy presents other disadvantages. Its cost is far greater than that of treatment with medication, and its execution is often very difficult and fraught with practical problems. Implementing a behavior therapy program for a child in the public school system, at least in the greater New York area, is not a simple matter. Teacher responses to the pressures that the treatment induces vary, as indicated by the fact that several children could not be accepted for treatment simply because their teacher refused to cooperate. (Since cooperation was secured *prior* to group assignment, teacher refusal to participate did not influence the groups' composition.) Nevertheless, behavior modification led to the child being perceived as improved.

Therefore, for children who cannot tolerate stimulants, or whose parents are resistant to their use, a behavioral approach offers a possible, if not equivalent, therapeutic alternative. More importantly, should stimulants be proved to induce lasting major side effects, a realistic, albeit difficult and less effective alternative is available for those vulnerable to the side effects.

Doubts regarding the quality of the behavior therapy used in this investigation may lead to reservations concerning the validity of the results obtained. Care was taken to hire individuals with a strong philosophical commitment to behavioral treatment, and individual management of the children was used in order to give each treatment the best chance. A more convincing argument, and one more to the heart of the quality of care issue, is the magnitude of improvement obtained with behavior therapy. Children treated with behavior modification alone had a mean improvement of .94 on the Hyperactivity factor of the Teacher Rating Scale.[2] This symptom reduction is similar to improvements of .82 and .93 scale points reported by others (O'Leary *et al.*, 1976; Rosenbaum *et al.*, 1975) on the same measure, in 4- and 10-week studies done at a university nationally famous for research in behavior therapy. Arguments that the behavior therapy in this study was less than adequate seem unwarranted.

Some concerned laymen have claimed that stimulant medication inhibits children, transforming natural exuberance into robotlike complacency. Others have viewed behavior modification in the same light, that is, as a dehumanizing form of control aimed at inhibiting adjudged deviant behaviors to placate the demands of irrational authority (Schrag & Divoky, 1975). The classroom observational data present a direct challenge to this claim. First, the one variable insensitive to drug or behavior therapy was Solicitation, which reflects the child's spontaneous, self-monitored interaction with the teacher. Second, at posttreatment, the observed levels of disruptive behavior and in-seat activity of the hyperactive children were either significantly greater or not significantly different from those of the normals (see Table 8.3). On no classroom measure did any of the treatment groups emit behaviors significantly less often than their normal comparisons. These results do not support the notion that either stimulant medication or behavior therapy transforms hyperactive children into abulic, overly compliant, anergic youngsters.

The treatment results from this expanded sample give added support to the tentative conclusion of our earlier report; namely, stimulant treatment is more effective than behavior therapy in hyperactive children. The clinical lesson is that if medication is not enough, behavior modification should be added. The reverse therapeutic strategy has been demanded by some who

[2]Arithmetic difference between actual posttreatment and pretreatment scores.

claim that behavioral techniques are the treatments of choice and medication is a last resort (Grinspoon & Singer, 1973). Clearly, this view is not supported by the results of this study.

ACKNOWLEDGMENTS

The authors wish to express their gratitude and appreciation to K. Daniel O'Leary and his staff, who very generously gave assistance and advice in developing the behavior therapy program and the observational techniques. We also wish to acknowledge gratefully the assistance of Lucille Westrich who managed so competently the difficult task of coordinating classroom observations. Jeffrey Felixbrod, Marion Pheterson, Bruce Hammer, and Edith Pollack were our dedicated behavior therapists. Our thanks to Pat Ramsey who performed the statistical analyses. Chris Gloisten and Wendy Kates, the study social workers, contributed greatly to the execution and quality of the study.

V

OPTIMIZING THE MATCH BETWEEN CHILD CHARACTERISTICS AND INTERVENTION STRATEGIES

9

The "Real" and "Ideal" Management of Stimulant Drug Treatment for Hyperactive Children: Recent Findings and a Report from Clinical Practice

JUDITH L. RAPOPORT

INTRODUCTION

There is growing concern with the inter- and intrapersonal issues surrounding diagnosis and drug treatment of the hyperactive child. The physician's behavior is often taken as a rather mechanistic "given," and the act of prescribing a drug becomes the starting point for discussion.

This chapter will discuss the clinical techniques for assessing hyperactive children, planning the use of medication, and maintaining drug treatment. The approaches presented here are simply good clinical practice, based on the author's clinical training and experience as well as on exchanges with pediatric and psychiatric colleagues. It should be stressed that this process of clinical manipulation is often overlooked when the effects of medicating are discussed; unfortunately, the process is sometimes also overlooked during the clinical training of pediatricians and child psychiatrists. However, that unfortunate situation is changing, and current textbooks of pediatric psychopharmacology increasingly stress the interpersonal issues surrounding the use of medication (Werry, 1978b; Wiener, 1977), as discussed in this volume.

When clinical practice is sensitive and flexible, the variables that are discussed elsewhere in this volume (e.g., parent and child attitudes, causal judgments about the patient's "illness") are considered in deciding how to present a diagnostic formulation, whether to use medication, and how to

HYPERACTIVE CHILDREN
The Social Ecology of Identification and Treatment

ISBN 0-12-745950-2

continue to monitor medication. An essential feature in sensible clinical training is to impress upon the trainee that the child must be viewed in his or her social–psychological setting, and that any therapeutic decision must take into account a network of relationships. Most importantly, the advantages of any therapy must be weighed against our present knowledge about alternative strategies. Finally, the preexisting causal attributions held by the child and family may be more powerful than the influence of medicating per se, and these cognitive factors should be considered in treatment decisions.

The ideal approach to diagnosis and planning is inevitably an interactional one in which neither the child's "defective functioning" nor environmental deficiencies are considered solely responsible for the deviant behavior. There is presently little justification for choosing one set of emphases over the other in the case of the hyperactive child. Clinical situations usually permit several alternate formulations. Such a flexible approach does not conflict with current scientific opinion because there is no firm basis to support a "defect theory" of hyperactivity. As will be discussed, the empirical usefulness of stimulant drug treatment does not verify physiological etiology.

DIAGNOSIS IN CHILD PSYCHIATRY

The controversial process of identification of behavioral deviance presents special challenges in child psychiatry, where reports from others about the patient are usually needed. The clinician must also evaluate the reporting source, which adds considerably to the workload. The need for such background material creates a bottleneck at most child diagnostic facilities. Careful developmental and current history from parents, school evaluation, psychological testing, and diagnostic interviews with the child are essential, but time-consuming, components of the diagnostic process.

It can be argued that such a collection of informal anecdotal material may have extremely low reliability and validity; however, the situation does not seem bleak. Recent studies have demonstrated the validity and reliability of clinical assessment processes in child psychiatry. Rutter and coworkers in England (Rutter & Graham, 1968; Rutter, Tizard, & Whitmore, 1970) and Herjanic and colleagues in this country (Herjanic & Campbell, 1977; Herjanic, Herjanic, Brown, & Wheatt, 1975) have demonstrated the validity of a standardized playroom diagnostic evaluation, documenting significant relationships between symptom reports by teachers and parents, as well as between these reports and direct observations of the child. In the Rutter and Graham study, the overall judgment of psychiatric disturbance also proved highly reliable (a 90% agreement between the two child psychiatrists on "definite abnormality"). Using a standardized diagnostic interview with children and their parents, Herjanic and coworkers found considerable agreement between interview information from child and from parent. Like the Rutter study, the Herjanic research showed that the structured interview validated independent diagnostic assessment of children when different populations were compared (Herjanic *et al.*, 1975: Herjanic & Wellner, 1977).

In addition to these encouraging reports that reliable clinical assessment is possible in child psychiatry, such assessments have proven valid in predicting neurotic and antisocial behavior in grade school, adolescence, and adulthood (e.g., Robins, 1966; Rutter, 1976; Wolff, 1967). Moreover, highly significant associations between psychiatric assessments and independent diagnoses of neurological dysfunction, speech disturbance, and mental retardation have also been demonstrated. Much work still remains to be done exploring alternate assessment approaches (e.g., group or family interviews) which may prove more useful for some diagnostic purposes.

The question of the nature of hyperactivity remains open. There is considerable debate between those who recognize a true motoric version of the syndrome and others who see a more generalized disorder of impulse control, with imperceptible shading into conduct disorders. The forthcoming diagnostic label of "Attention Deficit Disorder" to be used in the next Diagnostic and Statistical Manual (DSM lll) of the American Psychiatric Association will bypass this issue and focus instead on the commonly (if not inevitably) observed feature of inattentiveness during structured tasks. In spite of this debate, and the continuing difficulty of defining attention deficit in the absence of objective measurement, there is considerable consistency among raters in identifying disturbed classroom behavior.

Teachers' ratings have been shown to be the most consistent and sensitive measures of stimulant drug effects, perhaps because the teacher has the greatest number of structured activity periods with the child that demand task attention or peer interaction. There will be some information that parents or children are uniquely qualified to give, but in one study, teachers' ratings of activity correlated with home behavior *better* than did ratings made by the parent (Rapoport & Benoit, 1975). Furthermore, teachers' ratings over a 2-year period were more stable than parent ratings even with different teachers doing the rating, and even when the child had changed schools (Riddle & Rapoport, 1976). Because of this relative stability, researchers and clinicians have relied increasingly on teacher rating scales for diagnosis. However, the recognition of restless and impulsive behaviors in a grade school child is only a small part of a meaningful diagnostic evaluation.

CLINICAL INTERPRETATION OF FINDINGS TO SCHOOL AND PARENTS

A subtle but very important process is evaluation of the *meaning* of the child's problems to the parents, teacher, and child. Deviant behavior may be interpreted in many different ways. The fact that the child arrives at the physician's office with a deviant label and a particular network of causal ascriptions is consistently overlooked. In order to understand this preexisting process, the physician must obtain detailed information about what has been tried at home and at school and with what success. He must ask what the parents' and teachers' experiences have been with similar problems, and what they think is causing the child's problem behaviors. A teacher may be convinced that the family is "disturbed" and that the child has been mishandled; parents often project their own childhood onto the current problem. Without specific inquiry, this information may not be offered.

Parents often describe feeling helpless about their child's inability to manage at school or in the neighborhood. They have *already* arrived at labels about their child's defect and their own inadequate parenting (or that of their spouse). Alternate therapies—psychodynamic, behavioral, and educational—may have been tried without success, leading to further confirmation of the caretakers' sense of helplessness. These initial feelings are often powerfully entrenched, and diagnostic efforts must organize around such initial formulations. Interpretations of the child's behavior and treatment recommendations *must* take the parents' preexisting causal explanations into consideration; the physician has to decide which alternative emphasis will be most useful. For some parents, independent confirmation that their child has "difficulties with impulse control" reinforces their suspicion that they have a hopelessly defective child. For other families, a careful description of the child's temperamental qualities, including impulsivity, may serve to alleviate parental guilt and/or marital conflict; the parents may become more supportive of their child's problems, and focus their activities toward helping the child.

Using a clinical–intuitive foundation, this interpretive interview process is a basic feature of clinical training in child psychiatry. However, there have been no naturalistic studies of this diagnostic process that pinpoint the optimal means of presenting diagnostic and treatment information to the family. Research is needed on the influence of causal attributions on clinical referral and evaluation processes.

Part of the pressure surrounding initial clinical evaluation is the frequent report from parents and teachers that they feel their own behavior is out of control. Parents confess that they fear their own retaliative behavior; teachers describe their frustration with their own anger when they have tried unsuccessfully to handle the child. The child in this situation is perhaps the most disturbed, as his own sense of mastery depends in part upon his sense of the competence of the caretaking adults. Here medication may indirectly support the child's sense of mastery; in such a situation, the child's resulting sense of control will derive from multiple sources, not simply from drug control of impulsivity. A clinical example is that of the mother of a 9-year-old hyperactive boy. She was chronically agitated by her own unsuccessful punitive behavior toward the child. During family interviews, she described herself as feeling helpless, fearful that she would harm him physically, and unable to cope with either her son or her household routine. Following her child's beneficial response to stimulant medication, she described herself as in control for the first time in years. Her son no longer attacked her verbally during interviews and appeared to function more comfortably in the family.

EXPLANATION TO THE CHILD

During the initial diagnostic contacts with the child, an attempt always should be made to elicit the child's ideas about the causes of current difficulties. Obtaining information from a child during an initial interview may not be a simple matter. Children may seem reluctant or inarticulate during an initial contact, or they may merely parrot the labels and explanations used by parents and teachers.

Part of the diagnostic process must include some explanation presented directly to the child. Whether the child is seen individually or with the family will depend, of course, on the physician's comfort with family interviews. The experience of the writer is that family interviews are most useful for observing the child's interactions with others—a concept that pediatricians have accepted for a long time, and which child psychiatrists are now beginning to share.

Some attempts have been made to prepare a standardized explanation of minimal brain dysfunction symptomatology to the child (Gardner, 1973). These formulations are premature, however, because they fail to allow for the flexibility of explanation that often is appropriate; moreover, such explanations solidify the concept of organic deficit beyond the present stage of scientific agreement.

If medication is to be prescribed, the child must be told that this treatment may help him master tasks in school and control his own impulses. Medication may provide an important opportunity for the child to perceive himself as "in control." While medication *might* increase the likelihood of external explanations for behavior, the difficulties encountered before medication was initiated might have been even *more* likely to promote a defective sense of personal causation. A child on medication may perceive himself as gaining self-control for the first time in years. Studies are needed of this process, that is, changes in children's causal explanations during and following medication. Such studies will have to take into account more complex processes than have typically been pursued, and they must start with the acute, pretreatment period. For example, it would be difficult, but theoretically possible, to obtain locus of control measures on children at the time they are being rejected by peers, suspended from school, or confronted by local law enforcement agencies.

DECISION TO START STIMULANT DRUG TREATMENT

The need to evaluate the social and family setting before deciding whether and how to use medication is now stressed in current textbooks of pediatric psychopharmacology (Wiener, 1977, p. 97). As has been stated, the clinician is faced frequently with disheartened families and teachers who have been dealing with a deteriorating situation for months or years before seeking medical help. Clinical judgment in this case calls for a careful evaluation of whether the families and school have already tried reasonable limit setting and behavioral controls, and whether the child has shown some partial response to these efforts. Information is needed on whether there has been regular communication between teacher and parents about the child's school work and behavioral difficulties.

It is important that future research paradigms take the physician's decision-making processes into account, as well as considering the past history of the child. For example, in their provocative study, Bugental, Whalen, and Henker (1977) showed the importance of a "match" between causal attributions and type of intervention (behavioral or self-control) with hyperactive children. What remains unclear from their study is whether or not the children with the "right" attributional stance had arrived at their "position" choice from unknown or subjective sources, or if they were simply accurate observers of their own past history of attempts at self-control.

Similarly, the Bugental *et al.* (1977) study indicated that self-control intervention had greater benefit for children who were nonmedicated than for children who were medicated. One possible interpretation is that medicating creates powerful attributional biases in the child. An alternate explanation, however, is that physicians are more likely to prescribe medication for children who have not responded to self-control approaches in the past, while deferring medication for children with some self-control successes. My intention here is not to fault this thought-provoking research, but to emphasize that without knowledge of physicians' decision making processes, this incidental result concerning medication is uninterpretable.

There is obviously no simple formula that can be applied for choosing a treatment. Good judgment calls for management without medication, if that can be realistically expected. However, if the family has tried and failed with behavioral management or other nonpharmacological approaches, medication may be indicated. Here the final facts are simply not in, but it remains a strong likelihood that some hyperactive children cannot maintain in ordinary environments without the help of medication. Clinicians cannot afford the luxury of waiting until all of the facts are in; they must operate with the best information currently available.

STIMULANT DRUG RESPONSE AND DIAGNOSTIC FORMULATION

Empirically, stimulant drugs have proven useful at least for short-term treatment of hyperactive–conduct disordered children (Gittelman-Klein, 1975). However, endorsement of clinical use of these agents does not commit the prescriber to a particular attributional stand about problem etiology. It is unclear whether the drugs act differently on a hyperactive child than on a normal child, and preliminary data suggest, in fact, that they do not. In one study (Rapoport, Buchsbaum, Zahn, Weingartner, Ludlow, & Mikkelsen, 1978), 14 normal, well-rested grade school boys were studied following a single dose of .5 mg/kg amphetamine or placebo in a double-blind crossover design. The boys were between the ages of 6 and 12 years, with no behavior problems, above average academic performance, normal neurological examination, no history of pre- or perinatal difficulties, and no close family members with these difficulties.

The group was tested on a battery of cognitive and electrophysiological tests from .5 to 2 hr postmedication. Motor activity was also monitored. There were significant drug-related improvements on the Continuous Performance Test (a measure of vigilance) and decreases in reaction time. In addition, it was striking that the group performed significantly better on a verbal learning task when on stimulant than on placebo, and motor restlessness decreased even though the children were not considered hyperactive or even fidgety during baseline or placebo sessions. Age, baseline motor activity, and measures of arousal did not predict drug response within this sample. Most of the children experienced mild dysphoria. The results appear quantitatively and qualitatively similar to those for a group of 15 hyperactive boys matched for age, socioeconomic status, and IQ, who were studied in the same fashion (Rapoport, Buchsbaum, Zahn, Weingartner, Ludlow, Mikkelsen, in press). Thus, the effectiveness of stimulant medication may not be used to confirm a diagnosis of physiological alteration in the child.

It would be simpler if specificity of drug effect could have been demonstrated clearly; in that case, stimulants could be likened to insulin treatment for diabetes, or penicillin for bacterial infection. It seems, however, that this is not the case. Rather, the effects of stimulants are not specific to particular diagnostic groups; any child will be more attentive and less restless on the drug. Nonspecificity is, of course, no argument against therapeutic use. For example, diuretics, which act on the kidneys to promote excretion, are an important treatment for patients with congestive heart failure; however, this action is entirely nonspecific in that any normal person would also show this diuretic effect. Patients with congestive heart failure usually do not have any particular problem with their kidney function, and there is even some risk of kidney damage from the continual use of diuretic agents.

In summary, positive clinical response to medication does not confirm the presence of brain dysfunction or physiological imbalance, even though such lesions may be demonstrated in the future. It may prove to be most useful to stress to the family and child that *no* fixed imbalance has been identified, that maturation is continually increasing the child's ability to maintain attentional and behavioral control, and that drug response does not confirm a deficit.

LONG-TERM MANAGEMENT OF MEDICATION

A new prescription for medication will be followed by months to years of drug treatment for many hyperactive children. There are few guidelines for the long-term maintenance of medication, since empirical data are lacking and clinical techniques are notoriously weak. Ideally, the clinician should have some system for obtaining regular reports from the home, the school, and the child about his progress and the continuing effects of drug treatment. Here is the greatest divergence between ideal and real practice; few clinicians have organized methods for collecting such data, and many have had no training in the follow-up management of drug treatment for behavior disorder. This information is crucial for monitoring how medication is being handled and whether it is serving as an ally to the child's sense of self-esteem and his developing competencies. For example, a child whose behavior changes on medicine may be praised for an active role in keeping track of his or her own medication, for alliance with the physician in monitoring the medication process and reporting the results, and for exerting self-control with the extra help of stimulants. For the demoralized child who has "done nothing right" in previous months, this process may represent a potent and gratifying mastery experience, reinforcing his sense of personal control.

The physician must be on guard against "externalizing" uses of medication. Common problems are the irregular, nonscheduled use of the drug or alterations of dose and timing as a punitive manipulation, for example, calling a child to take medication because he is having a "bad day," or using medication as a "shaming" device. Clinical impressions indicate that a fixed medication routine, independent of the particular behavior of the moment, is less likely than a flexible schedule to be used punitively, although this remains a researchable question.

The meaning to parents, teachers, and the child himself of medication responsiveness must be continually monitored, since inferences may emerge during treatment that were not seen initially. For example, a teacher may perceive the child's response to medication as vindication of the position that the child was (and perhaps still is) "defective"; parents may see the child's response to drugs as evidence of their failure to control their child, an interpretation that may not appear until medication is in chronic use. School personnel may see the use of drugs as a sign of their own inadequacy. After a few months of drug use, it may be evident that a teacher's interpretation of stimulant drug response (as confirming a "biochemical abnormality" or as revealing his or her own inadequacy as a teacher) has decreased investment in helping the child. Similarly, parental disappointment in their own inability to handle their child without drugs may be reflected in decreased parenting efforts.

This continued monitoring requires regular input from family, teacher, and child, and information about peer interaction as well as academic achievement. A model for follow-up information of this sort has been prepared by Chapman and Associates, private practitioners in Virginia (Chapman & Michener, personal communication, 1975); the child's interactions in a variety of interpersonal situations are monitored monthly during long-term drug treatment. Information on home and school behavior is recorded, as well as information on medication effects and side effects. Unfortunately, the systematic approach that Chapman and his colleagues use is rare among private practitioners. Training of future pediatricians and child psychiatrists will have to improve in this area. Logistically, pediatricians must learn to work more closely with nurses, psychologists, and school personnel. Such coordinated team effort is still rare.

The child and his family need to appreciate the empirical nature of drug maintenance, that is, the *only* way to see if medication is still needed is to try off-drug periods, at regular intervals, usually during the school year. The only controlled study of long-term need for medication showed that 26% of the drug treated children could discontinue stimulants each year, that is, the behavior of these children did not deteriorate when placebo was substituted for drug (Sleator, Von Neumann, & Sprague, 1974). The physician must also continue to monitor the method of administration of medication in the school: Is the child's privacy being protected? Is it necessary for the school to be involved in medication? Is the drug still seen as an agent to maximize their efforts? Do the teacher and parent feel more optimistic and effective in their efforts to care for the child? Does the child feel less hopeless about his attempts to apply himself to school work or to achieve self-control? Interactions with the child should be discussed during drug follow-up visits in order to involve the parents in continued efforts to handle difficulties without additional medication.

During maintenance treatment, the appropriate interpretation to school and family may change; the impact of behavioral improvement may be greater if intrinsic determinants of behavior are increasingly emphasized to parent and child over time. Parents are gratified to see themselves reacting differently to their child. With long-term maintenance, the concurrent shift in the actual behavior of the caretaking adults, secondary to the altered behavior in the child, may be striking. The concept of "direction of effect" has been reviewed by Bell (1968) and Bell and Harper (1977) who have stressed the need to examine the influence of child behavior on that of the adult. Several studies of medicated hyperactive children illustrate Bell's point that the effect of the child on the parent must be taken into account. As part of a large outpatient drug study (Rapoport, Quinn, Bradbard, Riddle, & Brooks, 1974), parent diaries were scored for "negative interactions" between parent and child during drug and placebo treatments. Scoring was blind in that the raters did not know whether the child was on placebo or active medication. Significantly fewer negative interactions were reported during stimulant treatment compared with placebo. Qualitative reports from the mothers indicated that they perceived themselves as more in control and less likely to "fly off the handle" when their children were on stimulants.

Flynn (personal communication, 1975) made classroom observations of teacher behavior as part of the Rapoport study. Using the Classroom Observation Schedule and Record (OScAR) of Medley and Mitzel (1958a, 1958b), she found the teachers to be more adequate in classroom control and reinforcement of compliant student behavior when the children were on medication than when they were on placebo.

Fially, in a recent study of mother–child interaction, using hyperactive boys on methylphenidate or placebo, Barkley and Cunningham (1979) rated mothers as less directive and more attentive when their children were on stimulant than when these same children were on placebo. Self-perception was not directly measured in the Barkley and Cunningham study, but a reasonable inference is that these mothers felt more in control during periods of harmonious interaction with their children.

Thus a decrease in the child's acting out behavior alters the perception of caretaker adequacy by other adults and may also alter the caretakers' self-perceptions. Although these phenomena may be striking clinically, I am unaware of any formal demonstration of such an alteration in adult self-image, or (as can also be striking clinically) an increase in mutual esteem between parents following positive drug response in the child. The long-term effects of response to stimulant medication, therefore, may be to increase self-perceived adequacy in caretakers and, through identification with a more secure adult, the child's own sense of personal causation. The positive effects of these improved social interactions on the child may be *more* potent than any negative effects of the child's awareness that he is taking medication.

SUMMARY

Standard "good" clinical practice modifies preexisting, powerful models of behavior that families hold; the historical process of labeling and explaining the hyperactive child's deviant behavior is evaluated and the treatment process directed accordingly.

This chapter had been intended as a discussion of current clinical practices regarding monitoring and evaluating drug effects in children. Unfortunately, there is little empirical information on the medical practice of prescribing drugs for hyperactive children; in fact, it is not even known whether stimulant drug-treated children in the community usually show the major features of the hyperactive pattern! Hopefully, this information will be obtained in future studies.

The interrelationships among parental attitudes and expectancies, child attitudes and expectancies, and child and parent competencies can produce multiple outcomes. A "good" clinician is not one who unfailingly predicts the sum direction of these forces, but one who systematically collects these data during diagnosis and follow-up in order to make reasonable choices and, perhaps more importantly, correct these choices over time.

There are many examples in medicine where a condition is overdiagnosed and a good treatment is overprescribed. A common instance is the overuse of antibiotics, or the large number of unnecessary tonsilectomies that are performed each year. It would be wrong to deny treatment on this basis to a carefully diagnosed and monitored group of children, particularly when this treatment is probably the best available, given the current state of our knowledge.

This brief exposition of clinician behavior was stimulated by the lack of such explicit guidelines in the pediatric and child psychiatric literature. It is hoped that future practitioners will be more uniform in their compliance with a system of complete evaluation of attitudes toward problem behaviors and medication, before and during drug treatment. It they are to provide clinically useful information, future studies of the social effects of medicating must take into account the extent to which the physician bases a treatment plan on medication-related attitudes and attributions that precede and attend pharmacological treatment.

10

An Educational Analysis of Hyperactive Children's Achievement Problems

BARBARA K. KEOGH
CATHERINE J. BARKETT

INTRODUCTION

Hyperactive children are commonly described as poor achievers in academic subjects and as serious, persistent behavior problems in school. Curiously, there has been relatively little effort directed at specifying the nature of their educational problems, at documenting the course of development of their failure patterns, or at delineating the variables influencing their school failure. For the most part, research on hyperactivity has been focused on children's characteristics; consideration of school parameters has been left to educators concerned with curriculum and instruction. The lack of concern about possible effects of school programs on hyperactive children is particularly interesting, given the widely held view that hyperactivity is, in part, situationally specific, even situationally induced (Ellis, Witt, Reynolds, & Sprague, 1974; Werry, 1968b). We believe that understanding the school problems of hyperactive children requires differentiation of both child and program variables and, furthermore, that it is the interaction of these variables that provides the key to intervention and remediation.

Several excellent comprehensive reviews summarize current research and clinical evidence documenting the characteristics of hyperactive children (Grinspoon & Singer, 1973; Ross & Ross, 1976; Sandoval, 1977; Sroufe, 1975; Sroufe & Stewart, 1973). In the present chapter, we are concerned exclusively with the aspects of hyperactive children's functioning thought to

HYPERACTIVE CHILDREN
The Social Ecology of Identification and Treatment

ISBN 0-12-745950-2

be directly relevant to school success and failure. We suggest that too often social–behavioral, psychological, and educational components of hyperactivity are subsumed into a single failure category. We propose that these three domains are partially independent, and that they are affected differentially by various school programs and instructional demands. Our strategy in this chapter has been to examine the research literature and selected interventions with hyperactive children in order to determine which educationally relevant characteristics are amenable to particular settings and techniques. We touch upon some aspects of school programs that may influence hyperactive children's performance, and we argue for the importance of educational interventions in the treatment of hyperactive children. In the review of research on this topic, we pinpoint a number of methodological problems that seriously limit interpretation and generalization of research findings. These methodological limitations deserve comment before considering the substantive evidence.

METHODOLOGICAL LIMITATIONS

Delineation of the relationship between hyperactivity and school problems is complicated by the equivocal nature of the diagnosis. Diagnostic criteria and operational measures are inconsistent, even controversial (Salkind & Poggio, 1977; Sandoval, 1977; Zukow, Zukow, & Bentler, 1978). The professional discipline of the researcher may influence the character of research samples, and thus affect the interpretations and inferences derived from particular studies. The sampling problem is particularly relevant when the school performance of hyperactive children is at issue, as physicians, teachers, and parents may have different perceptions of what constitutes hyperactivity (Langhorne, Loney, Paternite, & Bechtoldt, 1976). Spring, Blunden, Greenberg, and Yellin (1977) note, too, that physicians and teachers frequently disagree as to the characteristics defining hyperactivity; the teachers rate as normal a number of children diagnosed by the physicians as hyperactive. It is unclear whether teachers and physicians are differentially sensitive to certain symptoms or characteristics, or whether situational influences mediate the significance of certain behaviors. By whom, and in what context should the diagnosis of hyperactivity be made?

Another source of potential sample bias complicates understanding the hyperactivity–school achievement relationship. A preponderance of identified hyperactive children exhibit school learning problems and function below grade level expectancy on achievement measures (see as examples, Huessy & Cohen, 1976; Lerer & Lerer, 1977; Palkes & Stewart, 1972; Stewart, Pitts, Craig, & Dieruf, 1966). Indeed, it is uncommon to find descriptions of hyperactive children who perform at or above grade level on school tasks. This is not to say that such children are not in schools. We suspect that when poor achievement is accompanied by social–behavioral signs of hyperactivity, the probability of identification is high; when hyperactivity is not accompanied by learning failure, identification is less likely. Furthermore, high achieving hyperactives who are referred for behavior problems may be labeled differently, for example, precocious, mischievous, even creative. Thus, the widely held generalization that learning problems are necessary correlates of hyperactivity cannot properly be made. Any empirically derived generalization about the relationship between hyperactivity and school achievement must be tempered by the obvious possibility of bias in subject selection.

A closely related point has to do with a possible confounding of general ability, hyperactivity, and school achievement. A common design in studies of hyperactive children is to compare clinically selected subjects with nonclinic peers of similar age and sex. In most studies, only children whose general ability (IQ) is presumed to be average or above are included in the samples. Estimates of ability for the hyperactive children are frequently obtained through individually administered intelligence tests; ability of "normal" comparison subjects is often estimated from group IQ tests or from teachers' ratings techniques that may lead to underestimation of actual ability levels. When mean IQs for hyperactive and normal groups fall within the average range, the two groups are presumed to be equal on general ability. However, examination of the research literature suggests that despite assessment on individually administered measures, in many studies hyperactive samples have lower mean scores on general ability tests than do their comparison peers (Huessy & Cohen, 1976). Although within a normal range, the poorer performance of hyperactive children on IQ tests may, in fact reflect somewhat below normal, even marginal, general ability. If so, the low achievement and learning problems that characterize identified hyperactive children may be a function of ability, not of hyperactivity (Palkes & Stewart, 1972). The frequent confounding of general ability and hyperactivity seriously limits inferences about causes of these children's school problems.

Unidentified sources of variance due to school or setting effects further confound generalization. Some classrooms may support disruptive behaviors because of the ways they are physically organized, and/or because of the treatment or the instruction program. With the exception of the early work by Cruickshank, Bentzen, Ratzeburg, and Tannhauser (1961), surprisingly little attention has been directed to the effects of classroom organization on hyperactive children's school performance. In one of the few recent studies in this area, Flynn and Rapoport (1976) looked at the behavior of hyperactive children in open and traditional classes, and reported that achievement test scores and activity levels did not differ significantly across classrooms. They noted, however, that hyperactive pupils in open classrooms were perceived by teachers as less distinctive and less disruptive than were hyperactive pupils in traditional classrooms. Weissenburger and Loney (1977) found that the teacher's style of interaction affected the amount of the child's hyperactive, off-task behavior. Rosenbaum, O'Leary, and Jacob (1975) reported higher activity levels when activities were teacher-specified and directed than in situations where options were available to the children. These findings are consistent with a single subject study by Hirst (1976) and with the current work of the Houston group (Doster, 1977). The results also corroborate the hypothesis of situational specificity proposed by Ellis *et al.* (1974) and supported by Schleifer, Weiss, Cohen, Elman, Cvejic, and Kruger (1975). Ellis *et al.* (1974) observed hyperactive children on the playground and in the classroom. Whereas clear differences in behavior between hyperactive and nonhyperactive children were observed in the classroom, activity differences were not significant on the playground. Taken as a whole, findings from these studies provide tentative evidence to suggest that classroom structure may influence identification of hyperactive children and thus may affect sample selection in research studies. It should be emphasized that few of the studies to date have addressed in a comprehensive fashion the question of possible differences in academic competencies relative to classroom structure. None has considered the effects of classroom structure over extended periods of time.

An additional methodological limitation deserves discussion. Understanding of hyperactive children's school achievement problems is difficult because of the measurement techniques used to document academic performance. In many studies, educational achievement is assessed through teachers' ratings of children's performance in the classroom. These rating systems are often subjective and global, including items that encompass social behaviors, attention, amenability to instruction, and the like. The validity and reliability of teachers' ratings may vary with the context and the rating system. Teachers who have training and practice in rating and observation techniques are more accurate perceivers of changes in children's classroom behavior than are teachers untrained in observation (Weinrott, 1977). Sprague and Gadow (1976) found teachers to be remarkably accurate in assessing effects of medication on children's behavior at school. Yet, in other studies where both teachers' ratings and objective measure of school performance were taken, children's objective performance scores were not necessarily consistent with the improvement perceived by teachers (Rie, Rie, Stewart, & Ambuel, 1976a). Parents' and teachers' ratings of improvement may even conflict (Spring, Greenberg, & Yellin, 1977). A related problem in documenting achievement change is that when psychometric measures are used, the tests are frequently neither comprehensive nor detailed. They provide only summary data. The reader is referred to the comprehensive review by Sandoval (1977) for detailed description of measurement approaches and problems. For purposes of the present review, it is sufficient to say that most measures of achievement used in studies of hyperactivity do not provide a differentiated view of a child's educational competencies, but rather yield only rough estimates of general performance level.

Despite methodological problems that seriously limit interpretation, the preponderance of evidence suggests that identified hyperactive children do have higher rates of social–behavioral and educational problems than do their nonhyperactive peers. Furthermore, aspects of these problems appear to persist into adolescence and young adulthood (Borland & Heckman, 1976; Huessy & Cohen, 1976; Huessy, Metoyer, & Townsend, 1974; Laufer, 1973; Mendelson, Johnson, & Stewart, 1971; Minde, Lewin, Weiss, Lavigueur, Douglas, & Sykes, 1971; Minde, Weiss, & Mendelson, 1972; Quinn & Rapoport, 1975; Riddle & Rapoport, 1976; Weiss, Minde, Werry, Douglas, & Nemeth, 1971). Long-term studies are of particular interest since even in cases where activity levels are lower and appear controlled, subjects continue to exhibit social–behavioral and educational problems. It is possible that severe hyperactivity during the school years may so impede the mastery of basic educational competencies that the child is at a continuing disadvantage in subsequent years. Although there is evidence to document the persistence of achievement problems, the reasons remain for the most part speculative (Douglas, 1972, 1974; Keogh, 1971).

BEHAVIORAL, PSYCHOLOGICAL, AND EDUCATIONAL DOMAINS

In studies of hyperactive children's school learning, or more precisely of their school failure, the tendency has been to lump together into a single descriptive category various aspects of failure; these studies treat as equivalent, even synonomous, disturbances in social behavior, psychological processes, and educational performance. Yet the interactions and interrelationships among the three domains are obscure. The three domains may be independent and respond uniquely to various intervention strategies and to different school settings. They may covary, interact, or be causally related. The nature of the interactions of social–behavioral, psychological, and educational domains is not only theoretically interesting, but has direct implications for therapeutic or remedial intervention programs. The goals, kind, and timing of interventions are, in large part, a product of the interveners' views of the nature of the relationships among these domains.

Most interventions with hyperactive children are directed at modification of social behavior, physiological functions, and/or selected psychological processes, for example, attention or visual perception. It is assumed that changes in these areas of the child's functioning will lead to improved academic competence. The inference is reasonable if one accepts the assumption of a causal relationship between child characteristics and academic performance. The view that the hyperactive child's learning problems are caused by his behavioral problems is indeed widely held. For example, after describing hyperactive children's characteristic behavioral overactivity and social disruption, Harlin (1973) added, "Of course, *because* of these problems he is an underachiever with a poor image of himself [p. 10; emphasis added]." The causal implication is clear. A logical extension of this point of view is that underachievement and school problems may be ameliorated through modification of the social–behavioral aspects of hyperactivity, or through remediation of deficient or disturbed psychological processes.

The assumption of covariance of behavioral, cognitive, and educational competencies may be found in a number of interventions. Operant procedures have led to a reduction of undesirable disruptive behaviors, and increases in "attending behaviors" (Patterson, Jones, Whittier, & Wright, 1965). Unfortunately, there is little direct evidence linking the behavioral changes to improved school achievement. As few operant studies have included assessment of educational performance or cognitive processes, it is difficult to determine the possible influence of behavioral changes on these functions. Studies of medication effects on hyperactive children have also provided extensive evidence of changes in behavior and selected physiological and psychological processes, as a function of drug intervention (Sroufe, 1975). However, evidence of drug effects on learning and educational achievement is inconclusive. Touching on the complexity of this issue, Conners (1975c) suggests that stimulant medication may affect academic skills such as spelling, arithmetic, and reading, when the learning problems are a function of impulsivity and attentional defects. He notes, however, that short-term drug effects may be a reflection of changes in motivation or other performance factors, rather than evidence of drug effects on ability (Conners, 1972c).

Further complicating questions about the nature of the interactions among behavioral, psychological, and educational domains are the findings of linear and curvilinear dosage effects (Sprague, 1977). Sprague and Sleator (1976, 1977) report that optimal dosage levels differ for different target behaviors. These findings are consistant with those of Sulzbacher (1973), and Eaton, Sells, and Lucas (1977) who also report changes in academic performance relative to dosage. Werry and Aman (1975) suggest that low dosages of a less widely used drug, haloperidol, facilitate performance on tasks of attention, immediate recognition memory, reaction time, and seat activity, whereas high dosages may cause some deterioration of performance on the same indices.

In short, despite impressive evidence of behavioral change following a number of different kinds of interventions, there is inconsistent and sometimes puzzling evidence regarding effects of particular interventions on particular processes. More importantly, there is little evidence that documents effects of interventions across behavioral, psychological, and educational domains, or specifies the causal interactions among domains. At issue is the assumed covariate relationship among various aspects of hyperactivity. Improvement in the hyperactive child's social behavior may be a desirable and agreed upon therapeutic goal, but such behavioral change may not have direct consequences for performance on educational tasks. As noted by Sroufe (1975), one of the major methodological failures in drug studies has been the "consistent failure to report intercorrelations among change scores following drug administration [p. 372]." The same criticism may be leveled against most intervention studies, and it is likely that some of the controversy surrounding interventions stems from this failure. As intervention effects may be selective, it is imperative that the nature of the interactions among functional aspects of hyperactivity be identified. In this chapter, we have approached the problem through review and analysis of research evidence describing intervention effects on social–behavioral, psychological, and educational competencies.

INTERVENTION EFFECTS

Although diverse in content and practice (Bower & Mercer, 1975; Prout, 1977; Ross & Ross, 1976; Werry, 1968b), most interventions with hyperactive children have common goals of reducing behavioral restlessness and distractability, directing attention, and improving social behavior. Few are directed specifically at increasing educational competencies, although almost all assume at least a secondary effect on school performance. For the purpose of this chapter, three types of interventions, representative of the state of the art, have been selected for more detailed discussion. These are interventions based on medication, behavior modification, and cognitive control training. No attempt has been made to provide a comprehensive review of the published literature on these interventions. Rather, we have based our interpretations on selected published research that uses each of these three approaches. We have attempted to determine the influence of the specific interventions on behavioral, psychological, and educational functions of hyperactive children. By inference, the analyses provide some clues as to the strength of the relationships among these domains.

Medication

The most extensive literature on intervention involves use of medication. The reader is referred to reviews by Sroufe (1975), and Lambert, Windmiller, Sandoval, and Moore (1976) that provide comprehensive and thoughtful looks at the use of medication with hyperactive children. Research by several sets of investigators, working independently, provides tentative clues as to the differentiated effects of various medications on hyperactive children; this work deserves detailed review. Rie *et al.* (1976a) reported few consistent effects of methylphenidate on school achievement of primary grade hyperactive children, although both parents and teachers rated medicated children as improved in behavior. Despite parents' and teachers' perceptions, improvement was demonstrated objectively on only one of six subtests of the Iowa Test of Basic Skills (Word Analysis), and on one subtest of the Illinois Test of Psycholinguistic Abilities (Auditory Association). Furthermore, the comprehension subtest of the Wechsler Intelligence Scale for Children (WISC), the only subtest on which change reached statistical significance, showed a decreased performance level under medication. Sociograms of classroom behaviors also suggested a decrease in socially acceptable behavior under medication. Although results were somewhat inconsistent, in general they supported a drug induced reduction in activity level, and an improvement in attention. Of particular importance for the present discussion was the finding that correlations between activity measures and achievement test scores were inconsistent and of low magnitude. From their results as a whole, Rie *et al.* (1976a) argue for the importance of specification of medication effects on particular functions, adding that, "although we observed the commonly reported changes in behavior, we find no support for the assumption that scholastic achievement (learning) improves [p. 258]." In a further interpretive comment implicating motivation, Rie *et al.* (1976a) cautioned that "the reactions of the children strongly suggest a reduction in commitment of the sort that would seem to be critical for learning. There would then appear to be not only a reduction of the disapproved behaviors that interfere with learning, but also of the desirable behaviors that facilitate it. The net effect on learning would presumably be nil, or precisely the findings of the present study [p. 259]."

In a second study, Rie, Rie, Stewart, and Ambuel (1976b) essentially confirmed their earlier findings, stressing again the lack of evidence to support a global positive effect of the drug under consideration. They suggest that methylphenidate is not a "suitable" treatment for learning problems, and note further that the use of the drug may mask or confound learning disorders; the child is perceived by parents and teachers as performing more effectively when, in fact, he continues to have deficits in basic educational skills. As a whole, the Rie *et al.* work is consistent with the hypothesis of partial independence among behavioral, psychological, and educational domains.

Further evidence for partial independence of behavioral, psychological, and educational functions in hyperactive children comes from two related studies by Gittelman–Klein and Klein (1975, 1976). These investigators addressed the question of the effects of medication on psychological processes of hyperactive and nonhyperactive children with learning deficits. Specifically, they attempted to determine the strength of relationship between change in overt behavior and change in performance on psychological and achievement measures. In the 1975 study, hyperactive elementary age pupils were randomly assigned to active treatment or placebo groups following extensive behavioral, psychometric, and achievement testing. Pupil data included parents' and teachers' ratings and observations, as well as structured behavioral rating systems. Possible drug effects were assessed at 4 and at 12 weeks. A major finding was that there was no relationship between behavioral and psychometric changes for the shorter time period, and only a weak relationship for the longer time period; these investigators concluded that psychometric and behavior changes are not necessarily correlated. They note that, "The notion that a primary, unitary, CNS function is ameliorated by stimulants, leading to remission of many secondary symptoms, seems unlikely [p. 195]." The findings were especially interesting in that after 4 weeks there were significant drug effects on behavior, but few on psychometric performance. That is, change in behavioral aspects of hyperactivity was not, especially in the short run, associated with improved performance on psychometric and achievement tests. In another study by the same investigators (Gittelman-Klein & Klein, 1976), children of elementary age, selected because of learning–achievement problems, but free from indicators of hyperactivity or behavior problems, were administered methylphenidate. The investigators reported that the drug improved performance on some psychometric tests, but did not have a direct positive effect on educational achievement. Performance on psychological subtests tapping particular abilities, for example, visual processing mechanisms, improved significantly under medication, but overall academic achievement appeared to be unaffected by the drug. It was significant that gains in performance on subtests requiring visual perceptual processes were not correlated with gains in educational tests of reading.

Recent work by Spring and his associates may clarify further the effects of medication on behavioral and psychological processes, especially perceptual–motor functions. In studies comparing effects of impramine and methylphenidate, Greenberg, Yellin, Spring, and Metcalf (1975) found that both drugs lead to improved behavior according to parent reports. However, in a related study, Spring, Yellin, and Greenberg (1976) found that hyperactive children improved on objective tests of perceptual–motor abilities only under methylphenidate. Furthermore, the drug effect was not comprehensive, but was limited to perceptual–motor tests requiring perseverance over extended periods of time; no improvement was found on tests that did not require "endurance," according to these investigators. The Spring *et al.* (1976) findings essentially corroborate the selective, and often limited, effects of medication described earlier by other investigators (e.g., Freeman, 1966, 1976).

The complexity of response to intervention is also demonstrated by studies comparing different therapeutic approaches. Christensen and Sprague (1973) suggested that a combination of medication and behavior modification was more effective than either technique used alone, but in another study, Christensen (1975) found that behavior modification procedures used with a placebo were just as effective as those used with medication for particular behaviors. In interpreting these apparently contradictory findings, Christensen (1975) suggested that there may be an inverse relationship between behaviors responsive to medication and those responsive to behavior modification; measures least responsive to the behavior modification were found to be most responsive to medication. The importance of the nature and range of outcome measures is underscored. The findings of Sprague and Sleator (1976) regarding dosage levels deserve further comment in this context. These investigators found that learning and behavior were differentially sensitive to dosage changes. In essence, teachers continued to report improved behavior at dosage levels that resulted in decrements in performance on a school-like, laboratory task (Sprague & Sleator, 1976). As Christensen (1975) pointed out, the temptation to achieve social–behavioral control through increased medication is great, but it must be tempered in light of the possible impairment of learning and cognitive functioning at higher dosage levels. Werry and Sprague (1972), Ayllon, Layman, and Kandel (1975), and Stablefore, Butz, Hasazi, Leitenberg, and Peyser (1976) all provide evidence supporting Christensen's caution.

It is important to emphasize that the most agreement about consistent effects of medication on psychological processes concerns changes in the ability of hyperactive children to sustain attention, to maintain on-task behavior. This effect is reported commonly in studies of elementary school children. It is also reported by parents of preschool children on medication (Gadow, 1977), and it recently received corroboration in a study of the effects of dextroamphetamine on behavior and cognition of normal prepubertal boys (Rapoport, Buchsbaum, Zahn, Weingartner, Ludlow, & Mikkelson, 1978). Ongoing work by Schain and his colleagues (1977) with clinically diagnosed hyperactive children provides independent support for the effects of stimulants on attention sustaining ability.

As the educational implications of increases in sustained attention seem obvious, it is somewhat surprising that there has been little direct demonstration of concomitant changes on performance of school tasks. Margolis (1973) found a significant positive relationship between performance on her sustained attention test and reading in a large sample of nonclinic third graders. However, work by Keogh and Margolis (1976) carried out in classrooms implicates functions in addition to sustained attention that affect performance. These investigators found that on a school-like test of sustained attention, Educationally Handicapped (EH) elementary school pupils did indeed perform significantly more poorly than did their normally achieving peers. Although the task was well within their competence level, EH children in the Keogh and Margolis study made more errors and showed an earlier decrement in performance than did the normally achieving pupils. Additionally, younger learning disabled pupils also had higher error rates on measures of impulsivity and perceptual organization compared to peers. These data demonstrate a relationship between ability to sustain attention and educational achievement but argue that other aspects of attention are also important influences on educational performance. To interpret improvement on sustained attention measures as indicating increased educational competence is an inferential leap unsupported by direct evidence.

Another point deserves attention. Assessment of medication effects on school performance may be clouded by possible state-dependent effects. A term derived mostly from animal studies, state dependency or "learned dissociation" refers to a condition in which "a response which is learned under the influence of a particular drug may recur with maximum strength only when the drug condition is reinstated [Aman & Sprague, 1974, p. 268]." Although Aman and Sprague found no evidence of state–dependent learning in their study of medication effects on learning and retention, other evidence (Swanson & Kinsbourne, 1976) suggests that state dependency may occur in cases where initial learning was facilitated by medication. The possibility of state-dependent effects warrants consideration in interpreting school relevant research findings. Specifically, as there are clear individual differences in children's response to medication, generalizations drawn from group means may mask important response patterns and child-specific state-dependent effects. Further, the interactions of state effects and particular learning or performance components are unknown; thus, the sequence of posttreatment measures relative to timing of medication becomes important. Finally, the regularity with which a medication regimen is followed may vary markedly according to parents' and children's attitudes about taking medication. It may well be that there is considerable within-sample variation in a group of children all presumed to be on controlled medication. Variability in adherence to a drug regimen may influence both test and school performance.

Taken as a whole, findings from medication studies allow tentative generalizations about the nature of the interrelationships among social behaviors, psychological abilities, and educational competencies. Certainly the evidence does not support an "across the boards" medication effect. It appears, rather, that the major effect of medication is on social behaviors and psychological processes involving selected attentional and visual–perceptual abilities; there is little evidence of direct drug effects on academic achievement. As noted earlier, exclusive reliance on a behavorial criterion of drug efficacy may lead to dosage levels that work to the child's disadvantage in academic subjects. In any case, change in behavior under medication will not necessarily be accompanied by improved ability to process information or to perform on school achievement tasks. When medication is the primary intervention, additional effort must be directed toward remediation of the deficits in educational skills that characterize many hyperactive children.

Behavior Modification

The use of behavior modification with atypical populations has been widely endorsed and, indeed, behavioral techniques have been the basis for a number of major educational programs for exceptional children (see Hewett, 1968). The reader is referred to several comprehensive sources (O'Leary & Drabman, 1971; Prout, 1977; Ullman & Krasner, 1965) and to a number of studies (Allen, Henke, Harris, Baer, & Reynolds, 1967; Becker, Madsen, Arnold, & Thomas, 1967; Patterson *et al.*, 1965; Twardosz & Sajwaj, 1972) that document the effectiveness of behavioral techniques for changing a variety of behaviors characteristic of hyperactive children. For the most part, behavior modification studies suffer from small sample size (single subject design and case studies predominate) and lack of evidence about the generalization of effects. Of particular concern for the present chapter, they provide limited data relevant to questions of learning and achievement in school subjects. Although the manipulation of reinforcement contingencies has been shown to reduce, even extinguish, hyperactive behaviors, the bulk of the studies, unfortunately, do not allow inferences about the consequences of these changes for school achievement.

Early efforts were directed toward modifying hyperactive behaviors through extinction techniques; recent work has utilized a counterconditioning paradigm in which hyperactive behaviors are reduced or supplanted through strengthening of alternative incompatible behaviors. A number of investigators of hyperactive behavior (Alabiso, 1972; Ayllon & Roberts, 1974; Christensen & Sprague, 1973) have suggested that attention to task is incompatible with symptoms of hyperactivity. Therefore, if attending behavior is increased through operant techniques, hyperactive behaviors such as distractibility, restlessness, and inattentiveness must necessarily decrease. The approach particularly appeals to those responsible for hyperactive children's educational programming; it has a clear situational relevance and avoids the complexities and possible negative consequences of behavioral management with drugs.

Several studies concentrated on the modification of attending behaviors. Allen *et al.* (1967) used social reinforcement to shape children's time performing activities, and Patterson and his colleagues (1965) relied on extrinsic reinforcers to bring about changes in attending behavior. Although behavioral change was demonstrated in both studies, neither provided a direct measure of learning or performance on school tasks. Therefore, it is not possible to determine if increases in "attention" were associated with improved achievement in school subjects. A single study by Doubros and Daniels (1966) hints at the possibility of a correlation between time spent attending to a task and learning; these investigators reported that reinforcement not only increased attending behavior and decreased nonattending behavior, but also improved the quality of mentally retarded children's play, leading the authors to infer that learning had occurred.

The question of interaction or relationship among behavioral and academic outcomes may be addressed by findings from Hewett's (1968) "engineered classroom" program. Hewett reported dramatic reduction in disruptive, hyperactive-like behaviors of emotionally disturbed children. He was able to show significant increases in in-seat behavior and attention to task, evidenced by gaze direction. The intervention had a powerful effect on social–behavioral aspects of disturbances in activity, but these changes did not necessarily lead to improvement in academic skills. When subsequent educational remediation was introduced, change in educational achievement was accomplished.

From a different perspective, Ferritor, Buckholdt, Hamblin, and Smith (1972) investigated the effects of behavioral and performance contingencies on classroom behavior and mathematics performance of normal, inner city school children. They found that reinforcement for acceptable classroom behavior increased attention and decreased disruptive behavior, but had no effect on adequacy of academic performance. When reinforcement was made contingent upon academic performance, skills improved while attention declined and disruptive behavior increased. It was not until contingent reinforcement was applied to both behavior and academic performance simultaneously that both improved. The authors note that reinforcement of acceptable classroom behavior did not in itself have the often assumed positive effect on academic achievement.

Recent work by Ayllon and his associates (Ayllon, Layman, & Burke, 1972; Ayllon *et al.*, 1975; Ayllon & Roberts, 1974) provides the most comprehensive evidence relating behavior modification strategies to school achievement of hyperactive children. These investigators noted that although drug interventions changed behavior, there was little evidence to suggest a direct effect of medication on academic achievement. Having demonstrated that task-oriented academic activity was incompatible with disruptive classroom behavior, they proposed that the disruptive behaviors characterizing hyperactivity might be reduced by reinforcing the incompatible academic behaviors. In the 1975 Ayllon *et al.* study, behavioral intervention was contrasted with medication. Importantly for this review, the dependent measures included actual performance on academic tasks: math and reading. Using a multiple baseline during math and reading periods, these investigators found that reinforcement of academic performance led to control of the disruptive behaviors comparable to the control achieved with medication. Concurrently, under reinforcement conditions both math and reading performance increased approximately 70%, leading these investigators to conclude that optimal social and academic results were achieved without medication. In the design of the 1975 study, all three hyperactive subjects experienced all treatment conditions (medication, no medication, reinforcement with math, and reinforcement with math and reading). The relationship between hyperactive behaviors and academic achievement within intervention conditions was of particular interest. Under medication, hyperactivity and achievement decreased; upon removal of medication, hyperactivity and achievement increased. Under the reinforcement program, achievement increased, but hyperactive behaviors decreased.

Finally, Varni (1976) elaborated and expanded Ayllon's work, showing that a combination of self-reinforcement and self-monitoring procedures improved task attention and decreased disruptive behaviors of three hyperactive children. Importantly, output in math and reading increased, and hyperactive behavior decreased. Varni's findings are especially interesting in that intervention approaches utilizing self-reinforcement may provide a bridge between the more traditional reinforcement programs and the self-management techniques encouraged in cognitive control interventions. Presumably, interventions stressing self-reinforcement are less situationally specific and have more long-term consequences than do externally controlled reinforcement programs. Masters and Mokros (1974) have reviewed comprehensively the evidence from laboratory studies documenting effectiveness of self-reinforcement in children's behavior. Demonstration of self-reinforcement effects in classroom settings is less extensive, but is essentially confirming (e.g., Drabman, Spitalnik, & O'Leary, 1973; Lovitt & Curtiss, 1969). As with other interventions, generalizability across behaviors is rarely demonstrated. Varni (1976), citing his own work with Rekers, suggests that compared with external reinforcement techiques, self-control techniques produce more stable responses. Unfortunately, with a few exceptions (e.g., Ballard & Glynn, 1975) the bulk of the work on self-reinforcement to date has not dealt directly with academic outcomes, but has instead focused on changes in, or maintainance of, specific behaviors, for example, reduction of disruptive classroom behavior (Bolstad & Johnson, 1972).

Findings from the behavior modification studies of hyperactive children throw some light on the nature of the interactions among social–behavioral, psychological, and educational domains. For the most part, however, the reported studies are seriously limited by the lack of demonstrable generalization or stability of effects. In the Ayllon *et al.* study (1975), for example, the reduction of disruptive behavior during math did not generalize to reading, unless reading was specifically reinforced. As in most behavior modification studies, there is little solid evidence to suggest stability of improved behavior; unless reinforcement continues, the changes in behavior appear temporary and specific. The research evidence from studies of drug and behavioral interventions is consistent with the position that social–behavioral, psychological, and educational competencies are relatively independent; hyperactive children's learning problems will not necessarily be remediated by treatment programs that are directed at changing specific behaviors.

Cognitive Control

Recognizing the central role of disturbed attention and impulse control in the behavior of hyperactive children, along with the relatively specific and often limited effects of drugs and behavior modification, a number of investigators have sought alternative therapeutic approaches directed at bringing about more enduring cognitive changes. Self-monitoring, verbal self-instruction, and modeling of problem-solving styles are examples of interventions that can be loosely grouped under the rubric, cognitive controls. Although varying in specific techniques, researchers have a common goal of modifying the attention and impulse control problems that are thought to impede problem solving and disrupt behavior. The interventions designed to improve cognitive control are intuitively attractive, as they stress internal controls that presumably lead to fundamental, long-term changes. The theoretical ties to attribution (see Whalen & Henker, Chapters 1 and 12 of this volume) are clear.

A good deal of the work on cognitive control interventions does not refer specifically to hyperactivity, but rather to "impulsive" children. The theoretical ties between hyperactivity and impulsivity have been discussed by a number of investigators (Keogh, 1971; Schain, 1968; Schleifer *et al.,* 1975; Sykes, Douglas, Weiss, & Minde, 1971), and have been delineated most clearly by Douglas (1972, 1974, 1976c). Douglas, Parry, Marton, and Garson (1976) concluded that distractibility and heightened activity levels, common clinical symptoms of hyperactivity, are "secondary to the attentional-impulsivity deficit [p. 39]." It is reasonable, then, that interventions aimed at modifying impulsivity would have appeal as interventions for hyperactive children.

The construct of impulsivity is a key one in cognitive control approaches; it provides a conceptual link between problem-solving strategies and hyperactivity. It is important on another level in that tests of impulsivity are frequently the dependent measure in intervention studies with hyperactive children. The work of Kagan and his colleagues (Kagan, 1965, 1966; Kagan, Rosman, Day, Albert, & Phillips, 1964) on impulsivity–reflection is, therefore, relevant to cognitive control interventions. In Kagan's conception, two dimensions of style are identified and assessed; response latency and perceptual accuracy. The operational definition of impulsivity–reflection is the Matching Familiar Figures Test (MFFT). The construct and the measure have been widely discussed and investigated (Kagan & Kogan, 1970; Messer, 1976), and despite some question and criticism (Bentler & McClain, 1976; Block, Block, & Harrington, 1974), the MFFT is a commonly used measure in research with hyperactive children. Indeed, there is considerable evidence to show that hyperactive children respond quickly and inaccurately, that is, they are impulsive in problem-solving situations (Douglas, 1972; Jacobs, 1972; Keogh & Donlon, 1972).

Modification of impulsive responding has been addressed through interventions based on modeling (Cohen & Przybycien, 1974; Yando & Kagan, 1968), instructions in scanning (Egeland, 1974), and self-instruction (Meichenbaum & Goodman, 1971). The question of importance for this chapter has to do with the relationships between changes in impulsivity and school performance. It is of interest that although many investigators infer that change toward a more reflective style will be associated with improved school achievement, there has been little direct demonstration of change on academic tasks. Tidberg, Parke, and Hetherington (1971), for example, showed that identified impulsive children became more reflective under a modeling intervention. These investigators added, "The underlying assumption of these training efforts is that a change in conceptual tempo may result in correlated improvement in areas of intellectual performance such as reading [p. 369]." Unfortunately, since no direct measure of reading was included, the findings are not definitive in regard to the question of academic achievement.

Egeland's (1974) study of impulsive children provides findings of more direct relevance to the educational achievement question. In his study, impulsive children were taught to be more efficient scanners through techniques that emphasized new search and scanning strategies or delay of responses. Both interventions led to improved scores on the MFFT immediately after training. Of importance for this discussion, improvement was correlated with higher scores on the vocabulary subtest of a standardized individual reading test administered 5 months after training. Subjects trained on scanning techniques also scored higher on the comprehension subtest of the same achievement measure. Experimental and control groups did not differ on a group administered standardized achievement test given immediately after training, however. It is possible that the group test was not sensitive enough to the types of changes brought about by the intervention, or as Egeland speculates, that it takes time for new ways of processing information to generalize to achievement measures. Necessarily then, the nature and timing of measurement are of concern in the study of hyperactive children's school problems. The important point is that remediation of impulsivity affected performance in the achievement domain, suggesting that improved psychological processing enhanced educational accomplishment.

Although not developed specifically for intervention with hyperactive children, the work of Meichenbaum and his colleagues (e.g., Meichenbaum, 1975; Meichenbaum & Goodman, 1969, 1971) has been widely applied to hyperactive samples. This approach to cognitive controls emphasizes the central role of language in the organization of problem-solving strategies. Meichenbaum and Goodman (1971) developed a training program that was aimed at facilitating verbal control over behavior. Meichenbaum had demonstrated that when self-directed verbalizations are absent, they can be taught, and that when they are nonfunctional, they can be changed (1971). Applying his procedures, Meichenbaum trained impulsive children to use self-directed speech during a problem-solving task. After 4 weeks, children trained in cognitive control improved their scores significantly on an impulsivity test and on subtests of the WISC, although no corresponding improvement in classroom behavior was noted.

Meichenbaum's techniques have been used by other investigators with mixed results (e.g., Bender, 1976), but few studies have included tests of achievement in educational subjects among the dependent measures. Of particular interest, thus, was the work of Malamuth (1977), who used a Meichenbaum type self-management training program with children identified by their teachers as poor readers. Not only did self-management programming lead to increased ability to sustain attention (as measured by the Margolis [1973] sustained attention test), but children improved in reading performance. The low correlations ($r = .21$) between the measure of sustained attention and reading, however, did not allow the interpretation that the self-management intervention had a unitary effect. Malamuth's subjects were in regular classes and were not identified as hyperactive; her findings, nevertheless, demonstrated effects of a cognitive control intervention on a specific school task, that is, reading.

Self-management techniques similar to the Meichenbaum approach have been used with clinically defined hyperactive children with generally positive results (e.g., Palkes, Stewart, & Freedman, 1971; Palkes, Stewart, & Kahana, 1968). Although Palkes and colleagues have demonstrated the effects of verbal self-commands on improved ability on planning tasks, for the most part they have not utilized direct measures of educational achievement. Thus, the link between the cognitive processes and academic performance remains an assumed one.

The most direct test of the effects of cognitive control intervention on educational performance comes from the 1976 work by Douglas *et al.* (see also Douglas Chapter 11 of this volume). These investigators worked with 18 clinically identified hyperactive children over a 3- month period. The training techniques were based on Meichenbaum's approach and were aimed especially at teaching children to deal with problems requiring "care, attention, and organized planning." Contingency management techniques were occasionally used, but the focus of the intervention was on self-regulated problem solving, coupled with control of impulsive responding. A group of 11 children served as a comparision sample at the end of the training and in posttest comparisons 3 months after completion of training. Differences in trained and comparison subjects were found at both posttest periods, suggesting that self-management training was effective in improving problem solving strategies. Specifically, differences were reported in favor of the training group on the MFFT, on tests of organization and planning and, importantly, on some reading achievement tests. The last deserves special note because the training was not directed specifically at remediating the children's reading problems, but rather at modifying aspects of cognitive control and problem solving. As with the Malamuth (1977) findings, improved reading scores on an objective reading test suggest generalization of changes in cognitive strategies to academic subjects. The Douglas *et al.* group did not find that the training resulted in improvement on the Bender Gestalt test, a measure of perceptual–motor performance; nor did they find differences on short-term memory tasks or on the WRAT arithmetic test. Of particular interest was the finding that trained and control children did not differ in scores on the Conners Behavior Rating Scale completed by teachers. Apparently cognitive control training, although leading to improved performance in a number of areas of functioning, did not generalize to classroom behavior, at least as perceived by teachers. This, of course, is in contrast to findings from interventions with medication and behavior modification.

Despite some inconsistencies in results, studies of cognitive control procedures with impulsive and/or hyperactive children provide tentative evidence of a direct link between changes in psychological processes and educational achievement. These findings are especially interesting when the same intervention did not bring about changes in social behavior, or in performance on visual–perceptual tasks. As with interventions utilizing medication or behavioral techniques, the cognitive control work is consistent with the suggestion that there is some independence among the social–behavioral, psychological, and educational components of hyperactive children's functioning, and that change in one domain is not necessarily correlated with change in others. From the educational point of view, cognitive control training is probably best viewed as an important, but not sufficient, intervention for children with learning problems.

FINDINGS FROM HIGH RISK STUDIES

We have proposed that behavioral, psychological, and educational components of hyperactive children's school functioning are at least partially independent, and that they may interact differentially with specific interventions and school settings. We argue, too, that despite the situational specificity of selected behaviors, that is, the social context view of hyperactivity, there are certain behaviors that characterize hyperactive children across situations and in a variety of settings. This is in contrast to the popular attitude that hyperactivity is primarily, even exclusively, a reaction to an overrestrictive and unsympathetic school setting (Schrag & Divoky, 1976). Although it is clear that hyperactive behaviors may be intensified or exacerbated by environmental conditions, considerable evidence may be interpreted to suggest that at the time of school entrance there are significant individual differences among children that affect their success in school. Some of thse dimensions of difference are reminiscent of characteristics of hyperactive school age children.

Studies of early identification of educationally high risk children, conducted through the UCLA Special Education Research Program, provide data that support, in part at least, an interpretation that risk for school is in part "locused" in children's characteristics. Our data from a number of studies are consistent in suggesting that children with hyperactive-like characteristics are identifiable early in school, even at the time of school entrance. Although behavioral manifestations of hyperactivity may be reduced through proper classroom management and socialization, a good number of these risk children are left with a residue of academic inadequacy, which may preclude success in the upper grades. Since these findings are pertinent to the discussion in this chapter, they deserve more detailed review.

Consider first the early recognition of children with hyperactive-like behaviors. Following work with suburban, middle socioeconomic status (SES) teachers (Keogh & Tchir, 1972), Keogh and Windguth (1973) interviewed kindergarten, first-, and second-grade teachers in inner city, low SES schools. Teachers were asked to specify child characteristics that in their experience signaled possible problems in school. Teachers' reports were made within the frame of reference of the grade levels they taught and the classification or categories of mental retardation (EMR) or educational handicap (EH). Teachers in both middle and low SES schools were able to distinguish between EMR and EH characteristics in young school children; although some attributes were similar, analyses according to co-occurrence matrices yielded two different clusterings of attributes. The co-occurrence matrix technique is a quasi-hierarchical clustering scheme (see Johnson, 1967) that allowed some idea of how teachers associated particular child attributes to EH or EMR designation. It should be remembered that all attributes were generated by the teachers and thus were not predetermined by the investigators.

The 23 high-frequency EH and the 24 high-frequency EMR characteristics were cast into two matrices. Two descriptors, hyperactivity and short attention span, had the highest number of co-occurrences with other descriptors in the EH matrix (80 and 90 co-occurrences, respectively). The next most co-occurring items were disruptive, talking, and noisemaking (74), and demands a great deal of teacher time (67). Within the EMR matrix, the highest co-occurrences were noted for short attention span (86), reversals and left–right problems (76), poor coordination (74), inability to work at academic level (71), inability to work with abstractions (68), and difficulty following directions (66). Hyperactivity was a co-occurring characteristic in 51 instances in the EMR matrix. The point is that even in the early school years teachers were sensitive to different behaviors as indicative of differing risk conditions. Importantly, the EH rubric carried a strong load of hyperactive type behaviors that are disruptive in school, as viewed by teachers. The EMR behaviors were, for the most part, related to academic deficiencies. Although it might be argued that teachers had predetermined "sets," it may also be argued that teachers were responding to already differentiated child characteristics. Children enter the school program with well-differentiated personality and behavioral characteristics; thus, hyperactivity within the school context is not so much a reaction to setting variables as it is an interaction of real individual attributes and the constraints of school.

Support for this interpretation may be found in results of other UCLA high risk studies. Observers identified risk and nonrisk children on the basis of their behavior in the kindergarten classroom (Forness, 1972, 1973). These children then were followed over a 4-year period. Compared to randomly selected nonrisk children, at the end of the kindergarten year it was found that risk children tended to be more impulsive, to have problems in perceptual organization, and to have difficulty in modifying or regulating their response strategies on both fine and gross motor tasks. Risk and nonrisk groups did not differ in measures of general ability, however (Becker, 1976). Follow-up at the end of first grade revealed that risk children were less successful in school than were their nonrisk peers (Keogh, Hall, & Becker, 1974).

Significant differences between risk and nonrisk children were noted in composite teachers' ratings, as well as in teachers' evaluations of four aspects of school performance—reading, arithmetic, classroom behavior, and attitude toward classroom rules and routines. In light of the argument previously presented on the need for differentiated analyses of hyperactive children's school performance, it is interesting to note that risk and nonrisk samples did not differ on general ability measures or on the general information subtest of an individually administered achievement test. Yet, differences favoring nonrisk children were found in reading recognition, spelling, and arithmetic subtests, differences confirmed by a group administered reading achievement test.

Taken as a whole, the analyses of first-grade follow-up data yielded two clusters of abilities or behaviors that characterized children at risk for school difficulties. Cluster one was composed of aspects of academic aptitude (IQ, verbal facility, problem-solving strategies, etc.); the second cluster captured aspects of behavioral adaptability, as expressed in social interactions and in classroom activities. These appeared to be relatively independent components, at least at first grade, and both contributed to risk and nonrisk status. When the primary problems were focused on the behavioral-adaptability area, and academic aptitude was strong (a condition often characteristic of older hyperactive children), school success was closely tied to the nature of the instructional program and to the classroom organization.

The academic aptitude–behavioral adaptability distinction has been supported by further case study follow-up of children from the kindergarten risk sample (Hall & Keogh, 1978) and by findings from an independently drawn sample of entering pupils in several different elementary schools (Sbordone, 1976; Keogh, Welles, & Hall, 1976). In the Sbordone study, 12 children were randomly selected from the total roster of children in each of 18 different kindergarten classes. Of the total 273 children, 185 remained in the same schools at the end of the first grade. Analyses of achievement in basic subjects and of classroom social behavior after 2 years of school suggested that differences identifiable upon school entrance were still apparent. Relationships among measures of academic aptitude were consistently high, as were relationships among social–behavioral indices; relationships *between* academic and social measures were less powerful, however.

Finally, work with preschool children and their families provides further argument for the notion of identifiable, consistent individual differences among children that influence success in school. Utilizing the temperament scheme proposed by Thomas, Chess, and Birch (1968), Keogh, Pullis, and Cadwell (1978) have gathered comprehensive temperament data on approximately 200 3- to 6-year old children enrolled in preschools or kindergartens in the Los Angeles area. Thirty-five teachers from three different schools have completed the Thomas and Chess (1977) Teacher Temperament Questionnaire; 126 mothers and 90 fathers have completed the Parent Temperament Questionnaire (Thomas & Chess, 1977). Of particular interest to the present discussion are the factor analysis results from subscale scores of the teachers' data. Although Thomas *et al.* (1968) propose that each of the eight subscales is relatively independent, our analysis of teacher data yielded three factors. The first loaded positively on persistence, and negatively on distractability and activity; it appeared to be a task-related or task orientation factor. A second factor loaded positively on adaptability, approach–withdrawal, and mood, and seemed to be a sociability factor. A third factor appeared more negative, loading on intensity, activity, threshhold of responsiveness, and the negative pole of the approach withdrawal and mood dimensions. The factor analytic findings suggest that clearly differentiated patterns of individual differences are definable by the time of school entrance. It is reasonable that such patterns of difference influence children's success and failure in formal school programs and, thus, are consistent with the interactive, rather than reactive, interpretation of hyperactivity.

DISCUSSION AND IMPLICATIONS

Taken as a whole, the empirical evidence provides some support for the proposition that interventions with hyperactive children must differentially address behavioral, psychological, and educational components of their functioning. Several generalizations are warranted. Stimulant medication changes social behaviors in school and sometimes affects selected psychological processes, especially sustained attention and perceptual–motor abilities.

Behavior modification techniques have powerful effects on specific social behaviors that characterize hyperactivity. Yet, neither intervention has been shown to transfer over time or setting, to have a generalized positive influence on performance on school tasks, or to have long-term effects on achievement in educational subjects. Cognitive control training, on the other hand, appears to modify impulsive responding and to lead to more effective problem-solving strategies compatible with better performance in school subjects; however, cognitive control training techniques do not necessarily reduce activity levels or socially disruptive behaviors. In short, interventions differ in their relative effects on social behaviors, psychological processes, and educational competence. None of the interventions reviewed had an "across the boards" effect, each having somewhat different degrees of influence on the three domains of hyperactivity targeted in this review.

The lack of consistent evidence documenting covariance among behavioral, psychological, and educational domains as a function of intervention deserves emphasis; it seems likely that some of the confusion of findings and interpretations in intervention work is related to blurring among these functional aspects. Consider the evidence used to evaluate the effectiveness of a given treatment program on a hyperactive child's school performance. For the most part, data pertaining to educational competence consist of reports of changed behavior as perceived by teachers and sometimes by parents. These reports tend to be global, focused primarily, even exclusively, on indicators of social adjustment and overt behavior. In few intervention studies is there detailed or differentiated analysis of ability to perform on school tasks. Thus, interventions that change overt, socially disruptive behaviors are viewed as educationally successful. Already cited evidence regarding effects of medication suggests that, in some instances, certain dosages may have seemingly positive effects on behavior, but negative effects on educational performance. The point is that poorly articulated outcome goals and global measures of change may lead to interventions that work to the child's disadvantage in the mastery of educational skills.

It is likely, too, that the impact of interventions differs as a function of time. Results from studies of long-term effects of behavior modification and medical interventions are for the most part disappointing; however, both interventions have been shown to have immediately powerful effects on hyperactive children. Cognitive control training effects appear less definite in short-term studies but may bring about more enduring changes over time. Thus, interventions must be differentiated in effects over time, as well as in terms of domains of functions.

It is important to emphasize, however, that when behavioral disruption is severe, it is often almost impossible to work effectively on educational skills.

Therefore, interventions that modify disruptive behaviors and affect educationally relevant psychological processes may lay the groundwork for educational techniques. There are likely direct and indirect effects of children's behavioral changes on those around them. Interventions that improve the child's ability to concentrate and attend affect his "teachability" and may lead to changed behavior on the part of teacher or intervener. Certainly the child's views on his capabilities for success in school and the teacher's views on the child's teachability are important ingredients in actual performance. The interesting and insightful work relating attribution theory to hyperactivity (Bugental, Whalen, & Henker, 1977; Whalen & Henker, 1976; Whalen & Henker, Chapters 1 and 12 of this volume) deserves serious study in this context. The perceived increased amenability of the child to instruction may strongly influence the teacher's opinion of that child and may shape the teacher's behavior with the child.

It seems possible that for some teachers the primary goal of intervention with hyperactive children is to gain behavioral control and to improve children's classroom social behavior. Time and energy directed to this end may preclude the intensive educational remediation needed by many hyperactive children. Because the child is more socially amenable following intervention, the teacher may have more opportunity for instruction. The hyperactive child's improved responsiveness may also provide teachers with more incentive to implement necessary remedial instruction. There is little conclusive evidence that interventions that change social behavior directly enhance educational achievement of hyperactive children. However, the same interventions may have important consequences for the social milieu that surrounds the child in school and, thus, may ultimately affect his educational accomplishments.

On the basis of this review, we argue vigorously for more differentiated and specific treatment goals and for more powerful and comprehensive measurement of outcomes. We cannot assume that change (improvement) in one area of functioning will necessarily be associated with, or lead to, change in another. Whereas long-term studies have demonstrated the continuing school achievement problems of hyperactive children, it seems reasonable, even imperative, that educationally specific interventions be included in any comprehensive treatment plan. We may speculate that behavioral hyperactivity in the early school years disrupts accomplishment of basic educational skills. In later periods of the child's life, the behavioral symptoms of hyperactivity may have diminished or been controlled, but the learning deficits remain, preventing mastery of higher order educational skills. Educational competence, thus, warrants inclusion as a primary component of hyperactive children's functioning.

11

Treatment and Training Approaches to Hyperactivity: Establishing Internal or External Control

VIRGINIA I. DOUGLAS

INTRODUCTION

The past few years have seen a proliferation of treatment and training approaches to hyperactivity. Indeed, it is not unusual to find parents and teachers who have sought help in dealing with a hyperactive child thoroughly confused by the conflicting advice they have received. Some professionals strongly recommend the use of drugs, usually the stimulants, whereas others point to disadvantages or even possible dangers resulting from drug treatment. This latter group is likely to advocate behavioral training as a safer and more effective alternative. Some behaviorists, however, endorse contingency management techniques, and others prefer a cognitive training approach. Even educators who limit their role to providing an optimal learning environment or designing effective instructional materials for hyperactive children are likely to disagree on how these goals can be best achieved. Some recommend stripping down both the classroom and the pages of textbooks to the bare essentials, because they believe that hyperactive children are unusually vulnerable to distraction. Others argue that the hyperactive child requires a particularly stimulating environment and colorful and novel instructional materials if he is to remain intellectually alert and motivated to learn.

It can be argued that some of this confusion could be reduced by well-designed studies to assess and compare different treatment methods. At a

HYPERACTIVE CHILDREN
The Social Ecology of Identification and Treatment

ISBN 0-12-745950-2

more fundamental level, however, a substantial proportion of the disagreement stems from an inadequate, and sometimes, distorted, understanding of the nature of the hyperactive disorder. Indeed, both the approach we take to treatment and our criteria for improvement are profoundly influenced by our views regarding the essential cognitive, behavioral, and social deficits that constitute childhood hyperactivity.

In one paper, Douglas and Peters (1979) have reviewed the research on hyperactivity and learning disabilities in an attempt to arrive at a clearer definition of the symptoms and defective cognitive processes that differentiate these two clinical groups from normal children and from each other. We concluded that most of the disabilities that define the hyperactive syndrome can be traced to deficits in three related processes. These include the mechanisms governing: (*a*) the investment of attention and effort; (*b*) the inhibition of impulsive responding; and (*c*) the modulation of arousal level to meet situational or task demands. Although some authors consider it desirable to establish one of these processes as the central or basic cause of the hyperactive child's difficulties (Keogh, 1971; Ross, 1976), we believe that present knowledge allows us to conclude only that the three mechanisms are intricately related and that they all play a major role in hyperactivity.

In another paper (Douglas, in press), I have expressed concern about the paucity of data describing higher order cognitive functioning in hyperactive children and the effects of treatment on these more complex skills. If one attempts to trace the long-term effects of malfunctioning in the hyperactive child's attentional, inhibitory, and arousal mechanisms, both theoretical considerations and the limited evidence available point to the likelihood that, unless treatment can be implemented to modify these faulty processes fairly early in life, limitations in conceptual capacity and problem-solving skills will become increasingly evident as the child matures. In the present chapter, I shall review briefly the evidence demonstrating the effects of basic deficits in sustained attention, impulse control, and arousal regulation mechanisms on the ability of hyperactive children to cope with a wide range of task and situational demands. These extend from relatively simple, vigilance-type tasks and social situations, which require a minimal degree of behavioral conformity, to complex perceptual, logical, and social problems, requiring organized, reflective effort and effective problem-solving strategies.

My purpose in reviewing this evidence is to provide the framework for a discussion of treatment and training approaches to hyperactivity. I shall argue that if an approach is to be effective it must be directed toward the defective processes I have described. It must, as well, produce lasting improvement in the entire range of attitudes, behaviors, and skills affected by them. Because I believe that the cognitive training approach offers the most promise for dealing with the problems of hyperactivity, I shall place most emphasis on this method. In addition, however, I shall consider some of the pros and cons of employing stimulant drugs, contingency management, and learning environments and instructional materials designed to bolster and supplement cognitive training.

ATTENTION VERSUS DISTRACTIBILITY: DEFINING OUR TERMS

There has been a growing consensus among researchers that attentional problems play a central rolc in hyperactivity. However, considerable confusion remains regarding the exact nature of these problems. Sometimes writers emphasize the *intensive* and/or the *sustained* aspects of attention. A critical aspect of these problems is the child's failure to invest sufficient effort in the attentional process and to maintain the effort over time. Other authors believe that the hyperactive child's problems lie in the *selective* aspect of attention. Here the author is usually referring to the youngster's "distractibility," that is, an inability to withstand the disruptive influences of external stimuli. To confuse matters even further, a few authors use the term *selective attention* in a different way. Their interest is in the child's failure to engage in an organized search for critical cues in his environment; instead, attention is "captured" by the striking or salient aspects of a stimulus situation.

The Distractibility Hypothesis

It is not unusual to find writers attributing a high degree of distractibility to the hyperactive child; terms like "stimulus bound," "stimulus driven," or "forced responsiveness" often are featured in clinical descriptions of the disorder (Cruickshank, 1967, 1977). Proponents of this emphasis on hyperactive children's vulnerability to irrelevant stimulation believe that their studies are supported by the "filter" theories of attention. These theories posit a filtering or attenuating mechanism which is necessitated by the limited capacity of the human nervous system to process information simultaneously from a variety of sources (Broadbent, 1971; Deutsch & Deutsch, 1963; Moray, 1969; Triesman, 1969). Thus, if one accepts this approach, the hyperactive child's attentional difficulties result from a defective filtering mechanism.

Some writers also seek support for a distractibility explanation of the hyperactive child's attentional problems from developmental and clinical studies of incidental learning in children: These investigations employ direct measures of a child's "acquisition of information that is extraneous or irrelevant to task performance [Hagen & Hale, 1973, p. 117]." Findings from incidental learning studies have been interpreted as demonstrating that young children and children who are learning disabled or hyperactive process more irrelevant information than older and normal children. This is thought to interfere with the capacity for processing task-relevant information (Hagen, 1967; Hagen & Hale, 1973; Hallahan, Kauffman & Ball, 1973; Maccoby & Hagen, 1965; Pelham & Ross, 1977; Ross, 1976; Tarver, Hallahan, Kauffman, & Ball, 1976).

However, I believe that the portrayal of the hyperactive child that emanates from the distractibility and incidental learning hypotheses is quite misleading. After reviewing 11 studies in which investigators attempted to prove that the task performance of hyperactive children is unusually susceptible to the disruptive effects of extraneous stimuli, such as loud noises, flashing lights, irrelevant pictures, contradictory colors, and manipulable objects, Douglas and Peters (1979) concluded that there is little evidence to support this hypothesis. In addition, our review of the incidental learning literature forced us to conclude that serious weaknesses in the basic assumptions, methodology, and statistical procedures employed in many of the incidental learning studies render their findings highly questionable.

Interestingly, there was indirect evidence from some of the distraction studies to suggest that hyperactive children may have an unusual need for stimulation; I shall discuss this interpretation when I present the evidence for an arousal defect in hyperactive children. In addition, we reviewed several studies in which investigators attempted to improve the task performance of hyperactive children by placing them in learning cubicles where extraneous stimulation was minimized. Contrary to expectations, these researchers frequently reported an *increase* in restless movement. Thus, studies with hyperactive children have yielded little support for the distraction hypothesis or for treatment approaches that emphasize protecting them from extraneous stimuli.

STOP, LOOK, LISTEN—AND THINK!

On the other hand, evidence of a sustained attention or concentration deficit in hyperactive children is very compelling. Since this deficit is observable even when the children are tested in stimulus reduced conditions, it cannot be attributed to the influence of external stimuli. We must look, rather, to the internal mechanisms that enable a child to direct, guide, and focus his own attentional processes.

In another paper (Douglas, in press), I have listed the tasks on which hyperactive children have been shown to perform more poorly than normal children. The list, together with a description of the behaviors assessed by each task, is reproduced in Table 11.1. When we consider the nature of these tasks, I believe that certain common elements become apparent. To be successful, the child has to take the task demands seriously; he must then muster sufficient self-discipline and organized effort to remain effectively involved with the problem over a fairly lengthy period of time. Almost always, there is the reciprocal requirement that the child avoid responding carelessly or thoughtlessly; thus, the attentional demands and the necessity for inhibitory control are very intimately linked.

The argument that these are the critical task demands for revealing the hyperactive children's deficits is, I believe, further supported by the children's ability to cope successfully with the tasks listed in Table 11.2. A comparison of the tests included in Tables 11.1 and 11.2 reveals that they make similar demands on processes such as visual discrimination, speed of motor responding, and auditory memory. However, a closer examination of the tasks on which hyperactive children do well points to certain factors—either in the tasks themselves or in the way they are administered—that serve to reduce the requirements for independent and sustained effort. For example, hyperactive children respond as quickly as normal children on reaction time tasks if the experimenter elicits the children's attention before each trial; but, if they are left on their own to deal with a series of automatically programmed stimuli, their performance drops below that of the control group.

Similarly, hyperactive children perform successfully on the Picture Completion subtest of the Wechsler Intelligence Scale for Children (WISC) but have difficulty with the Matching Familiar Figures Test (MFFT). Since both tasks require rather fine visual discrimination, the essential difference seems to rest in the fact that the MFFT requires an exhaustive, self-sustained search through several stimuli.

THE ROLE OF AROUSAL

Modulating Arousal to Meet Task Demands: Findings from Drug and Reinforcement Studies

A third mechanism, involving the modulation of arousal level to meet task demands, appears to be closely related to the hyperactive child's attentional and inhibitory difficulties. It has been shown that administering stimulant drugs, which are thought to increase arousal, results in improved perfor-

TABLE 11.1
Tasks on Which Hyperactive Children Perform Poorly[a]

Task	*Facilatory behaviors*	*Inhibitory behaviors*
Continuous performance test: vigilance task (Anderson, Halcomb, & Doyle, 1973; Doyle, Anderson, & Halcomb, 1976; Dykman, Ackerman, Clements, & Peters, 1971; Sykes, Douglas, & Morgenstern, 1973)	Establish response set for designated stimuli Concentrate on responding quickly Maintain response set (vigilance) over time	Inhibit responding to inappropriate stimuli
Reaction time tasks with preparatory interval (Cohen & Douglas, 1972; Firestone & Douglas, 1975; Parry, 1973; Zahn, Abate, Little, & Wender, 1975)	Establish response readiness on basis of warning signals Concentrate on responding quickly to reaction signals Establish response readiness repeatedly over time	Inhibit responding at inappropriate times
Kagan's Matching Familiar Figures Test (MFFT); reflection–impulsivity (Campbell *et al.*, 1971; Cohen, Weiss, & Minde, 1972; Juliano, 1974; Parry, 1973; Peters, 1977; Schleifer *et al.*, 1975)	Concentrate on finding exact match to target picture Conduct exhaustive, organized search of all alternatives in a visual array Systematically compare standard and alternatives on critical perceptual features	Inhibit choosing pictures only superficially like standard
Embedded figures test: field dependence (Campbell *et al.*, 1971; Cohen *et al.*, 1972)	Concentrate on forming clear visual image of target figures Conduct exhaustive, organized search for correct figures embedded within a visual array	Ignore embedding context Inhibit responding to superficially similar figures
Porteus mazes (Parry, 1973)	Concentrate on finding safe route to goal Conduct careful search at critical points to discover consequences of taking alternate routes	Avoid entering blind alleys Inhibit cutting corners, crossing lines, etc.
Tests with multiple choice format (Hoy *et al.*, 1978)[b]	Concentrate on finding correct logical choice among several alternatives Conduct exhaustive logical search of all alternatives	Inhibit responding to superficially correct answers

Wisconsin card sorting task (Parry, 1973)[c]	Concentrate on finding all possible legitimate categories for sorting Systematically examine patterns on cards for common features Abstract class concepts from patterns (e.g., color, form, number)	Inhibit responding with salient but unacceptable categories Inhibit idiosyncratic responses
Matrix solution tasks (Tant, 1978)	Concentrate on finding strategies that will eliminate most cards Scan and analyze visual display Classify stimuli into groups and label each group Choose questions that will elicit most information Make correct deductions from feedback provided Remember which possibilities previous questions eliminated Coordinate a series of questions into a planful approach	Avoid being misled by salient but less informative cues
Rule learning tasks (Tant, 1978)	Concentrate on finding the rule connecting stimulus attributes that will enable correct sorting Conduct careful perceptual analysis of stimuli appearing on cards Code stimuli logically, depending on the presence or absence of key attributes Use feedback to assign classes of stimuli to positive and negative categories Remember logical implications of feedback	Avoid responding only to *perceptual* aspects of stimuli (as opposed to *logical* classes they represent)
Memory for paired associates: arbitrary associations (Benezra, 1978)	Concentrate on finding best way of remembering paired associates Consider possible strategies, mnemonic devices Choose most effective strategy	Inhibit choosing readily available but less effective strategies
Story completion task: frustrating stories (Parry, 1973)	Concentrate on understanding a social situation from several perspectives Consider possible motives of frustrator Consider consequences of own behavior Consider possible substitutes for lost object or event	Inhibit aggressive responses

[a] Table reproduced from Douglas, in press.
[b] Hyperactive children did *not* show deficit when number of choices was limited to two.
[c] Hyperactive children have no problem with shifting set.

TABLE 11.2
Tasks on Which Hyperactive Children Perform Relatively Well[a]

Task	*Task requirements*	*Factors minimizing demands on attention and effort*
Simple reaction time task: continuous reinforcement (Parry, 1973)[b]	Concentrate on reaction signal Concentrate on reacting quickly	Child receives reinforcement for every response
Choice reaction time task (Sykes *et al.*, 1971)	Concentrate on pushing buttons corresponding to geometric figures on screen Concentrate on responding quickly	Trials are discrete E. elicits child's attention before each trial
Serial reaction time task (Sykes *et al.*, 1971)	Concentrate on pushing buttons corresponding to particular lights as lights appear Concentrate on responding quickly	Stimuli are self-paced Stimuli remain in view until child responds
Picture completion subtest: Wechsler Intelligence Scale for Children (Douglas, 1972)[c]	Concentrate on finding missing part on individual pictures Conduct visual search of picture for missing part	E. elicits child's attention before presenting each picture Pictures are presented one at a time Only one item must be found in each picture
Concept identification task: continuous reinforcement (Freibergs & Douglas, 1969; Parry, 1973)[d]	Concentrate on discovering the "correct" concept from series of visual stimuli presented in pairs Abstract stimulus dimensions from the task stimuli Assign stimuli to nominal categories (e.g., "bird," "flower") Modify response strategies on basis of information feedback	Equipment is novel, interesting Test stimuli are colorful Child receives immediate and consistent reinforcement for every correct response Concepts to be discovered are very familiar

[a] Table reproduced from Douglas, in press.
[b] Significant hyperactive–normal differences *do* occur on partial reinforcement schedule.
[c] Hyperactive children performed very poorly on same task on a partial reinforcement schedule.
[d] In the continuous reinforcement condition, hyperactive children showed excellent transfer to a second concept. Hyperactive children also were able to reverse concepts when feedback changed—no evidence of perseveration.

mance on vigilance and reaction time tasks; the improvement has been reported on both sustained attention scores and on measures of impulsive responding (Barkley & Jackson, 1977; Cohen, Douglas, & Morgenstern, 1971; Conners & Rothschild, 1968; Knights & Hinton, 1969; Porges, Walter, Korb, & Sprague, 1975; Sykes, Douglas, Weiss, & Minde, 1971).

It also appears, however, that treatment with the stimulants may cause unexpected impairment on more complex tasks. Sprague and Sleator (1977) have reported interesting dose response data from hyperactive children who were being treated with methylphenidate. These investigators found improvements on a memory recognition test when the children were on relatively low dosages of the drug; however, at a higher dosage their performance decreased. It is rather disturbing to note that teachers were more likely to report improvement in classroom behavior when the children were receiving the high dosages. Since we do not have comparable dose response data for normal children, we cannot conclude from these findings that arousal patterns in normal and hyperactive children differ. Nevertheless, the findings do point to the importance of monitoring arousal and its cognitive and behavioral consequences carefully when stimulants are being used to treat hyperactive children.

Similar cautions apparently apply to the use of contingency management techniques with hyperactive children. It has been shown that their performance on a simple reaction time task and on a delayed reaction time task (DRTT) improves with the introduction of contingent positive reinforcement (Cohen, 1970; Firestone & Douglas, 1975; Parry, 1973). As with the stimulants, it seems reasonable to postulate that the reinforcers act to increase alertness and involvement in these somewhat dull and repetitive tasks; some evidence for this interpretation comes from psychophysiological indications of increased arousal during the reward condition (Firestone & Douglas, 1975).

It also appears, however, that investigators and clinicians who use reinforcement techniques with hyperactive children may sometimes unintentionally raise arousal to a supraoptimal level and thus produce unexpected deterioration in performance. Firestone and Douglas (1975) report that hyperactive children improved reaction times but increased impulsive responding on the DRTT when positive reinforcement was introduced. The incidence of impulsive responses in normal children, on the other hand, was not affected by the reward condition. Interestingly, negative reinforcement, which was found to be physiologically less arousing than reward, produced the positive effect on reaction times in hyperactive youngsters but did not increase impulsive responses. Parry (1973) found that randomly administered praise improved the performance of normal control children on the DRTT but caused a deterioration in the performance of hyperactive children. It is possible that the praising statements increased arousal without providing the specific cues to guide attentional processes, which hyperactive children require and which are provided by contingent reinforcement.

Reward schedules also have been shown to affect the performance of hyperactive children on more complex tasks. Freibergs and Douglas (1969) and Parry (1973) found when hyperactive and normal samples were receiving continuous positive reinforcement for correct responses on the Concept Identification Task (described in Table 11.2), the two groups did not differ in number of trials taken to solve the task. However, when a partial reinforcement schedule was employed, the performance of the hyperactive group was significantly poorer than that of the control group. Parry (1973) demonstrated that the poor performance of the hyperactive children in the partial condition was not due to decreased feedback. Consequently, she agreed with the interpretation offered by Freibergs and Douglas, that is, the hyperactive children were unusually frustrated and disrupted by the failure to receive reinforcement on the nonreinforced trials.

These findings have important implications for the use of reinforcement with hyperactive children, either in contingency management programs or as a supplement to cognitive training. It appears that reinforcers are extremely salient for these children. As a consequence, the therapist who employs them may inadvertently create shifts in arousal, which lead to impaired performance. In addition, disruptions are likely to occur if the child fails to receive expected rewards. This means, I believe, that particular care must be taken in using reinforcement techniques with hyperactive children. We have made it a point, for example, to "wean" the children from continuous schedules gradually, making sure that they understand how the schedules are being used and helping them deal with their reactions to the decrease in rewards. We take great care, as well, to define and administer the contingencies in each situation in a clear and precise manner, frequently reminding the child about exactly what is being rewarded. In addition, the findings from Firestone and Douglas (1975) have encouraged us to experiment with the use of mild negative feedback and response costs. Provided there are also sufficient positive inducements in the situation, these methods seem to encourage hyperactive youngsters to exert greater control over their inclination to respond impulsively.

Manipulating Arousal through Teaching Materials

Zentall, Zentall, and Booth (1978) unintentionally demonstrated that very stimulating teaching materials can sometimes interfere with learning in hyperactive children. These investigators added arousal enhancing qualities, such as color and movement, to materials used for teaching spelling lessons. Contrary to their expectations, they found that the learning of hyperactive children was more impaired in this high stimulation condition than when they were taught with regular materials; normal children, on the other hand, learned more effectively with the novel materials. As I have discussed previously (Douglas, in press), there is some reason to believe that the novel aspects of the stimuli may have interfered with the hyperactive children's performance, particularly during early exposures to the materials, because the novel qualities sometimes added salience to nonessential or competing aspects of the teaching materials. For example, color was used in the background, rather than in the letters of the words to be learned. It is important to note, however, that after several exposures to the teaching materials, the hyperactive children began to benefit from the more stimulating condition.

This latter finding underlines the importance of carrying out studies to assess the long-term effects of interventions that influence arousal levels. It also highlights the necessity of taking account of both the inherent interest of tasks and the hyperactive child's reactions to them over time or repeated exposures. We have found, for example, that their alertness drops rather precipitously over time when they are performing dull, repetitive tasks (Sykes, Douglas, & Morgenstern, 1973). On the other hand, they have shown good involvement and transfer through repeated testing on more challenging and colorful problems (Freibergs & Douglas, 1969; Parry, 1973; Tant, 1978).

Autonomic and Central Indices of Arousal in Hyperactive Children

The behavioral evidence suggesting peculiarities in the arousal patterns of hyperactive children has been somewhat substantiated by studies employing psychophysiological and central indices of the children's arousal responses. After reviewing the extremely complex and confusing findings from numerous investigations in the area, Hastings and Barkley (1978) concluded that the data point to diminished autonomic and electroencephalic responsivity to specific stimuli in hyperactive children. Equally important, they report that few investigators have found differences between hyperactive and normal children on arousal indices when the children were in a resting state. In previous papers (Cohen & Douglas, 1972; Douglas & Peters, 1979), my colleagues and I have suggested that the arousal abnormalities of hyperactive children may involve not a general condition of over-or underarousal, but a failure to modulate their own arousal levels in order to meet specific task demands. I have speculated that this could be due to any of the following causes:

1. The range of arousal within which hyperactive children can function effectively is unusually narrow, so that small shifts from optimal levels result in impaired performance.

2. Arousal patterns are particularly labile in hyperactive children.
3. The children are less capable than normal children of controlling or modulating their own states of motivation.

Whichever of these explanations proves to be the most accurate, we have come to believe that any treatment approach should involve continuous monitoring of the hyperactive child's state of arousal or alertness. In addition, in our cognitive training programs we work toward both increasing the child's awareness of his own arousal state and teaching him ways to gain more control over his arousal levels.

Arousal, Stimulus Seeking, and Vulnerability to the Salient Aspects of Stimuli

Before leaving the topic of arousal, I wish to return briefly to two hypotheses regarding hyperactive children that have been mentioned in the previous discussions. The first is that much of the children's abnormal behavior represents some form of stimulation seeking; the second is that they tend to react to the salient aspects of a stimulus situation and fail to process less subtle aspects.

A few authors have concluded that the stimulus seeking behaviors of hyperactive children may be necessary in order to maintain activation at an adequate level (Douglas, 1974; Dykman, Ackerman, Clements, & Peters, 1971; Satterfield & Dawson, 1971; Zentall, 1975). As mentioned earlier, evidence from studies in which hyperactive children have been placed in stimulus reduced environments suggest that they may compensate for the consequent drop in arousal by engaging in increased restless movement; indeed, some investigators explain the hyperactive child's typically high activity levels in a similar manner. In addition, results from a few of the distraction studies have been interpreted as pointing to the possibility that hyperactive children perform tasks more efficiently when a reasonable amount of stimulation is present (Browning, 1967; Scott, 1970; Zentall & Zentall, 1976). Finally, I have been intrigued by the interesting observation from a few distraction studies that hyperactive children looked at task-irrelevant stimuli more than normal children, but did not experience any greater interference with task performance as a result of this (Bremer & Stern, 1976; Steinkamp, 1974). Although all of these results are suggestive, we need investigations that test the stimulus seeking hypothesis more directly. Equally important, we must learn a good deal more about the positive and negative effects of various kinds of stimulation on the hyperactive child's cognitive functioning. If we had this information, it should be possible to manipulate extraneous stimulation in ways that would enhance learning. From the viewpoint of cognitive training programs, it might also become possible to teach hyperactive children to perform these manipulations themselves in order to gain greater personal control over factors influencing their arousal levels.

A tendency on the part of hyperactive children to react to the salient aspects of stimuli could also be seen, at least in part, as resulting from a need for stimulation; many of the qualities of salient stimuli, such as novelty, intensity, and incongruity, are thought to increase arousal (Berlyne, 1960). We have found some evidence that hyperactive children do react to the salient qualities of stimulus situations and fail to process less obvious aspects. Parry (1973) reports that hyperactive children often ignored the number category on the Wisconsin Card Sorting Task (see Table 11.1) in favor of the color or form categories. This occurred in spite of the fact that they were capable of discovering the number category, as was revealed by subsequent questioning. Similarly, Tant (1978) found that hyperactive children remained unaware of less obvious dimensions that could have been used in solving her Matrix Solution Task (Table 11.1).

Findings of this kind may prove useful in designing training programs and teaching materials for hyperactive children, particularly if we can learn more about the children's salience hierarchies. Fading techniques could be employed, for example, to focus the children's attention on critical aspects of learning situations. In accordance with my emphasis on helping hyperactive children achieve *inner* control of their attentional processes, however, I would prefer to make them aware of their unusual reactivity to salience; they could then be taught and encouraged to continue processing beyond obvious aspects of problems, in order to deal with more subtle but essential aspects.

EXAMINING THE PROBLEM-SOLVING STRATEGIES OF HYPERACTIVE CHILDREN

As we have just seen, differences in the arousal patterns of hyperactive children appear to influence their method of dealing with many kinds of problems. In addition, it is important to take a closer look at how deficits in their attentional and inhibitory mechanisms limit their problem-solving strategies.

If we examine again the tasks described in Table 11.1, the role of sustained attention and inhibitory control is perhaps most obvious in the vigilance and reaction time tasks listed at the beginning of the Table. Here, children must watch out for particular stimuli or stimuli occurring at particular times and avoid responding either to the wrong stimuli or at the wrong time; furthermore, they must stick with the tasks over a considerable time period.

Although the tasks listed later in the Table make more complex demands, I believe that here, too, the critical requirements for hyperactive children involve deployment of attention and effort. Thus, for example, on the MFFT several alternatives must be scanned carefully for critical differences. When we look at the way hyperactive children deal with this and similar perceptual tasks, we find that they make their choices more quickly than normal control children and give less consideration, in a less organized fashion, to the other alternatives (Douglas & Peters, 1979).

To choose a second example from Table 11.1, Hoy, Weiss, Minde, and Cohen (1978) found that hyperactive children coped successfully with spelling and word knowledge tests when they had to deal with only two possible answers. When a five-choice format was used, however, their scores were significantly worse than those of normal children. Thus, when they must choose among several logical alternatives, they seem, again, not to give sufficient thought to all the possible answers.

In the tasks we have been discussing thus far, the correct solution is provided for the child among other possible choices. In the case of the Matrix Solution Task used by Tant (1978), however, the youngsters must produce their own solution. Furthermore, they are told that they should search for the most efficient solution possible. Obviously, some fairly sophisticated strategies must be employed if a child is to be successful on this task. Fundamental requirements, however, involve the following: (*a*) Examining all of the clues that could help toward a solution; (*b*) considering all of the possible solutions; and (*c*) evaluating each of these possibilities in order to arrive at the one that is most effective. Again, I would stress that each of these strategies requires the investment of a good deal of controlled effort. As mentioned earlier, the hyperactive children in this study failed to even notice some of the possible dimensions that could have contributed to better solutions on the Matrix Tasks. Over and above this, however, Tant was able to demonstrate that her hyperactive subjects did not make effective use of the categories they did manage to discover. For example, the hyperactive youngsters were more likely than their peers to guess single items in the array rather than to ask categorical questions that systematically eliminated several possibilities. Thus, although Tant's groups were matched on IQ, she found that the solutions produced by her hyperactive group were inferior in quality to those of both a normal and a reading disabled control group.

Let us consider the requirements of one final task listed in Table 11.1, the Paired Associates task involving *arbitrary* associations. Benezra (1978) demonstrated that her hyperactive subjects had little difficulty with a wide range of other verbal memory tasks, including the recall of series of digits or letters (both forwards and backwards), rather lengthy lists of words, and a Paired Associates task involving *meaningful* pairs. Benezra points out that the children's problems became apparent only when the task required them to develop fairly sophisticated rehearsal strategies in order to commit the material to memory. Her suggestion that their poor performance is attributable to a failure to engage in these strategies is supported by the children's replies when they were asked how they had gone about remembering the unrelated (arbitrary) word pairs. Normal children were much more likely than hyperactive children to report using mnemonic strategies and elaborative rehearsal, whereas the hyperactive children usually said that they had "just listened" or that they had repeated the pairs to themselves several times. It seems not to have occurred to many of the hyperactive children that special effort of a strategic nature was required.

I have been emphasizing the demands of the tasks included in Table 11.1 because our approach to training has been dictated to a considerable extent by what we see to be the basic causes behind the failure of hyperactive children to cope with these particular tasks successfully. In the past, cognitive training programs usually have emphasized teaching the children effective problem-solving strategies, and the preceding analysis certainly points to serious deficiencies in the strategies used by hyperactive children. The important question, however, is why hyperactive children do not employ these strategies. Both teachers and trainers in our cognitive programs repeatedly complain that these children do not continue using sophisticated strategies, even when they have been taught painstakingly, and apparently learned. I have argued, therefore (Douglas, in press), that the children do not use sound strategies because their defective attentional, inhibitory, and arousal mechanisms have interfered with their learning them; and even when strategies have been learned, the same deficits interfere with the children employing them in a consistent manner. To complicate matters further, several sequelae of the original deficits (which will be discussed in the next section) compound these problems. These insights have led to a gradual shift in emphasis in our programs away from a concentration on strategy training, and toward a somewhat greater emphasis on trying to ameliorate both the original defective mechanisms and the resulting motivational, attitudinal, and cognitive consequences.

LONG-TERM CONSEQUENCES OF THE ORIGINAL PROBLEMS

If we think about the long-term effects of the attentional, inhibitory, and arousal deficits of hyperactive children, I believe that we are forced to conclude that these deficiencies must have serious consequences for functioning in virtually all complex problem-solving or information processing situations. These consequences have been discussed more completely in Douglas (in press). However, because of the serious implications for training, I shall review them briefly here.

The Development of Schemas and Effects on Future Learning

First, attentional theorists (e.g., Bindra, 1976; Gibson, 1969; Hebb, 1976; Neisser, 1976) hypothesize that an individual's perceptions of events are guided by prior learning; these earlier acquisitions are represented in such neural organizations as "schemas" (Neisser), "higher order cell assemblies" (Hebb), or "contingency organizations" (Bindra). Since hyperactive children examine events in their environment less carefully and think less reflectively about their experiences, it seems highly likely that the schemas or neural traces resulting from their prior learning will be considerably less elaborated and organized than those of normal children. Consequently, an acceptance of the above theories leads to the conclusion that this impoverishment must, in turn, set limits upon future learning.

The Role of Metacognitive Processes

Secondly, as suggested above, the impact of hyperactive children's faulty attentional, inhibitory, and arousal mechanisms on problem-solving capacities appears to extend beyond interfering with the learning of problem-solving strategies. These defective mechanisms seem to have an even more fundamental influence on the children's ability and motivation to assume the role of an active problem solver.

As I mentioned earlier, trainers and teachers frequently complain about the children's apparent unwillingness to commit themselves to tasks, even when an adult has worked hard to teach them the necessary skills. The findings of investigators who study the "metacognitive" development of children (e.g., Brown, 1975; Vygotsky, 1962) can, I believe, help us gain some understanding of this most perplexing and disturbing behavior. These authors emphasize the difference between knowledge that can be gained automatically and knowledge that must be acquired by exercising self-conscious, deliberate, and stategically applied effort. To cope successfully with problems of the second kind, the individual must work methodically through a series of "executive" operations including: (*a*) analyzing and characterizing the problem at hand; (*b*) reflecting upon what he knows or does not know that may be necessary for a solution; (*c*) devising a plan for attacking the problem; and (*d*) checking or monitoring his own progress (Brown, 1975). Until recently, psychologists have given too little empirical consideration to these essential skills; however, we cannot take either their acquisition or the motivation to use them for granted. Brown, Campione, and Barclay (1979) have been able to demonstrate the effectiveness of training in metacognitive skills with a group of educable retarded children. Improvement on memory tasks was found following training in "metamemory" strategies; even more encouraging, Brown was able to demonstrate maintenance and transfer of the skills 1 year later.

We currently are engaged at McGill in studies designed to shed more light on hyperactive children's metacognitive skills and attitudes toward problem solving. Hopefully, knowledge of this kind will help us improve our cognitive training programs. In the meantime, however, we are attempting to apply the insights we have gained from observing these children approach the tasks included in Table 11.1 in order to help them become more willing, more deliberate, and more effective problem solvers.

Effectance Motivation

Observations of hyperactive children in our training programs reveal another characteristic closely related to their failure to assume the problem-solving role; it appears, also, to stem, both directly and indirectly, from the defective mechanisms I have postulated. I am referring to the fact that the children appear to take no great interest in mastering a problem for its own sake; that is, they seem to lack intrinsic motivation. Trainers report that the children often try to mimic mindlessly the solutions offered to them, apparently because they are more interested in appeasing the trainer than in understanding the problem.

It is interesting to speculate about the origins of this characteristic. Describing hyperactive children as anhedonic and unresponsive to reinforcement, Wender (1972) has developed a neurological model to account for these characteristics. However, as I have reported, there have been several empirical demonstrations of hyperactive children's sensitivity to reinforcement contingencies. It seems more likely that their lack of effectance motivation, like their failure to engage in metacognitive strategies, stems from the fact that they cannot remain intensively involved in most problems long enough to learn much about them or to master them. Instead, hyperactive children experience repeated failure.

Thus, a trainer is faced with the necessity for a "boot straps" operation. If the child can be induced to focus effectively on tasks for a sufficient length of time, the success experienced and the knowledge gained will hopefully contribute to future successes. Particularly in the beginning, these learning experiences must be carefully orchestrated. The difficulty level of tasks must be gradually increased and the length of "concentration periods" gradually extended. In addition, as I shall describe shortly, we try to follow the advice of Harter (1978) that the child should be reinforced for independent *attempts* at mastery, as well as for successes.

USING DRUG TREATMENT AND CONTINGENCY MANAGEMENT TO SUPPLEMENT COGNITIVE TRAINING PROGRAMS: SOME ADDITIONAL CONSIDERATIONS

Further Comments on Drug Treatment

An acceptance of the preceding analysis leads, I believe, to the inevitable conclusion that providing meaningful help for the hyperactive child is not going to be an easy task. Those who look to stimulant drug treatment as a total solution must assume that the stimulants exert a specific corrective influence on the very mechanisms I have described. Even if this highly optimistic assumption proved valid, it also would be necessary to assume that the children have the capacity to compensate, without special help, for all of the defective learning that preceded drug treatment.

It is not possible to consider these assumptions in detail here. However, as the preceding discussion implies, combating the long-term effects of the hyperactive child's deficits is likely to be a long and difficult process. With regard to the locus of action of the stimulants, there is some controversy in the current literature regarding stimulant effects on the kinds of complex problem solving that I just discussed. Most reviewers have concluded that the efficacy of the drugs has been demonstrated only on simple, repetitive tasks. They argue that when investigators have employed more complex assessment measures involving problem solving or academic achievement, the findings usually have been negative (Barkley & Cunningham, 1978; Rie, Rie, Stewart, & Ambuel, 1976a, 1976b; Sroufe, 1975). A few authors, in fact, have gone so far as to suggest that the stimulants would be expected to *impair* performance on tasks that require a flexible problem-solving approach (Margolin, 1978; Sahakian & Robbins, 1977). They refer to animal studies demonstrating that animals receiving the stimulants focus in a narrow manner on particular cues in a stimulus situation and engage in repetitive responding; the extreme of this behavior is stereotypy. These authors believe that the improvement observed in hyperactive children on vigilance tasks when they are given stimulant medication may simply reflect this kind of narrowly focused, perseverative behavior.

However, there is some reason to think that this pessimistic evaluation of the action of the drugs may be overdrawn. As Sprague and Berger (in press) have argued, methodological weaknesses such as faulty assessment techniques or inappropriate drug dosages make the findings from several of these studies questionable. Furthermore, as I have discussed elsewhere (Douglas, in press; Douglas & Peters, 1979), a few investigators have reported improvement following drug treatment on several fairly complex perceptual and cognitive tasks, including the MFFT, Porteus Mazes, and Paired Associates involving arbitrary associations (Campbell, Douglas, & Morgenstern, 1971; Conners & Rothschild, 1968; Dalby, Kinsbourne, Swanson, and Sobol, 1977; Sroufe, 1975). In addition, Sprague and Berger (in press) have obtained preliminary results with a specially constructed arithmetic task that also suggest positive drug effects. It must be stressed, however, that all of these studies have been of rather brief duration. We still know very little about the long-term effects of the stimulants, and, as Barkley and Cunningham (1978) have concluded, the little information we do have does not appear promising.

Equally serious, Swanson and Kinsbourne (1976) reported findings they believe demonstrate that the effects of the stimulants on hyperactive children are state dependent. If this assertion is correct, it has serious implications for drug treatment; we would be forced to consider the possibility that, when treatment is terminated, children will show poor retention of material that was learned during the period when they were receiving medication. Or, alternately, once children began treatment with the stimulants, it would be necessary for them to remain on them indefinitely. Since few physicians have been willing to maintain children on these drugs for more than a few years, it is impossible to predict the consequences of using them for such extended periods. Thus, although we see some advantages in using stimulants in conjunction with our training programs, until these doubts are resolved, we are reluctant to do so.

Additional Considerations in Using Contingency Management

Although I believe that the cognitive training approach provides the "best fit" for dealing with the hyperactive child's problems, we have found that it usually is necessary to supplement this method with contingency management techniques. The need for these techniques is particularly evident in the early stages of training; they are needed also when the youngster's symptoms have led to a breakdown in the rationality and predictability of the disciplinary methods used by parents and teachers. As a result, the first objective often must be to demonstrate to the child, in very concrete ways, that his own actions elicit predictable and reasonable consequences. The contingency management approach has the additional advantage of encouraging teachers and parents to model rational, consistent behavior; in the process of establishing a contingency management program, adults who deal with the child are forced to think more objectively about their interactions and, as a result, their own behavior often becomes more reflective and controlled. I have stressed these points to emphasize the fact that contingency management techniques can be employed in ways that promote either inner or outer control. Our purpose in using them is to work toward helping children develop a sense of mastery and to achieve purposeful control over their own behavior.

A COGNITIVE TRAINING APPROACH

In planning a cognitive training program, it is important to realize that temporary alleviation of more obvious symptoms, such as disruptive behaviors or excessive movement, is not enough. What must be changed is nothing less than the basic mechanisms that guide the hyperactive child's perceptions, cognitions, and behavior, as well as the faulty learning and attitudes that have developed as the results of defects in these mechanisms. Thus, it is quite unrealistic to look to training programs that invest less time and expertise than we might devote to teaching a child an athletic, academic, or musical skill.

In addition, since the defective mechanisms permeate virtually all aspects of the child's life, it is essential that training extend beyond the clinic or laboratory to the home, school, and playground. The child must be made aware that what is learned in the training situation is applicable to work at school, relationships with friends, and dealings with parents and siblings. Also, significant individuals in the child's life, including parents, teachers, and older siblings, should be knowledgeable about the training methods and goals and, whenever possible, should participate in the training program.

My colleagues and I have completed two empirical investigations of the effectiveness of a cognitive approach (Douglas, Parry, Marton, & Garson, 1976; Garson, 1977). We are attempting, as well, to improve our techniques by using the approach in a more "clinical" fashion with a few individual children who represent extreme examples of the hyperactive disorder. Our contacts with some youngsters in this latter group have extended over a period of 3 or 4 years. Because our ideas about training strategies have evolved since the first study (Douglas *et al.*, 1976), I shall present here our current thinking; however, the reader is cautioned that we have not yet completed an adequately controlled evaluation of the revised approach. To avoid confusion, I shall try to be clear about changes that have been introduced since our first publication.

Levels of Training

It is possible to conceptualize our training approach as representing three levels of intervention. At the first, or most basic, level, our goal is to help the children understand the nature of the disabilities that are creating problems for them: As discussed earlier, these include difficulties in maintaining attention, inhibiting impulsive responding, and modulating arousal in accordance with situational requirements. At the second level, we attempt to increase the youngsters' awareness of their own roles as problem solvers and to motivate them to assume this role more actively and successfully. At the third level, the emphasis is on teaching them specific problem-solving strategies. A summary of the three levels of intervention, together with the major goals of each level, appears in Table 11.3.

LEVEL 1: HELPING THE CHILD UNDERSTAND THE NATURE OF HIS DEFICITS

When we begin working with hyperactive children, our initial goal is to give them some understanding of the nature of their deficits, how they are creating difficulties for themselves and how we propose to help them overcome them. Often it is necessary, in the beginning, to combat the notion that the child is "silly" or "dumb," because erratic behavior is likely to have earned the child these labels. We may assure the child, for example, that the tests we have given prove that he is really quite clever (see Douglas *et al.,* 1976).

We then try to convince the child that one kind of problem behavior lies behind almost all of the difficulties he is experiencing both at home and at school. Using words we hope he will understand, we define this behavior as being related to his failure to "stop, look, and listen," and to think carefully before acting. We explain that he often does not look over a problem long enough to understand exactly what the problem is asking, and he also does not think hard enough about possible ways of solving the problem before "jumping in." In our second training study (Garson, 1977), we began involving the children more actively in this discussion by asking them to tell us about recent events where they got into trouble because they had not stopped to think before acting. Although these children have trouble with introspection, they frequently can produce such examples.

We then tell the child that we can help him overcome these difficulties and that we are going to do this by working together on some games and problems. We explain that we will do the problems or games first to show him how to work on them, and that in the beginning we will say everything we are doing and everything we are thinking out loud, so that he will know exactly what is going on in our minds. Then the child will take a turn at solving a similar problem, and he, too, will say out loud what he is thinking so that we will know what is going on in *his* head. We stress, as well, that we both should be reminding ourselves to check our work very carefully; we

TABLE 11.3
Levels of Training in the Cognitive Approach

Level I

HELPING THE CHILD UNDERSTAND THE NATURE OF HIS DEFICITS AND HOW TRAINING CAN HELP

1. Providing an explanation of the nature of the child's attentional, inhibitory, and arousal modulating deficits
2. Helping the child recognize how these deficits affect his daily functioning and create problems for him
3. Convincing him that the deficits can be modified and motivating him to share actively in the process
4. Introducing child to the basic elements of the cognitive training approach.

Level II

STRENGTHENING THE CHILD'S MOTIVATION AND CAPACITY TO DEAL WITH THE PROBLEM-SOLVING ROLE

1. Providing success experiences within the training sessions by:
   breaking tasks into component parts
   presenting tasks in gradually increasing order of difficulty
   tailoring teaching material to individual child's capacities
   providing systematic reviews of material covered
2. Arranging success experiences at home and at school by:
   helping parents and teachers organize demands made on child to coincide with his ability to meet them successfully
   encouraging parents and teachers to reward genuine attempts at mastery, as well as successes
3. Teaching child general rules for approaching tasks, including:
   defining task demands accurately
   assessing one's own relevant knowledge and/or the available cues in a situation or problem
   considering all possible solutions
   evaluating relative effectiveness of solutions considered
   checking work carefully
4. Discouraging passivity and encouraging independent effort by:
   addressing child with a title like "Mr. Problem Solver"
   discouraging undue dependence on trainer
   discouraging mimicking of trainer's strategies or parroting of instructions; encouraging child to produce his own strategies and to restate instructions in his own words
   shifting responsibility for correcting work and administering rewards to child
   helping child learn to differentiate between his careless errors and errors that reflect genuine problems with understanding
5. Making child aware of behaviors and attitudes on his part which interfere with problem solving by:
   drawing his attention to flagging attention or "hyped up" behavior
   discouraging excessive talking
   reminding him to "work beyond" superficial aspects of a situation or problem
   discouraging unreasonably low criteria for success

Level III

TEACHING SPECIFIC PROBLEM-SOLVING STRATEGIES

1. Modeling and teaching strategies directed toward improving attention and concentration. These strategies might include:
   organized and exhaustive scanning techniques

TABLE 11.3 (continued)

focusing strategies; checking for critical features
careful listening for essential information
2. Teaching strategies and offering management suggestions directed toward increasing inhibitory control and developing organizational skills. This might be accomplished by:
teaching child to sit on hands until he has thought through possible solutions
encouraging parents and teachers to provide special places for keeping important materials and helping the child remember to use them
encouraging the use of a special notebook for classroom assignments; keeping notebook in special place
modeling the use of lists of events or assignments to be remembered, assembling necessary materials for projects, laying out clothes and books for following day
3. Teaching strategies and offering management suggestions directed toward improved control of child's level of alertness and arousal. This might include:
labeling of arousal states
teaching the child to exhort self or calm self using verbal self-commands
suggesting interesting "breaks" between periods of concentrated work
being sensitive to the fact that child may need stimulation to combat boredom
4. Teaching other specific strategies child has failed to learn, for example:
rehearsal strategies and mnemonic devices
strategies required for particular academic activities (e.g., steps involved in adding fractions or in writing an essay)

will do this as we go along and, again, when we think we have finished a problem. More detail about the games and problems and how we use modeling, self-verbalization, self-monitoring, and self-reinforcement techniques is provided in our first training paper (Douglas *et al.*, 1976). The rationale for choosing these particular techniques will be discussed in the next section.

In our earlier studies, our trainers did not use academic material in the training sessions because we were interested in discovering whether the strategies we taught would generalize to classroom activities. The child was assured, however, that the very same strategies we were teaching would "work" on school assignments. In addition, in our first training study (Douglas *et al.*, 1976), teachers were rather heavily involved in the program. In our subsequent clinical work, we have been applying the principles and strategies of the cognitive training program more directly to the academic work being covered at school. I shall give a few examples of how we accomplish this, shortly.

More recently, we also have stressed making the children aware of how their own state of arousal or alertness can interfere with doing a good job. We point out that, if they are not fully "awake," they will not be "sharp" enough to solve problems; we remind them, too, that they sometimes have the opposite problem, that is, they get too excited to think clearly. Again, we assure the children that we can show them some ways of dealing with these difficulties.

We suspect that many of our explanations are grasped only vaguely in the beginning. However, they gradually make more sense to the children as we introduce them to coping techniques that are specifically directed toward the difficulties we have described to them.

LEVEL 2: STRENGTHENING THE CHILD'S MOTIVATION AND CAPACITY TO DEAL WITH THE PROBLEM-SOLVING ROLE

Before we begin modeling specific problem-solving strategies, we draw the child's attention to some essential questions that must be asked when approaching most problems. These are questions like: Exactly what am I supposed to do here? What do I know about problems like this? What possible solutions can I think of? How would this particular solution work out? Which of these solutions is best?

While the child is being encouraged to pose such questions, we may address him with a title such as "Mr. Problem Solver," in order to emphasize that *he* is in charge of the problem-solving process. We try, as well, to discourage undue dependency on the trainer or simple mimicking of specific strategies. The youngster is encouraged to think of his own strategies and, when he produces ones that are reasonably sound, they are accepted and praised. Similarly, we discourage rote learning of our instructions. To avoid this, we ask the child to restate them in his own words. In this way, we can be reasonably sure that the youngster understands and is not just parroting words. In addition, we sometimes reverse roles, placing the child in the position of the one who poses the problems.

As part of this goal of promoting self-reliance, we also encourage the child to monitor his own work for correctness and, whenever possible, we have him "mark" it. The trainer models the monitoring and correcting process, talking out loud about the importance of checking each item (or part of a solution) carefully. If the child fails to find his own errors, the trainer provides feedback to the effect that an error has been made, provides some clues as to where it can be found, and encourages the child to return to the task of discovering it. In the case of older children, we try to help them differentiate between careless errors and errors that occur because of a genuine difficulty in understanding the problem. Occasionally, we introduce response costs for careless errors that the child has failed to discover. On the more positive side, the trainer uses modeling to teach the youngster how to correct errors without undue upset, and how to reinforce himself for each part of the task that he has mastered successfully. Comments like "I've done very well so far" and "that was a really good job" are used fairly frequently, as the trainer tries to communicate to the child that mastery of a problem can produce joy and pleasure.

Feelings of mastery are also promoted by very careful programming of the problems, games, or academic material used in each session. Tasks are broken down into their component parts, and the trainer tries to make sure that the child is taught all of the essential elements. Similarly, tasks are arranged in order of difficulty, and the difficulty level of the tasks presented in the sessions is increased very gradually. For example, if we are teaching reading, we go back to the most common phonemes and pace the introduction of new sounds and combinations of sounds to the child's progress. Systematic reviews of material already covered are frequent. In addition, reading material is tailored specifically for the individual child; this is necessary in order to avoid exposing him to sounds that he has not already mastered. When it becomes necessary to teach the child about exceptions to the rules, we announce this explicitly. Sometimes we bolster our explanation with a whimsical little poem about the vagaries of the sounds in the English language; in this way, we hope to show him that everyone has trouble mastering some of the peculiar exceptions to the rules.

Finally, we draw the child's attention to his own behaviors or attitudes that are interfering with success as a problem solver. Often, for example, the children try to engage the trainer in irrelevant conversation. If a child seems to be using this gambit to avoid taking the problem-solving role seriously, we gently point this out. Also, if attention begins to flag, or if a child becomes too excited to work effectively, we try to increase his awareness of these internal states. Similarly, if we believe that the youngster has been "seduced" into reacting to superficial but compelling aspects of a problem situation, we draw this to his attention and help him experience the success that comes from "working beyond" these more obvious clues. We find, too, that many hyperactive children accept very low criteria for success. One boy, for example, had adopted the position that getting 50% (a pass) on examinations represented adequate performance; once he had experienced a reasonable amount of success in the training sessions, we moved toward dissuading him from this attitude. As the sessions progress, we try to transfer responsibility for recognizing the occurrence of these "foibles" or self-defeating behaviors to the child himself. Usually, on the way toward this goal, the trainer and child develop "shorthand" ways of communicating to each other that one of these behaviors has just occurred; a hand to the mouth, for example, may signify that the youngster is talking too much.

In this section, we have been considering ways of enhancing hyperactive children's capacity and motivation to become more effective problem solvers. Before leaving this topic, it is important to recognize that these goals can be accomplished only if we are successful in maintaining the children's motivation to cooperate actively in the training sessions themselves. Almost by definition, we are asking them to engage in activities that are "against their nature." It is frustrating to a hyperactive child to have to slow down in order to evaluate the demands of a task carefully, to consider the pros and cons of possible solutions, and to work through a solution in a methodological, step-by-step fashion. It can be annoying, too, to have to voice each step aloud before embarking upon it. Thus, it is necessary to bolster the success experiences we arrange for the children with other inducements. We have found that young, energetic, and optimistic trainers work out well with these children. We try, too, to vary the material covered, dividing the sessions into periods that do not overtax the children's ability to concentrate. The length of periods in which they are expected to work on difficult material is lengthened very gradually, and more playful activities are interspersed between the periods. Sometimes it is necessary to tell the children how long they will be asked to work on a particular activity; this provides a guarantee that they will not be expected to cope with it indefinitely and, hopefully, enables them to deploy their concentration for a brief but concerted effort.

In addition, we reassure the children that they will not always have to verbalize their plans aloud; we explain that, later, we will move toward whispering them, and then to just saying them to ourselves. Similarly, the children are told that once they have disciplined themselves to consider all of the important steps in solving problems, they will be able to move through the steps much more quickly. Perhaps most important of all, we try to assure successful generalization of what is learned in the training sessions to the children's lives outside the sessions. Whenever possible, we work closely with parents, teachers, and occasionally, siblings. We help these important individuals in the children's lives structure opportunities for them to apply their new skills in "real life" situations. They are constantly reminded, as well, of the importance of rewarding both successes and genuine effort enthusiastically. Thus, the training sessions hopefully become associated in the children's minds with positive experiences outside the sessions.

LEVEL 3: TEACHING SPECIFIC PROBLEM-SOLVING STRATEGIES

The specific strategies taught to a particular child vary considerably, depending on the youngster's age and capabilities. All strategies, however, are directed toward ameliorating one or more of the three deficits I have postulated to be most critical in the hyperactive disorder: (*a*) an inability to sustain attention and effort; (*b*) poor impulse control; and (*c*) problems involving the modulation of alertness and arousal. Since these deficits are highly interrelated, a strategy directed toward one is very likely to influence the others as well; in fact, as we begin thinking about particular strategies, it quickly becomes apparent that clear delineation among the three target problems is impossible.

Some of the strategies emphasize helping the child deploy attention and effort more effectively. At the most basic level, this involves making him a more efficient viewer, listener, and explorer. He may be taught, for example, how to develop more organized and exhaustive scanning techniques (e.g., working methodologically from left to right when information is organized in rows, and from top to bottom of a page). Other activities involve training in focusing strategies, for example, teaching the child to check in an organized manner for critical attributes, and perhaps crossing out examples that do not fit the criteria. Listening strategies are also important. The child can be asked to repeat essential information from instructions or from a story that has been read to him; he may be required to reconstruct a visual design from oral instructions. This last activity provides a good opportunity for reversing roles, thus placing the child in the position of the person who gives the orders for the design. Often the children find, in the beginning, that the instructions they give are too incomplete or incomprehensible for another person to follow and, as a result, they learn to be more explicit and clear.

As mentioned earlier, hyperactive children frequently have failed to learn some of the more sophisticated strategies practised by other children their age. It then becomes necessary to teach the missing strategies, and also to convince the children that these strategies are superior to their own. Some of the rehearsal techniques and mnemonic devices mentioned in the previous discussion of metamemory provide good examples of these kinds of strategies. Also, in teaching academic material, it often is necessary to emphasize that a series of operations or rules must be followed meticulously and in a particular order. Here, the trainers must know the material sufficiently well to define the rules that apply to particular types of problems. We usually write the rules down and keep them in view in order that the child can check off each step as he proceeds.

Many of the strategies our trainers model are directed toward the children's impulsivity and carelessness. Since hyperactive children are very likely to blurt out a response or write down an answer before giving the matter much thought, it sometimes is necessary to teach them to sit on their hands or cover their mouths until they have thought through a problem. By requiring them to verbalize their thoughts aloud, the trainer can assess how effectively they are using this "waiting" period.

We find, too, that it is extremely important to teach the children strategies for organizing their time and their activities more effectively. Since they typically lose belongings, we ask parents and teachers to provide special places for storing essential clothing and school supplies and to check that they are put away safely. Similarly, since the children forget things, we encourage them to write down assignments and to keep them in a special notebook, in a particular pocket or section of their school bag. In this way, the teacher can see that the assignments are understood accurately and that they accompany the child when he leaves school. At the other end, the parents make sure the notebook arrives safely, and they are kept informed about the teacher's expectations. Other organizational strategies taught include how to make and use lists, how to assemble the necessary materials for a project, how to lay out clothes and books that will be needed the following day, how to keep reasonably straight rows and columns when printing, writing, or working on arithmetic problems. In addition, it usually is necessary to find ways of preventing careless errors; for example, the children can be asked to circle "plus" or "minus" signs to make sure that they notice which operation is to be performed, or they may be required to enter the amount "carried" when adding columns in a special box. We find, too, that using specially lined paper can reduce "sloppy" errors and, hopefully, it also contributes toward an appreciation of the necessity for order.

We have only recently begun to appreciate the possible importance of helping hyperactive children gain better control over their own state of arousal or alertness. Consequently, when we carried out our two training studies (Douglas *et al.*, 1976; Garson, 1977), we did not emphasize teaching techniques for accomplishing this in a consistent fashion. In addition, more research is required to verify the arousal deficit hypothesis and to define the effects of different manipulations on the children's physiological arousal and behavioral effectiveness.

In the meantime, however, we have begun to draw the children's attention to their own arousal states during the sessions; we try, also, to make them aware that certain tasks make particular demands for alertness and commitment on their part. Occasionally, these children arrive at a session in a state that appears so "high" and erratic that serious work is impossible. Since experience has shown that the same behavior may not be repeated in the following sessions, we simply let the children know that we understand how they feel. We try to engage in activities that will avoid confrontations and, hopefully, help the children become more controlled.

Many of the strategies we teach the children for recognizing, labeling, and controlling their own states of arousal are similar to the methods used by the trainers to assure involvement during the sessions. We may, for example, show both child and parents how to organize homework sessions to provide for interesting breaks between carefully defined work periods. Modeling of self-encouraging statements during the sessions will, hopefully, enable the child to use similar methods of self-exhortation at home and at school. In addition, we are trying to learn more about the effects of providing nonintrusive stimulation, such as music, during the training sessions. If this method seems to help a particular child concentrate better, he and his parents can institute the same procedure at home. Although we have not, ourselves, used biofeedback techniques with hyperactive children, this method may provide another means of giving the children more control over their own arousal states.

Rationale for Emphasizing Self-Verbalization, Modeling, Self-Monitoring, and Self-Reinforcement in Training Programs for Hyperactive Children

As mentioned earlier, in our training sessions with hyperactive children we place considerable emphasis on four methods: self-verbalization, modeling, self-monitoring, and self-reinforcement. I believe that these methods are particularly appropriate for combating the deficits I have attributed to hyperactive children and for accomplishing the training goals that have just been delineated.

In the preceding discussion of reinforcement studies with hyperactive children, it was suggested that the use of external reinforcers may involve certain disadvantages; if hyperactive children are particularly influenced by the salience of reinforcers and unusually sensitive to their loss, having the children administer their own reinforcements may help reduce the disruptive effects of these problems. In addition, giving the children responsibility for reinforcements enhances active, independent participation in the learning process. It also increases the likelihood that they will develop a clearer understanding of the contingencies being taught, since they must have an accurate appreciation of the contingencies in order to deliver the reinforcers appropriately.

Self-monitoring shares some of the advantages of self-reinforcement. In this case, the children are given responsibility for improving the accuracy of the problem-solving process. The method also helps combat hyperactive children's tendency to react impulsively, since they must stop to evaluate their own productions from time to time. The importance of the method for these children is perhaps best demonstrated by the inordinate difficulty trainers encounter in getting them to monitor and check their own work; going back over assignments they consider completed is anathema to them, perhaps because the material is no longer novel, and the monitoring process itself requires diligent effort and considerable attention to detail.

Like the methods already discussed, self-verbalization also enhances the active involvement of the children in training activities. In addition, the youngsters' own verbalizations would be expected to exert a guiding, controlling function over their impulsive tendencies. As mentioned earlier, self-verbalizations can also exhort children to remain alert or encourage them to persevere in the face of difficulties. The method has the additional advantage of providing the trainer with ongoing information about how a child tackles a problem and what difficulties he encounters; this information enables the trainer to provide more accurate and immediate feedback.

The advantages of the final method, modeling, have been appreciated by behaviorally oriented therapists for some time. Modeling seems particularly appropriate for hyperactive children because of the action that accompanies the method; the children's attention is more likely to be captured by a trainer who acts than by one who simply lectures. If roles are reversed during modeling, activity increases for the child as well and, in addition, he gains valuable experience in the "teacher's" role. Finally, the modeling approach helps make the nature of the strategies being modeled more clear and explicit for both trainer and trainee. A parent or trainer must have thought through a strategy or solution very carefully in order to model it successfully, and, from the child's perspective, the steps are likely to be laid out much more clearly.

TWO EMPIRICAL STUDIES OF THE TRAINING APPROACH

Thus far, we have completed two investigations of training programs based upon the methods I have described. The first was a rather substantial program, covering a 3-month period and involving 24 sessions with each child, 12 sessions with one or both parents, and a minimum of 6 sessions with the child's teacher (Douglas *et al.,* 1976). The second was a brief remedial "exercise" that extended over a 3-week period and involved only 3 sessions with the child (Garson, 1977).

Description of Subjects

Children in the first study were screened to meet fairly stringent criteria for a diagnosis of hyperactivity (see Douglas & Peters, 1979, for a discussion of diagnostic issues). The subjects in the second study can be more accurately described as relatively normal children who demonstrated evidence of some attentional and impulsivity problems. They were chosen by a statistical procedure, which took account of their scores on a series of tests that had been shown to define an attentional–impulsivity factor. The training group for the first study consisted of 18 boys; there were 15 subjects (9 boys and 6 girls) in the training group for Study 2. Ages of subjects in the two studies ranged from approximately 6 to 10 years; IQs were in the average or above average range. Families of subjects in Study 1 were middle class or upper lower class; a larger proportion of the children in the second study were from lower socioeconomic status homes, with several coming from immigrant families.

Methods and Materials

Because of the relative length of the two programs, the range of materials and activities used in Study 1 was much greater. In the briefer study, training was limited to four activities: constructing jig-saw puzzles, building patterns with blocks, completing tracking tasks, and working on items from the Raven Progressive Matrices test (Raven, 1958). Care was taken to choose materials for training that differed as much as possible from tests used in the assessment battery (see below). Both studies featured the general approach to problem solving and the more specific kinds of problem-solving strategies that have been described. As mentioned earlier, at the time these studies were carried out, we were placing somewhat less emphasis on arousal training than we currently do. In addition, the sessions did not involve any direct training with academic materials.

Assessment Batteries

The battery of tests and measures used to evaluate the effectiveness of training in Study 1 included tests that had been shown in previous investigations to differentiate between hyperactive and normal children; some of these, the MFFT, the Porteus Mazes, and the Story Completion Test involving frustrating events, are described in Table 11.1. In addition, we assessed generalization of the training to academic activities by including reading and arithmetic achievement tests; the Conners Teacher Rating Scale (Conners, 1969) was used to assess changes in classroom behavior. The assessment battery for Study 2 included all of the measures that had loaded significantly on the attentional–impulsivity factor; it will be recalled that these same measures were used to select subjects for the training group.

Control Groups

In both studies, effectiveness of training was assessed by comparing changes between the training group and a control group, both at the time training ended and again 3 months later. The control group for the first study consisted of hyperactive children who had been screened in the same manner as children in the training group; they were matched with the training group on age, sex, IQ, socioeconomic status, and scores on the Conners Teacher and Parent Rating Scales. Children in the control group were placed on a waiting list and were offered no training during the period covered by the study. We felt that it was unethical and impractical to include an "attention" or "placebo" control group because of the duration of the study and because parents and teachers participated in the training. Children in the control group for Study 2 were matched with children in the training group on scores derived from the attentional–impulsivity factor, age, sex, socioeconomic level, and IQ. Control subjects in this study constituted an "attention control" group. They participated in the same number of sessions with the same trainers and worked with the same materials as the control group. However, they were simply allowed to go about completing the tasks in any way they wished; the trainer offered encouragement but made no effort to influence the child's style of working with the tasks.

Results

Findings from both studies were rather encouraging, both at the time of posttesting and after a 3-month period in which no training occurred. In the case of Study 1, a multivariate analysis performed to compare pretest–posttest differences for the training and control groups was highly significant, $F(9, 19) = 3.53$, $p < .009$. Analyses of variance performed on individual measures from the assessment battery revealed significant Group (training versus control) × Treatment (pretest versus posttest) interactions ($p < .05$) on several of the measures; these included time and error scores from the MFFT, aggressive and realistic coping responses on the story completion test, and a measure of time taken to complete the Bender Gestalt test. In addition, the following three variables approached significance ($p < .10$): Porteus Mazes, the withdrawal measure from the Story Completion Test, and an auditory memory measure from the Detroit test. Because of missing data, separate analyses of variance had to be performed on measures obtained from the Durrell Analysis of Reading Difficulty, the Arithmetic test from the Wide Range Achievement Test, and the Conners Teacher Rating Scale for hyperactivity. A significant Group × Treatment interaction was found on one of the Durrell measures ($p < .05$) and trends ($p < .10$) were obtained on two other measures from the Durrell. Interestingly, there were no significant differences on the Arithmetic measure or on the Conners Teacher Rating Scale.

The multivariate analysis performed on pretest and follow-up scores closely approached significance, $F(9, 19) = 2.36$, $p < .055$. Individual analyses of variance produced significant Group × Treatment interactions ($p < .05$) on error and latency scores from the MFFT and on two measures from the Story Completion Test; trends ($p < .10$) were obtained on aggressive responses from the Story Completion Test and on the Bender Gestalt time measure. Separate analyses also revealed that gains made by the training group were greater than those of the control group on two Durrell measures. Again, no significant differences were found on the Arithmetic test or on the Conners Teacher Rating Scale.

An overall comparison of pretest and posttest measures from Study 2 revealed a significant Group × Condition interaction, $F\ (18, 10) = 4.02$, $p < .01$. In addition, gains made by the training group were significantly greater than those of the control group ($p < .05$) on latency and error scores from the MFFT and on a score derived from a "Matching Sounds" task, which had been designed to parallel the task demands of the MFFT; trends were obtained on two other measures, one of which was derived from the "Matching Sounds" task and the other from a Haptic Matching Task. Somewhat surprisingly, the control group surpassed the gains made by the trained group on one measure, the Porteus Mazes.

As in Study 1, there also was some evidence that the superior gains of the trained group were still present at the time of the 3-month follow-up. On the overall comparison there was a trend toward a significant group × Condition interaction, $F\ (18, 9) = 2.43$, $p < .08$. The Group × Condition interactions on individual measures proved significant ($p < .05$) for the MFFT errors measure, one measure from the Haptic Matching Task, and one measure from the Matching Similar Sounds Task; trends toward significance ($p < .10$) were obtained on two other measures from the sound matching task. There were no comparisons on which the gains of the control group surpassed those of the trained group.

Comments on Findings

The findings from these two cognitive training studies compare favorably with results that have been obtained from other treatment approaches with hyperactive children. This is particularly true when we consider the fact that measures taken 3 months after all contact with the children had ended still showed a substantial advantage for the trained groups. As mentioned earlier, evidence for long-term effects of drug treatment with hyperactive children has not been promising. It would be interesting to test the effects of the stimulants, over a comparable time period, on the kinds of cognitive and academic measures that were used in the present study. Since many proponents of drug treatment believe that hyperactive children must be kept on the stimulants indefinitely, it would be necessary to measure the long-term effects both while the children were still receiving treatment and after they were taken off the drugs. To this writer's knowledge, the long-term effectiveness of contingency management techniques with hyperactive children also has not been demonstrated on as wide a range of measures as those reported here.

The apparent generalization of the effects of cognitive training to performance on the Durrell reading test in Study 1 is also encouraging. It seems reasonable to expect that the inclusion of training specifically directed toward academic difficulties would result in even greater gains on reading and, hopefully, arithmetic performance could be improved as well.

On the other hand, some of the measures used failed to show superior improvement in the trained groups. The most noteworthy of these is the Conners Teacher Rating Scale. It is perhaps not too surprising that this measure is not particularly influenced by cognitive training, especially since judgments made by teachers using the scale apparently reflect changes on readily observable negative and disruptive behaviors, rather than changes in actual academic performance (see Barkley, 1977a, for a review of this evidence). Nevertheless, these behaviors can be extremely important, particularly for those who must live with hyperactive children. This is one reason for considering combining cognitive training with drug treatment or contingency management, as discussed earlier. Alternatively, it might be possible to use the cognitive approach to impress the child with the negative consequences of his disruptive behaviors, and thus work more directly toward helping him bring them under control.

A CONCLUDING WORD OF CAUTION

As the reader has no doubt noticed, in writing this chapter I have placed much more emphasis on elucidating the rationale behind our approach to cognitive training than on describing particular activities or materials to be used in training programs. This emphasis is intentional. We have had numerous requests for our training "handbook" since our first study was published. A number of people have contacted us, as well, asking to be trained in the approach. Frequently, however, the requests come from educators or researchers who have a very mechanistic notion about what goes on in our training sessions. It is hoped that the previous description of levels of training (see Table 11.3) will convince the reader of the importance of dealing with the attitudes, cognitions, and behaviors considered at Levels 1 and 2, as well as with the more specific strategies taught at Level 3. (I have found that a quick method of identifying "mechanical" trainers is to observe the amount of mindless mimicking and parroting that goes on in a training session.)

In addition, even when modeling specific strategies, it is desirable to tailor the activities and materials to the needs of the individual child. Sometimes, it is possible to establish several levels of the same task and then use the task at its appropriate level for a particular youngster, as we did in our two training studies. When unhampered by the restrictions of research design, however, the trainer should be free to develop materials and activities in an even more individualistic fashion. Again, I would emphasize the importance of the trainer being intimately familiar with the material he is trying to teach in order that he can lay out each step for the child. I have seen dramatic instances where an apparent "learning disability" in a hyperactive child was dramatically "cured" by a trainer who knew how to discover essential information that the child had failed to pick up and how to lead him methodically through the stages leading to and from these gaps in his knowledge. (For a discussion of the differences between hyperactive children and children with specific learning disabilities, and the implications of these differences for training, see Douglas (in press) and Douglas and Peters (1979).

The type of individualized "total push" program that I have been describing is, admittedly, difficult to study empirically. It is clear that, along with multifaceted group studies like the ones discussed here, we require more sophisticated separate case studies. Also needed are carefully controlled investigations that focus on single ingredients of the training process and on their combinations. The results obtained thus far suggest that the cognitive approach merits this kind of investment.

VI

CONCLUSIONS AND EPILOGUE

12

The Changing Faces of Hyperactivity: Retrospect and Prospect[1]

BARBARA HENKER
CAROL K. WHALEN

DISAPPEARING MYTHS

One way of integrating many of the diverse findings reported in the preceding chapters is to reconsider some myths that have been enjoying popular support despite incremental empirical refutation. As with most myths, each has a kernel of truth, and it is this kernel that has often resulted in wholesale acceptance of these poorly substantiated propositions. The empirical details refuting each myth are delineated in earlier chapters and are only summarized below.

Myth 1. Hyperactivity Resides in the Child: Child D The Child Deficit View

Children labeled hyperactive are not simply afflicted by the "Hyperactive Child Syndrome," the "Hyperkinetic Impulse Disorder," or "Minimal Brain Dysfunction." Although it is relatively easy to construct a global profile of the hyperactive child, the more details that are added, the more difficult it is to find children who fit the profile. There is substantial evidence that many children labeled hyperactive have atypical behavioral and physiological characteristics. It is also clear, however, that prevalence rates vary with

[1]Portions of the research reported in this chapter were supported by National Institute of Drug Abuse Grant DA 01070 and National Institute of Mental Health Grant MH 29475.

HYPERACTIVE CHILDREN
The Social Ecology of Identification and Treatment

ISBN 0-12-745950-2

parental attitudes and competencies, with social system definers, and with a host of other environmental characteristics. The implication is that the problems attributed to—or experienced by—hyperactive children cannot be understood or ameliorated until these environmental variables are included in our conceptual paradigms, and person-by-situation matrices become prime research targets. Paternite and Loney (Chapter 4) and Routh (Chapter 2) illustrate approaches to the study of environmental influences on childhood hyperactivity.

Myth 2. Hyperactivity Is in the Eyes of the Beholder

The converse of the child deficit view is the presumption that hyperactivity itself is a myth, and that the diagnostic process is used primarily to satisfy the personal, social, economic, or political needs of the people doing the labeling (cf. Conrad, 1975; Schrag & Divoky, 1975). One kernel of truth here is that the diagnosis of hyperactivity is often a relatively subjective process, with child specialists relying necessarily on the impressions and reports of a child's parents and teachers, rather than on impersonal, quantifiable criteria. A second kernel of truth is that individual differences and person perception processes significantly influence people's evaluations of children's behaviors (see pages 340–343). Despite these realities, there is now objective documentation of the learning and performance difficulties experienced by many hyperactive children, as illustrated throughout this volume.

Myth 3. Hyperactivity Vanishes with Adolescence

The assumption that the hyperactive youngster's problems are age-specific and time-limited is not supported by recent outcome data. Although it appears that some hyperactive children may indeed "outgrow" their problems, many of them continue to have social and academic difficulties during adolescence and even adulthood (Ackerman, Dykman, & Peters, 1977; Allen & Safer, 1979; Borland & Heckman, 1976; Hoy, Weiss, Minde, & Cohen, 1978; Huessy & Cohen, 1976; Weiss, Hechtman, & Pearlman, 1978). The problems do tend to change in form or at least in mode of expression. Problems may also decrease in intensity as these individuals leave highly structured academic environments and enter more flexible school or work settings, which offer greater options for achieving a match between personal styles and situational demands. In general, however, social and attentional problems often persist.

There are also indications that some adults who were never diagnosed during childhood are experiencing the problems characteristic of hyperactivity and may in fact respond to the same pharmacologic treatment (e.g., Huessy, Cohen, Blair, & Rood, 1978; Preis & Huessy, 1979; Wood, Reimherr, Wender, & Johnson, 1976). The evidence on adult hyperactivity is still too new and sparse to engender firm conclusions, although the findings to date do challenge the wisdom of assuming that hyperactivity is a time-limited developmental problem.

Myth 4. Psychostimulant Treatment Is Increasing to Epidemic Proportions

The media coverage and popular outcry against stimulant treatment in 1970 was based on the faulty assumption that perhaps 10% of United States school children were receiving drugs for behavioral control. As explicated by Bosco and Robin (Chapter 6) and by Sandoval, Lambert, and Sassone (Chapter 5), recent prevalence studies indicate that only between 1 and 2% of school-aged children are receiving psychostimulants. (These figures refer to the proportion of children taking stimulants at any one point in time; the proportion that has ever taken stimulants is, of course, somewhat greater.) Moreover, findings from a continuing prevalence study provide no evidence of increased usage (Krager, Safer, & Earhart, 1979).

Myth 5. There Is an Optimal Response to Psychostimulant Medication

For many children considered hyperactive, medication appears to improve behavioral regulation. A single rating of "improved" or "unimproved," however, obscures the individual reaction. There is no single desirable response to stimulant treatment. For one child, improvement may mean less squirming and fidgeting, for another it might mean enhanced ability to concentrate and less frequent changes of activity, whereas for still another it might mean smoother interpersonal transactions. There are no ready relationships among these diverse responses. Behavioral changes observed in one child may not be related to those observed in another and, for a particular child, improvements in one behavioral domain are not necessarily related to improvements in another. Both interindividual and intraindividual variability appear to be the rules rather than the exceptions.

There is also evidence suggesting that different dosage levels effect changes in different behavioral domains. Sprague and Sleator (1977) have demonstrated that some types of cognitive performance improve with a low dose of methylphenidate and that higher doses may impede learning and performance. In contrast, teacher ratings, amount of movement (wiggling), and side effects such as cardiac changes show a monotonic rather than a curvilinear relationship to dosage level. Thus, it is no longer tenable to consider psychostimulant effects as unitary, homogeneous phenomena. Additional details are given in Keogh and Barkett (Chapter 10) and in Whalen and Henker (Chapter 1).

Myth 6. Hyperactive Children Respond Paradoxically to Stimulant Medication

Rapoport and her colleagues presented data indicating that normal prepubertal boys show enhanced learning and performance following a single dose of dextroamphetamine (cf. Rapoport, Chapter 9; Rapoport, Buchsbaum, Zahn, Weingartner, Ludlow, & Mikkelsen, 1978). These findings dispute the popular assumption that stimulants have paradoxical effects on hyperactive children, exerting a calming influence on this subgroup in contrast to the arousing, energizing effects expected in normal organisms. Although there is some tentative indication that normal and hyperactive children may show opposite drug responses on occasion (Swanson & Kinsbourne, 1976, 1978), the growing consensus is that psychostimulants have similar effects on hyperactive children and normal individuals, whether children or adults. The major influences seem to be enhanced ability to focus and sustain attention, to inhibit extraneous responses, and to modulate behavior in accord with situational cues. The appearance of increased calm in medicated hyperactive youngsters may actually be a side effect of enhanced focal attention; when the ongoing, situationally appropriate task consumes a child's attention, atypical motoric patterns, impulsive acts, and disruptive maneuvers may diminish naturally. The Rapoport *et al.* (1978) findings not only challenge the notion of a paradoxical effect, but they also illustrate the hazards of reasoning backward from treatment to etiology, that is, assuming that a positive medication response confirms a physiological deficit (Whalen & Henker, 1976, 1977).

Myth 7. Psychostimulants Are Necessary and Sufficient for the Treatment of Hyperactivity

Although the immediate effects of psychostimulants are often gratifying, the long-term outcomes have been quite disappointing (e.g., Huessy, Metoyer, & Townsend 1974; Weiss, Kruger, Danielson, & Elman, 1975). Clearly, drugs are not enough; pills do not create skills. In addition, stimulant treatment carries certain physiological and psychological risks, as detailed in Chapter 1. Studies of nonchemical interventions, for example, operant and cognitive behavior modification, indicate the promise of these approaches as adjunctive or perhaps alternative treatments (see Camp,

Chapter 7; Gittelman, Abikoff, Pollack, Klein, Katz, & Mattes, Chapter 8; and Douglas, Chapter 11). However, there are still vast limitations in knowledge about these and other alternate approaches, as well as problems with their feasibility and palatability vis-a-vis stimulant treatment. These consequential issues are discussed further in a later section.

EMERGING RESEARCH ARENAS AND SOME ILLUSTRATIVE DATA

The field of inquiry surrounding hyperactivity has become rich and provocative to scientists from many disciplines. Ironically, perhaps, the intrigue and challenge of the research area are increased by the high ambiguity surrounding the syndrome, as well as by the large numbers of children whose lives are affected.

Empirical Examination of Environmental Variables

The past two decades have witnessed a burgeoning awareness of the behavioral effects of omnipresent environmental variables once considered inconsequential. Congruent with this *zeitgeist,* some investigators are now studying possible links between hyperactivity and aspects of our everyday environment. Three examples follow.

FOOD ADDITIVES AND DIETARY MANAGEMENT

Interest in food allergies and possible adverse effects of flavors, dyes, and preservatives has been growing steadily as more and more studies suggest relationships between specific foodstuffs and various types of cancer, schizophrenia, depression, etc. Links between hyperactivity and diet have been postulated in several forms for several years. Contemporary interest in this area was boosted quite dramatically in the mid-1970s by Feingold's (1973, 1975, 1976) claims that 30–50% of hyperactive children improve when placed on a salicylate-free diet. Called the Kaiser–Permanente or K–P diet, this regimen excludes all artificial flavors and colors. Because of clinically observed relationships between aspirin intolerance and adverse reactions to specific food dyes, all foods containing salicylates are also eliminated, even those with natural salicylates, for example, almonds, apples, and tomatoes.

The early claims used to buttress this hypothesis were not compelling; the first studies were impressionistic and replete with methodological flaws. Adequate dietary management studies are exceedingly difficult and costly.

Food additives are endemic to our society, and controlling a child's food intake requires almost around the clock monitoring of his every activity. The quality of parental care and energy necessary to reorganize the household and maintain the diet is itself sufficient to change markedly the child's behavior.

Fully cognizant of these difficulties, several investigators are currently tackling the problem in sophisticated and innovative ways. Systematic experimental designs involving placebo controls, random assignment, and double-blind procedures have been implemented. A detailed control diet has been developed that matches the K–P diet in required preparation time, types of restricted foods, palatability, and plausibility. Special cookies have been manufactured that contain either "challenge" doses of additives or placebo ingredients. Compliance with the special diets is, of course, a critical factor in these studies, and attempts are made to record each infraction. Harley, Ray, Tomasi, Eichman, Matthews, Chun, Cleeland, and Traisman (1978) have gone to extraordinary lengths to maximize dietary compliance, including (*a*) placing the entire family on the special diets; (*b*) removing previously purchased foods from the home and delivering the family's entire food supply each week; (*c*) arranging for weekly home visits by a dietician to monitor dietary practices and maintain motivation; and even (*d*) delivering special treats to the entire classroom when any one of a target child's classmates has a birthday. These investigators also use a number of "pseudo-dietary manipulations and distractions" to prevent families from cracking the experimental code. Within a particular diet phase, for example, hot dogs, potato chips, and cookies might be included one week and excluded the next; to some family members this change might suggest two distinct diets, when in fact there had been no shift between experimental and control conditions.

The results of these ambitious diet studies are just beginning to emerge, and thus far the data do not support the enthusiastic claims of dramatic improvements in a substantial proportion of the children. There are, however, some suggestive glimmers against a background of generally negative results. Findings from the most rigorously controlled studies *tentatively* indicate that (*a*) a subgroup of hyperactive children may show behavioral improvement when placed on diets free of additives, dyes, and perhaps also natural salicylates, (*b*) preschool children may respond more positively than older youngsters, (*c*) diet-related changes may not be as dramatic as stimulant-induced changes, and (*d*) dose–response and time–response relationships may be critical, as is true with stimulant treatment. Moreover, an intriguing order effect has emerged in two of the most methodologically sound studies: Children placed first on the control diet and then on the experimental (additive-free) diet showed some improvement, whereas no changes were noted in youngsters given the two diets in the reverse order (Conners, Goyette, Southwick, Lees, & Andrulonis, 1976; Harley *et al.*, 1978). This puzzling difference may be more than a simple rater practice effect, and further empirical work clearly is indicated. For additional details about individual studies, the reader is referred to Conners *et al.* (1976), Harley *et al.* (1978), Levy, Dumbrell, Hobbes, Ryan, Wilton, and Woodhill (1978), Swanson and Kinsbourne (1978), and Williams, Cram, Tausig, and Webster (1978). For critical reviews of the literature, see Spring and Sandoval (1976) and Williams and Cram (1978).

Many of these programs are continuing, and data from other ongoing studies are still to be published. In the next few years, more conclusive findings should emerge from these investigations of the direct effects of food additives. Side effects need careful monitoring, given the possibility that the K–P diet may reduce a child's total nutrient intake, especially Vitamin C (Conners *et al.*, 1976; Wender, 1977). The large number of families adopting this diet without consultation from health specialists makes such information particularly important.

Also needed are studies of the emanative effects of the dietary treatment, for example, the ready acceptance and rapid popularity of the food additive notion. Obviously, the stage was set by contemporary interests in ecology and natural products—and the accompanying distrust of artificial ingredients, including drugs. But this *zeitgeist* cannot fully explain the public fervor, the wholesale and uncritical adoption of the food additive notion. The authors have heard dramatic testimonials during interviews with parents of hyperactive children, and similar "conversion" phenomena have been reported by other investigators (e.g., Bierman & Furukawa, 1978; Spring & Sandoval, 1976). Entire families are undergoing radical lifestyle changes to insure that the hyperactive child does not ingest additives. The "Feingold hypothesis" has spawned mutual support groups who create "do-it-yourself" prepared foods, a special cookbook is available at major bookstores, and the hypothesis has received multimedia publicity and even legislative hearings. In a sense, the introduction of the food additive notion could be considered a large-scale natural experiment. If validated, even in part, the notion may have preventive and treatment implications for all youngsters, hyperactive or not. Given the importance of this question, competent studies hopefully will receive continued support.

FLUORESCENT LIGHTING

A second environmental variable that has been implicated in the hyperactivity puzzle is fluorescent lighting. Some authorities have asserted that children show more hyperactive behaviors in classrooms using artificial fluorescent lights than in those using full-spectrum lighting, which more closely approximates natural sunlight (Mayron, Ott, Nations, & Mayron, 1974). Hypothesized causes of negative fluorescent effects include a growth-inhibiting distortion of natural wavelength energy (Ott, 1968), radiation stress (Ott, 1976), and the 60-per-sec flickering that occurs with fluorescent but not with incandescent illumination (Colman, Frankel, Ritvo, & Freeman, 1976).

As in the case of the food additive notion, the early studies of this lighting hypothesis were more dramatic than rigorous, and methodological flaws were apparent. Using improved methodology, O'Leary, Rosenbaum, and Hughes (1978b) conducted a systematic classroom test and found no behavioral differences between standard fluorescent and daylight-simulating illumination. There is no compelling evidence at this time to support the fluorescent lighting hypothesis, but the variables are complex and the debate continues (Mayron, 1978; O'Leary, Rosenbaum, & Hughes, 1978a). Although much smaller in scale than the food additive movement, there has once again been a premature bandwagon effect, with widespread publicity and classroom interventions occurring in the absence of adequate empirical justification.

ENVIRONMENTAL LEAD

Lead is another ecological variable that is receiving increasing research attention. The concern is *not* that hyperactive children are suffering from acute lead poisoning or plumbism, but rather that some of these youngsters may be carrying excessive but "subclinical" body burdens of lead; that is, lead levels in amounts substantial enough to exert chronic, though subtle, effects on learning and performance. The minute fragments that wear off tires, exhaust from certain factories, common urban topsoil, gasoline additives, fruits and vegetables, metal food containers, or paint and plaster from old buildings are but a few of the substances that may contain dangerous lead levels. Risk of high lead burden goes up with the condition known as pica, or indiscriminate mouthing and eating of inedible substances. Normal babies and toddlers, especially those who are unusually lively and incautious, are also prone to indiscriminate mouthing and eating.

Much of the evidence suggesting a possible link between hyperactivity and lead absorption is indirect. One data source is long-term clinical studies of children exposed to undue lead levels during early developmental periods (e.g., de la Burdé & Choate, 1975). A second data source derives from animal models involving purposeful and controlled exposure of rodents to lead during specified developmental periods. In both types of studies, lead exposure often results in behaviors similar to those observed in hyperactive children, including atypical motoric activity, irritability, and learning difficulties (see Silbergeld, 1977, for a comprehensive review).

More direct investigations of the link between lead and hyperactivity in children are currently underway. Using blood and urine tests, David (1974) found that a subgroup of hyperactive children have elevated body lead levels. David, Hoffman, Sverd, Clark, and Voeller (1978) documented behavioral improvements in some hyperactive children following treatment with lead chelating agents that diminish body lead stores.

The elevated lead levels found in these studies are generally considered nontoxic because they do not cause the encephalopathic symptoms of acute lead poisoning, yet such levels may interfere with learning and behavioral regulation. Indeed, a large-scale and carefully executed study of dentine lead (Needleman, Gunnoe, Leviton, Reed, Peresie, Maher, & Barrett, 1979) indicated that youngsters with relatively high lead levels performed more poorly than those with low levels on tests of intelligence, attention, and language processing. Those with high dentine lead levels were also rated more negatively by teachers on such items as "distractible," "impulsive," and "does not follow sequence of directions."

The perennial chicken-or-the-egg question about causality is of paramount importance in our understanding of lead levels. Are hyperactive children more likely than their peers to have elevated body lead burdens because they tend to be impulsive, indomitable, and "always getting into things?" Do elevated lead levels produce the learning and behavior problems? Or can both of these questions be answered in the affirmative? In an attempt to untangle this issue, David, Hoffman, Sverd, and Clark (1977) have presented preliminary data indicating that chronic low-level lead exposure may indeed be a causal agent for some hyperactive children.

Although much research remains to be done, these and related studies suggest that standard criteria for "acceptable" and "unacceptable" body lead levels may require revision (David, Hoffman, & Koltun, 1978). Also needed are studies of the interactions of lead and nutritional variables, particularly the ingestion of trace metals. In a review of recent research, Chisolm (1977) has suggested that, "Nutritional variables may well be the most significant factors affecting responses to minimal increases in lead absorption [p. 5]." Moreover, evidence is now emerging that suggests a link between hyperactive behaviors and trace metals such as copper and zinc (Krischer, 1978). The complex interactions among these various elements merit detailed empirical investigation.

Specifying Response Domains: Behaviors-in-Contexts

Since the completion of plans for this volume and the development of the conceptual model presented in Chapter 1, the authors have, in collaboration with Barry E. Collins, launched an intensive series of studies on the social ecology of hyperactivity and psychostimulant treatment. Given the fact that these studies were designed to yield answers to many of the questions delineated in the opening chapter, it seems appropriate to preview and summarize some of the major findings that are emerging.

The easiest way to introduce this research program is to describe the context in which it was done. The goal was to combine the best components of laboratory and naturalistic methodologies. To this end, we implemented a summer school program in which children were brought to a university environment (UCLA) daily to participate in academic and social activities. They were given ample opportunities to become familiar with the research settings, apparatus, staff, and procedures, and the development of peer and child–staff relationships was encouraged, all in order to insure that data would be collected under conditions as naturalistic—and also as rigorously controlled—as possible.

The boys who participated were 7–11-year-olds enrolled in one of two 5-week summer sessions. There were two classes per session. The program was designed so that each class had 16 boys, 10 of them normal youngsters with no known history of serious school or social problems, and 6 of them considered hyperactive by referring physicians. All of the hyperactive boys were taking methylphenidate; morning dosages ranged between 5 and 40 mg (M = 12.27) or between .11 and 1.28 mg/kg (M = .41).

During two mornings each week, the boys participated in a series of modular experiments designed to assess peer interaction styles and attentional patterns. The boys were in a classroom setting two other mornings each week, permitting observation of their responses to changes in classroom tasks and teaching styles. We hired an experienced elementary teacher to conduct the classes and kept her blind to the purposes of the research program. She knew that we were studying variations in classroom environments, but she knew nothing about the focus on hyperactivity and psychostimulants.

This structure provided an ideal context for an evaluation of hyperactivity and medication responses. The research strategy enabled between-group comparisons of hyperactive and unlabeled children and within-group comparisons of placebo and medication conditions for the hyperactive sample. The research staff were highly trained, the teaching staff were the same for all children, and all procedures were standardized in order that each child was observed under conditions as nearly identical as possible. To reduce novelty effects and promote familiarization, the boys were in the setting for 2 weeks before the structured experiments began. A few examples of specific research methods and findings are presented below.

CLASSROOM ENVIRONMENTS

In the classroom, the goal was to create both "provocation ecologies," designed to highlight differences between unmedicated hyperactive boys and their peers, and "rarefaction ecologies," designed to diminish such differences. Notions gleaned from theory, research, and clinical reports guided these endeavors. One hypothesis, for example, was that other-paced situations pose particular difficulties for hyperactive children; these youngsters appear most likely to show performance decrements when required to modulate their behaviors in accord with external cues (Douglas, 1972). A second hypothesis was that hyperactive children may function quite adequately when their academic work is not challenging but tend to "fall apart" when given difficult assignments.

In one study, these two dimensions were systematically varied using a 2 × 2 experimental design. During the least challenging, easy/self-paced period, the boys worked on simple arithmetic and graphing assignments, using individual worksheets and regulating their own pace. In contrast, the most challenging (difficult/other-paced) period involved more difficult problems, which were presented via an audio cassette recorder. Thus the boys were required to adjust their performance to a nonresponsive, external source. The two other (moderately challenging) combinations were also presented: easy/other-paced and difficult/self-paced.

Approximately half of the hyperactive boys were on their regular dose of methylphenidate during this study, while the other half were on placebo. A double-blind format was followed throughout.

Objective observers time-sampled the behaviors of the boys during the school day. These observers were, of course, blind to the group and medication status of individual children, and most were also blind to the purposes of the studies. A new coding system was developed specifically for this research series. The goal was to cast a wide net to insure delineation of classroom behaviors that distinguish hyperactive children. One of the hypotheses was that these children may differ in behavioral style as well as in behavioral content, and for this reason the system includes discrete acts (e.g., verbalization and fidget) as well as more qualitative aspects (e.g., energy level and appropriateness). Brief definitions of the behavior categories are presented in Table 12.1.

These studies demonstrate that specific behaviors can be accelerated or decelerated *either* by modifying classroom environments *or* by withholding medication. In many instances, the most interesting patterns are the Drug × Situation interactions. For example, task attention rates for all three groups (hyperactive–placebo, hyperactive–medication, and normal comparison) dropped during the difficult/other-paced period; in addition, boys on

TABLE 12.1
Brief Definitions of Behavior Categories

1. *Task attention:* On task is coded when the child is completing class assignments or following the teacher's directions.
2. *Out of chair:* Child is not supporting his weight with a chair.
3. *Translocation:* Child moves from one place to another a minimum of 2 steps or about 3 ft, for example, walking, scooting while seated in a chair.
4. *Movement:* Child moves his trunk or entire body while in a relatively stationary position, for example, wiggling, stretching.
5. *Fidget:* Child's hands, head or feet are in motion for at least 2 sec, for example, tapping fingers, poking holes in notebook, drawing on self.
6. *Regular verbalization:* Spoken words that are neutral in affective content.
7. *Positive verbalization:* Spoken words that are friendly, pleasant, approving, complimentary.
8. *Negative verbalization:* Spoken words that are threatening, derogatory, offensive, aggressive.
9. *Vocalization:* Nonverbal noise with mouth, for example, humming, throat clearing, tongue clucking.
10. *Noise:* Audible sound other than verbalization or vocalization, including tapping pencil, slapping face, banging chair.
11. *Physical contact* (positive or regular): Nonaversive contact with another person, for example, shaking hands, hugging.
12. *Negative contact:* Aversive or unpleasant physical contact, for example, tugging, tripping, slapping. Includes clear entries into another's personal space, for example, grabbing a pen out of a shirt pocket or throwing objects within 6 in of another.
13. *Grimace:* Facial contortion or distortion, if child seems unaware of the behavior. Grimace is not scored when the facial expression appears to be a nonverbal message, for example, nose wrinkling in response to a teacher's demand.
14. *Bystand:* Nonparticipant observation or onlooking.
15. *Social initiation:* Clear attempts to begin a social interchange, for example, starting a conversation.
16. *Ignore:* Refusal to acknowledge a clear social bid.
17. *High energy:* Acts that are vigorous, effortful, intense, vehement, rapid, or loud.
18. *Disruption:* Action has observable consequences that interrupt other people's behavior.
19. *Stand-out or inappropriate:* Nonnormative behaviors that tend to violate the observer's expectations of appropriate behaviors in specific social settings.
20. *Sudden:* An abrupt change in the direction, quality, or type of activity that cannot be predicted from the ongoing stream of behavior.
21. *Accidental:* Coded in conjunction with noise or physical contact when behavior is clearly unintentional.

placebo showed the lowest overall task attention rates. As can be seen from Figure 12.1, however, the placebo group's relatively low rate of task attention is largely attributable to a disproportionate drop during the most challenging (difficult/other-paced) period. During the least challenging period these youngsters did not differ from their peers. Hyperactive boys on placebo also showed disproportionately high rates of inappropriate behavior and physical contact, but only under other-paced conditions. They tended to fidget more than their peers, but this relatively high rate of minor motor movement was not seen during the most challenging period of the day.

In another classroom study the two environmental dimensions were ambient noise level and source of pacing. Rock music was played in the classroom during the "noisy" periods, and regular classroom conditions prevailed during the "quiet" periods. As in the previous study, class assignments were presented via audio cassette tapes during the other-paced periods, whereas individual worksheets containing all necessary information were distributed during the self-paced periods. This second classroom study yielded findings quite consistent with those reported previously. Hyperactive boys on placebo behaved differently from the medicated and comparison groups, and variations in classroom dimensions resulted in some intriguing Medication × Situation interactions. For example, when ambient noise levels in the classroom were high, child-generated noise (e.g., chair scraping, book dropping) increased and this increase was particularly noteworthy in the placebo group. These results are presented in Figure 12.2.

To summarize, hyperactive boys on placebo were not distinctive throughout the school day. Rather, their behaviors were discordant within specific contexts. These initial findings represent a first step toward mapping the social ecology of hyperactivity. Hopefully, the results of these and subsequent studies will be useful in the design of optimal treatment plans that include environmental restructuring and other nonpharmacologic components, as well as stimulant medication. Additional details about these classroom studies are presented in Whalen, Collins, Henker, Alkus, Adams, and Stapp (1978) and in Whalen, Henker, Collins, Finck, and Dotemoto (1979a).

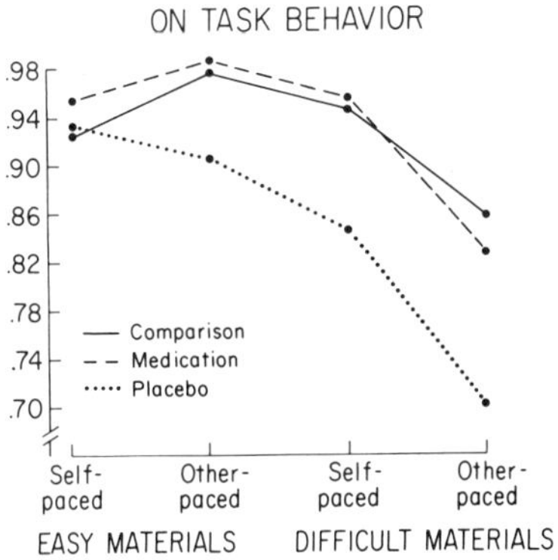

FIGURE 12.1. Probability of task attention seen in comparison boys (——), hyperactive boys on methylphenidate (–––), and hyperactive boys on placebo (· · ·). [Reprinted by permission from the **Journal of Pediatric Psychology**, 1978, **3**, 177–187.]

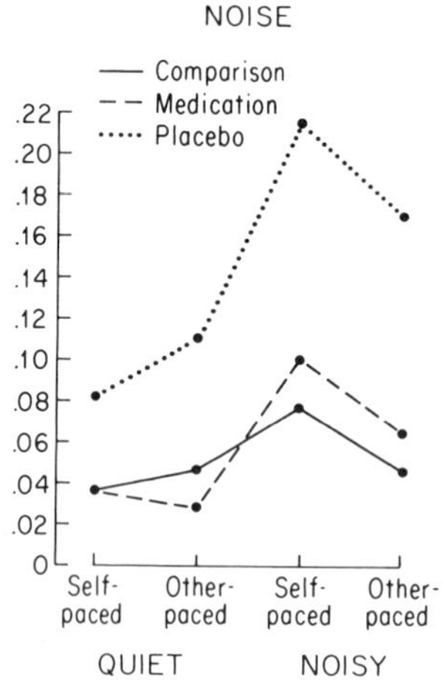

FIGURE 12.2. Probability of noise-making seen in comparison boys (——), hyperactive boys on methylphenidate (---), and hyperactive boys on placebo (· · ·). [Reprinted by permission from the **Journal of Applied Behavior Analysis**, 1979, **12**, 65–81.]

It is important to note that the studies summarized in the preceding paragraphs represent only an initial step toward understanding hyperactivity as an interactional process. An advantage of the approach is that both sides of the Person × Situation equation are included in the research design, thus allowing personal *and* environmental factors to emerge as codeterminants of behavior. A disadvantage is that this research approach cannot do full justice to the continuous and multidirectional nature of these phenomena. Behavior is not merely a function of situations; it also changes these situations. This dynamic process is illustrated by the Campbell, Endman, and Bernfeld (1977) data suggesting that the presence of a hyperactive child in a classroom significantly increases the amount of negative feedback teachers give to *normal* children in the same classroom. In other words, hyperactive children generate changes in their behavior settings, and these changes, in turn, have an impact on their subsequent behaviors. Studies are needed of these reciprocal, *transactional* processes as well as the more static and unidirectional elements of Person × Situation interactions. (See Endler and Magnusson [1976] and Magnusson and Endler [1977] for a detailed discussion of these issues.)

PEER INTERACTION STYLES

In one of our analog tasks for assessing peer interaction, children are presented with a poster containing pictures of 20 related items, for example, types of foods or camping gear. Their task is to select the 3 "healthiest foods" or "best things to take on a camping trip." First they make their own individual choices; then they discuss their opinions, with the goal of reaching a group consensus. This is a natural and engaging task for the youngsters, one that approximates everyday group decision-making activities, for example, a family's selection of a restaurant or a class' choice of foods to bring to a holiday party.

In the first study using this "Decisions" task, the boys worked in small groups including, as often as possible, one hyperactive boy on medication, one on placebo, and two comparison boys. All children participated twice during 2 consecutive weeks of the program, working with a different group of peers each time. A randomly assigned half of the hyperactive boys were on methylphenidate Session 1 and placebo Session 2, whereas the other half were on placebo first and then medication during the subsequent week.

The interactions were videotaped and later analyzed using coding systems developed specifically for this research program. One system, affectionately known as "Globals," focused on seven qualitative aspects of communication: behavioral intensity, task involvement, communicative efficiency, responsiveness, positive affect, negative affect toward self (sadness, self-denigration), and negative affect toward others (hostility, threats, ridicule). Following each minute of interaction, each of these dimensions was rated on a 5-point scale ranging from "low or not at all" to "high or extreme." The raters were, of course, blind to group and medication status.

It is noteworthy that medication status was the important variable for some of the dimensions, whereas others were influenced by group membership (hyperactive versus comparison) independently of medication. Medication exerted a significant effect on intensity, task involvement, and positive affect. When they were on Ritalin (compared to placebo), hyperactive boys were perceived as less vigorous or intense, more involved in the task, and less positive. The findings for intensity are presented in Figure 12.3.

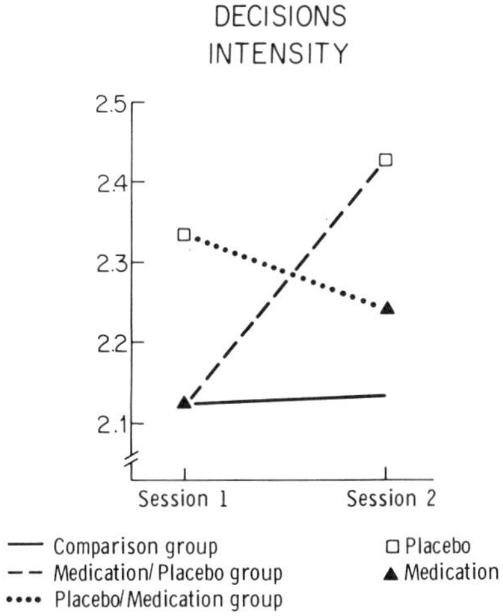

FIGURE 12.3. Mean intensity ratings during a group decision-making task.

The pattern of results was quite different for communicative efficiency and responsiveness. Whether they were on medication or placebo, hyperactive boys were perceived as significantly less responsive—and their verbal messages were rated less efficient—during their first than during their second exposure to the task. There were no differences between the two sessions for the comparison group. By the second session, the hyperactive boys reached the level of the comparison boys in terms of communicative efficiency and even surpassed this level for responsiveness. The results for communicative efficiency are presented in Figure 12.4.

These latter findings suggest that hyperactive boys have a more difficult time than their peers "warming up" or "learning the ropes." They evidently require more than the expected amount of time to settle into a task, and this temporal pattern may be responsible for some of their difficulties in classroom settings. A more complete description of this study is given by Whalen, Henker, Dotemoto, Vaux, and McAuliffe (in press).

Similar results were obtained in a more highly structured referential communication task called "Space Flight." Here the boys work in pairs, one serving as the message sender ("Mission Control") and the other as message receiver ("Astronaut"). Mission Control is given a photograph showing a layout of wooden shapes or "equipment parts"; the Astronaut is given a set of the shapes but no photograph indicating their correct locations. Mission Control's task is to guide the Astronaut in the correct placement of the blocks "so that the Astronaut will be able to repair his own space capsule when it breaks down in outer space." To increase veridicality, a large ward-

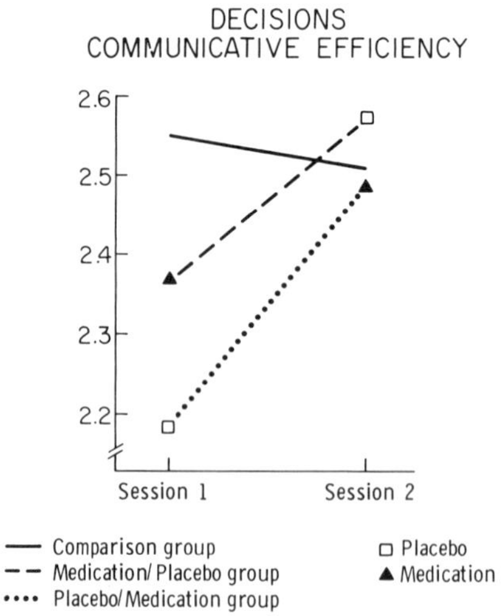

FIGURE 12.4. Mean communicative efficiency ratings during a group decision-making task.

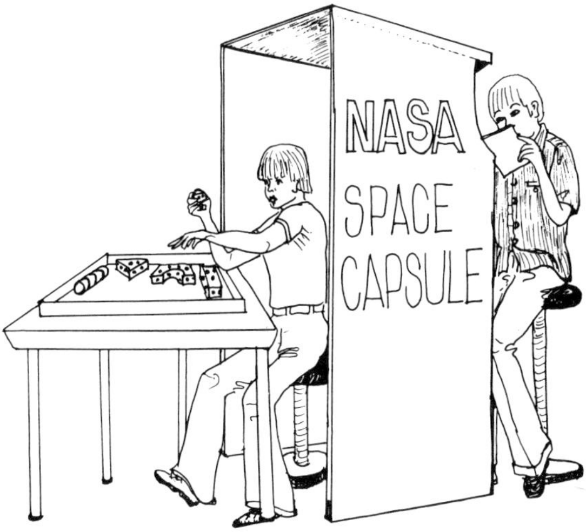

FIGURE 12.5. Illustrated is "Space Flight," a dyadic referential communication task for assessing peer interaction patterns.

robe carton was painted silver and lettered "NASA." The Astronaut was seated within this "space capsule," while Mission Control stood behind the capsule and observed through a window. The materials and physical arrangement are shown in Figure 12.5.

The same double-blind, crossover design was used to facilitate analyses of medication effects as well as group differences. Each boy served in each role during the first session and again during the second session, working with a different partner and a different block design on each of these four occasions.

In terms of the qualitative dimensions (the 1-per-min Global ratings), the findings were similar to those from the group consensus study. Hyperactive children serving as Mission Control were perceived as more intense when on placebo than on medication. Positive affect was lower on medication than on placebo (in the Mission Control role), and there was a medication-induced increase in negative affect toward self in the Astronaut role. As in the previous study, the communicative efficiency dimension yielded a group difference that was independent of medication status. Both groups of hyperactive boys were perceived as less efficient than comparison boys during Session 1, although their efficiency scores increased to the level of the comparison group during Session 2.

These findings suggest that, at least in these types of interpersonal encounters, psychostimulants do not influence competence (e.g., communica-

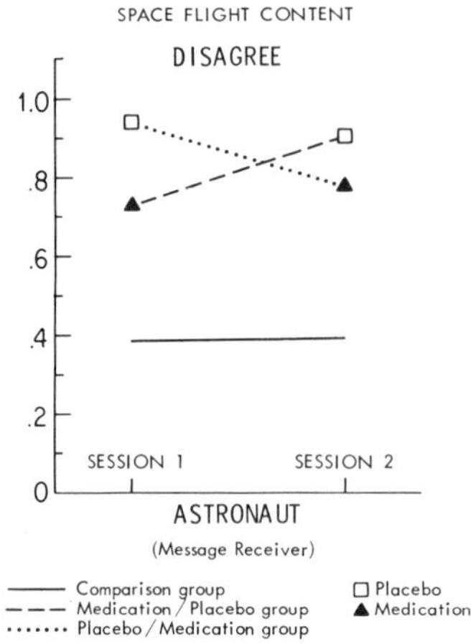

FIGURE 12.6. Frequency of disagreement in the message receiver role.

tive efficiency).[2] What the medication appears to do is modulate excitement and affect levels—behavioral style and task approach. Hyperactive boys are less intense and slightly more dysphoric when on medication as compared to placebo. Although these changes are small in a clinical sense, they are detectable and reliable. It seems reasonable to speculate that behaviors judged to be vigorous, energetic, or intense are those likely to get a child into trouble during social and academic transactions. Regardless of what he says, the youngster who typically talks a bit too loud—or too fast—or too much—is likely to elicit negative sanctions.

The Mission Control and Astronaut roles were designed to elicit quite different types of interpersonal behaviors. Mission Control is the leader who knows the correct answers and has the responsibility of guiding his partner. The Astronaut is placed in an other-directed, follower role that requires sustained attention and responsiveness to his partner's bids. Thus this task also yielded information about role appropriate behaviors and response modulation in accord with shifting external cues. As one means of assessing such variables, we developed a system for rating the content of the verbal messages. Frequency counts of 12 types of communicative content were obtained from an independent group of videotape raters. The categories included giving directions, requesting directions, giving various types of feedback, requesting feedback, and commentary (small talk and nonfunctional comments about the task).

[2] It should be noted that these particular tasks were designed to assess interpersonal rather than cognitive performance and thus were not intellectually challenging. Previous research indicates that psychostimulants do influence competence when sustained attention is required or when heavier information loads are involved (e.g., Douglas, 1976a; Sprague & Sleator, 1977).

Very few medication effects emerged in these analyses. There were, however, several group differences that have intriguing implications. For example, hyperactive boys (regardless of medication status) were not as likely as their peers to engage in role appropriate behaviors. When they were serving as Astronauts, and thus unable to evaluate their own performance independently, hyperactive youngsters were less likely to request feedback or confirmation and more likely to disagree with their partners than were comparison boys (see Figure 12.6). We also found that communicative content was more similar across the two roles for the hyperactive than for the comparison boys, suggesting again that hyperactive boys do not readily modulate their behaviors in accord with shifting external cues. Are hyperactive children less attentive to social cues, is it just that they do not care as much, or do they lack the requisite skills to match behaviors to social circumstances? These are important questions that cannot yet be answered.

Another interesting finding was that hyperactive boys were less consistently oriented toward the task and more willing to "break task set," for example, by engaging in tangential small talk. (Our favorite to date is one 8-year-old's query of another, "How's your love life?") It is noteworthy that this difference appeared only during the second session, as shown in Figure 12.7. We view this finding as an empirical representation of the often noted "doctor's office effect" discussed in Chapter 1. Hyperactive children often behave quite appropriately during an initial clinic or laboratory visit when novelty and uncertainty are high; dysfunctional social behaviors are more likely to emerge in familiar and comfortable settings.

In the preceding paragraphs, the results of the Space Flight study were merely sampled. The complete set of findings, along with additional details

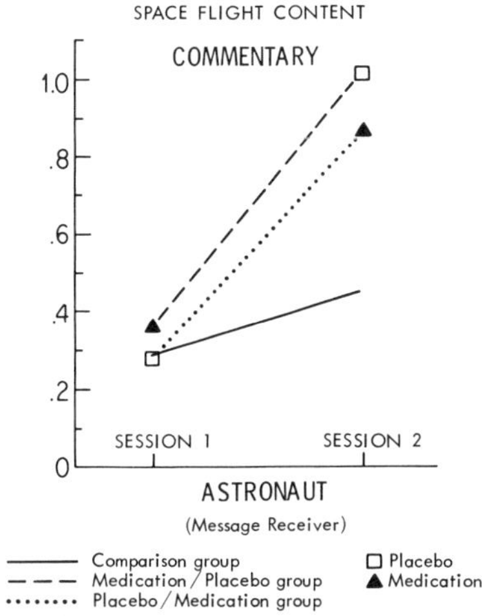

FIGURE 12.7. Frequency of commentary found in the message receiver role.

about methodology, are presented in Whalen, Henker, Collins, McAuliffe, and Vaux (1979b).

Perceiver Processes: Person Perception and Individual Differences

Very little is known about how cognitive and motivational processes in the observer influence the identification and treatment of hyperactive children. As discussed in Chapters 1 and 2 of this volume, much of the information now available is based on rating scales and checklists completed by parents and teachers. As Routh (Chapter 2) underscores, our picture of hyperactivity is often passed through the filter of other people's perceptual processes. It seems quite reasonable to assume that rating scales tell us a good deal about the respondent and the situation, as well as about the target child. One research topic concerns the types of causal ascriptions that are generated by specific diagnostic labels and treatment programs. When a child is identified as hyperactive and begins to receive psychostimulants, what types of explanations and expectations are created in his parents, teachers, and peers? A related question concerns the role of individual differences in the perceiver. Some teachers are more likely than others to give negative ratings and to identify particular children as deviant and in need of special help. In some situations a child will be labeled quite readily, whereas in others he may escape the labeling process entirely. What specific variables relate to high or low "detection thresholds," and how important are these variables in the identification and treatment of hyperactivity? In other words, what are the situational variables and perceiver characteristics that mediate the links among child behaviors, the labeling-medication intervention, and perceptions of improvement?

Although a large literature on person perception, causal attributions, and Person × Situation interactions exists within social psychology, there have been few attempts to study the impact of such processes on clinical decision making, particularly on decisions regarding children. The following paragraphs preview some of the results from ongoing studies of perceiver characteristics and situational factors in the identification and treatment of hyperactivity.

As a first step in the delineation of the attitudinal consequences of specific diagnoses and treatment modalities, the authors have developed a set of videotapes portraying behaviors considered characteristic of hyperactive children (e.g., impulsive acts, rule-breaking, inattention). Different groups of adults are given various kinds of information before they view these tapes. In one study, for example, all subjects are first given the same minimal information about the target child's problems. Next, they receive one of three kinds of information about treatment. Those randomly assigned to the "medication" condition are told that the target child received a trial of Ritalin. In the "school–home" condition, subjects are told that the treatment included systematic use of rewards, individualized academic programming, and exercises to enhance family communication. The third group was told that the child had received no treatment of any type. All subjects viewed the identical videotape and were then asked a series of questions about the causes of the child's problems, the seriousness of his difficulties, the most likely long-term outcomes, etc.

One interesting finding is that people do, indeed, tend to commit "treatment–etiology" fallacies (Whalen & Henker, 1976, 1977), reasoning that the same factors involved in a treatment program are the ones that caused the problem initially. Respondents led to believe that a school–home intervention program was implemented were more likely to attribute the problems to "other people" than were those told that the child had received medication ($M = 4.06$ versus 3.42), $F(1, 125) = 4.04$, $p < .05$. In contrast, the school–home group were less likely than the medication group to endorse "nervous system dysfunction" as a cause of the child's problems ($M = 1.65$ versus 2.60), $F(1, 125) = 6.31$, $p < .05$. A particularly consequential finding is that subjects who were told that the child had received Ritalin viewed the child's problems as more serious than those in either the "school–home" or the "no treatment" conditions. An intriguing sex difference also emerged: When the videotaped excerpts were sequenced so as to suggest behavioral improvement over time, females were significantly more likely than males to note this improvement.

These data suggest that knowledge about the type of treatment a child is receiving may influence a respondent's global impression of that child—independently of the child's actual behaviors (since all respondents viewed the same videotape). If replicated in more naturalistic contexts, this type of effect could have weighty implications for standard clinical practice; treatment decisions and program evaluations are often based on subjective ratings obtained from teachers and parents who are involved in a child's treatment program. Given the importance of these processes, the authors decided to take a closer look at the influence of a respondent's knowledge or "suspicions" on his or her assessment of children's behavior.

The summer school program previously described provided an ideal context for a study of this type. Some of the staff (primarily graduate students) knew the research objectives and experimental design, whereas others (primarily undergraduates) did not even know that the research focus was on hyperactivity and medication effects, believing instead that the goal was to study the development of interpersonal and attentional styles during middle childhood. All staff provided Conners (1973c) Abbreviated Symptom Questionnaire (ASQ) ratings routinely after each experimental module or at the end of each school morning. When those staff members who knew that some of the children would be on placebo a portion of the time were asked to guess medication status, they indicated a partial ability to break the double-blind code. Despite this ability, the pattern of ASQ ratings obtained from these "knowledgeable" staff was quite similar to the pattern obtained from the "naive" staff, a finding indicating that positive psychostimulant effects are not attributable to rater sensitization. These results are detailed in Henker, Whalen, and Collins (1979).

The fact that rater knowledge of psychostimulant treatment did *not* elevate symptom ratings is somewhat reassuring. Still, why were elevations seen in the videotape study? In comparing these two studies, it is important to pinpoint several differences in context and methodology. The raters in the summer program knew the youngsters and interacted with them daily. They were asked to evaluate child behaviors during discrete periods of time (e.g., a single task or a single morning in the classroom) rather than to provide an overall impression. They used the Conners 10-item ASQ rather than a single, global rating of problem severity. Finally, several ratings of the same children were obtained during both medication and placebo conditions. The fact that treatment information significantly influenced judgments in the videotape study but not in the naturalistic study suggests the importance of both specificity in method and familiarity. When the raters knew the children well, were also familiar with the rating instrument, and were asked relatively specific questions, their responses were not influenced by their treatment knowledge. When these conditions did not prevail, there was a tendency for treatment information to affect the evaluation of a child independently of the child's actual behavior.

These findings also have implications for double-blind methodologies. It is well known that sophisticated observers who are looking for drug effects may be able to crack the double-blind code, since behavior changes or side effects may signal the presence of active medication (e.g., Werry & Sprague, 1974). What is not known is whether or how such knowledge influences the assessment process. The findings of the Henker *et al.* (1979) study suggest that failure to maintain perfect double-blind conditions is to be expected when comparing psychoactive drugs with placebos; however, this does not necessarily invalidate data on drug effectiveness.

A related set of empirical questions, largely unexplored, concerns the relationships among perceiver characteristics and responses to child behaviors. For example, Stollak, Messé, Michaels, and Catlin (1977) found that fathers' interpersonal perceptual styles were related to specific behaviors toward their own children during family interaction tasks. More specifically, fathers who tended to give negative ratings to an unknown ("standard stimulus") child portraying various activities on a videotape also tended to be antagonistic, evasive, etc., while interacting with their own children. Although it is not possible to specify direction of causality on the basis of these findings, studies of this type can provide important information about assessment processes and intervention practices.

Syndrome and Subgroup Issues

A syndrome, according to the conventional medical model, is characterized by a consistent symptom pattern that shares both a consistent etiology and a consistent response to treatment. As discussed in the opening chapters, there is growing agreement among many child specialists and investigators that no unitary syndrome or disorder of hyperactivity will be demonstrated. In spite of this consensus, the prevailing clinical sentiment seems to be that true or primary hyperkinetics do exist and that, although they are relatively uncommon, experienced clinicians "know them when they see them." So far, however, data-based attempts to demonstrate the existence of this "classical hyperactive" have fallen short of meeting scientific criteria. One of the most perplexing findings is that characteristics that correlate conceptually and theoretically often fail to correlate (or show only modest relationships) when empirical studies are conducted (Klein & Gittelman-Klein, 1975; Langhorne, Loney, Paternite, & Bechtoldt, 1976; Routh & Roberts, 1972; Sandberg, Rutter, & Taylor, 1978; Werry, 1968b). For example, in a recent study of multiple measures of attention and activity level, Ullman, Barkley, and Brown (1978) found no consistent relationships between these two response domains; in other words, predictions of attentiveness from measures of motoric activity (or vice versa) could not be made at better than chance levels.

There are several possible explanations of the low intercorrelations that researchers typically obtain. Situational or environmental variations may generate differences in child behaviors—or in adult interpretations of child behaviors. Differential perspectives, orientations, and role responsibilities may also result in low congruence among measurement sources, for example, when behavior observation data are obtained from nonparticipant university undergraduates versus from classroom teachers. A third critical factor concerns specificity of assessment instruments and pervasiveness of measurement errors.

Most of the time when someone sets out to measure some aspect of hyperactive children's behavior, those measurements take place over a short period of time or in a relatively novel context or both. Cross-response covariation is rarely seen. But how surprising is that? Children have complex and variegated repertoires and adaptive skills; inconstancy may be the rule rather than the exception, simply because our measurement windows are too narrow. Moreover, some of the target response classes may be functional alternatives for each other, with children engaging sometimes in one (e.g., fidgeting) and sometimes in another (e.g., noise-making) under ostensibly similar conditions.

It would be instructive, for comparison purposes, to study response covariation or situation–behavior linkages in normal youngsters. One broad hypothesis might be that the behavior patterns of normal children, in contrast to those identified as hyperactive, would be more accurately predictable from a knowledge of situational norms or implicit constraints. A complementary hypothesis would be that behaviors sampled randomly, or without regard to situation, would show greater variability or less response covariation in the normals. That is, in spite of the common notion that hyperactive children are "unpredictable," they should nonetheless show greater cross-situation consistency than their unlabeled peers. Suggestive data along these lines were reported by Barkley and Ullman (1975).

It is noteworthy that, given better measuring instruments and recognition of potential moderator variables, improved interrater and cross-modality correlations are beginning to be seen (e.g., Copeland & Weissbrod, 1978; Goyette, Conners, & Ulrich, 1978; Kupietz & Richardson, 1978; Stevens, Kupst, Suran, & Schulman, 1978; Whalen *et al.,* 1979a). Further discussions of measurement strategies and issues appear in Conners (1977), Werry (1978a), and Whalen (in press).

One result of the relatively nonproductive syndrome search is the increased focus on environmental effects and Person × Situation interactions, as discussed previously. A second outcome is a call for standardization of subject selection criteria as well as of measurement instruments and settings. In a general discussion of child development research, Bell and Hertz (1976) suggest the use of standard marker variables to improve comparability and generalization across studies, and Keogh (1978) and her coworkers (Keogh, Major, Reid, Gandara, & Omori, 1979) are attempting to define such marker variables for research on children with learning disabilities. Another step toward standardization is the collaborative effort under the auspices of the Psychopharmacology Research Branch of the National Institute of Mental Health to generate an assessment battery for use in pediatric psychopharmacology (Guy, 1976), although the resultant battery has not achieved large-scale adoption.

The Conners (1973b) symptom questionnaires (usually the abbreviated form) have recently been adopted by several prominent research teams as selection measures. Typically a score around two standard deviations above the mean is set as a cutoff. Also, it is becoming common practice even for those investigators who do not use these Conners scales as selection criteria to nonetheless report Conners scores for their samples. Of course, the inherent subjectivity of the rating scales makes it difficult to interpret the scores in other than a "global problem" sense. If a set of marker variables and instruments is to be developed for hyperactivity, it will be necessary to include more precise measures of specific behavioral domains (e.g., sustained attention, interpersonal competence).

Still a third outcome of the syndrome quandary is an accelerating interest in the delineation of relatively homogeneous subgroups within the global rubric of hyperactivity. Most investigators now agree that hyperactivity is a heterogeneous category that probably subsumes multiple etiologies and symptom clusters (e.g., Conners, 1975b; Fish, 1971; Hastings & Barkley, 1978; Preis & Huessy, 1979; Ross & Ross, 1976), and recent empirical efforts are demonstrating the utility of this view. For example, Loney, Langhorne, and Paternite (1978) have identified two distinct behavior factors, Aggression and Hyperactivity. Some children scoring high on the Hyperactivity factor also obtain high scores on the Aggression factor but others, with identical Hyperactivity scores, obtain very low Aggression scores. The importance of this distinction is demonstrated by evidence that the two factors relate differently to various etiologic and prognostic variables, for example, parenting adequacy, socioeconomic status, and response to medication. The distinction to date stems from ratings made by judges on the basis of case history documentation in medical records; direct behavioral observations are now needed to facilitate separation of the contributions of (*a*) actual behavioral covariation from those of (*b*) conceptual covariance, that is, the implicit personality theories held by the chart readers.

Other attempts to delineate distinct subgroups are also quite promising. Some investigators are studying differences between hyperactive children who do and do not show various deviations in central or autonomic nervous system functioning (e.g., Porges & Smith, Chapter 3; Satterfield, Cantwell, Saul, Lesser, & Podosin, 1973). As discussed previously, David and coworkers are distinguishing between those with high and low body lead burdens (e.g., David *et al.*, 1977), and Conners (1973a, 1975b) has used specific clinical characteristics and patterns of psychological test scores with some success. The American Psychiatric Association is now recommending two new diagnostic categories: Attention Deficit Disorder with Hyperactivity, and Attention Deficit Disorder without Hyperactivity (Gittelman-Klein, Spitzer, & Cantwell, 1978). Although this distinction has not yet been documented empirically, it is certainly congruent with the Ullman *et al.* (1978) findings that various measures of activity level and attentiveness are relatively independent. To cite a final example, another group of investigators is studying differences between "situational" hyperactive youngsters, whose problems may be specific to home environments, and "true" hyperactive youngsters who show transsituational difficulties (Campbell *et al.*, 1977; Campbell, Schleifer, Weiss, & Perlman, 1977; Schleifer, Weiss, Cohen, Elman, Cvejic, & Kruger, 1975).

In summary, intriguing findings are emerging from studies in which children considered hyperactive have been subclassified along diverse behavioral, situational, or psychophysiological dimensions. Investigators are also attempting to delineate behavioral characteristics that distinguish between hyperactive children and nonhyperactive youngsters considered to have learning disabilities, conduct disorders, or general behavior problems (e.g., Firestone & Martin, 1979; Lahey, Stempniak, Robinson, & Tyroler, 1978). Additional research along these lines should serve several purposes, for example (*a*) clarifying contradictory findings in the published literature, (*b*) pinpointing distinct etiological patterns, (*c*) enhancing the match between child characteristics and treatment strategies, and (*d*) increasing the ability to predict immediate and long-term outcomes for hyperactive children.

Neglected Subgroups

In studies of hyperactivity, one of the most formidable hurdles is recruitment of an appropriate research sample. Practical difficulties and ethical constraints have resulted in a relatively narrow focus on children—primarily boys—who have been referred for professional evaluation. There are at least two other subgroups that merit careful study: school-aged girls considered hyperactive, and children (of either sex) whose checklist scores are as deviant as those of hyperactive children, but who have not been diagnosed or treated.

In normative studies, female children generally receive less negative ratings from parents and teachers than do males (Goyette *et al.*, 1978; Sprague, Cohen, & Eichiseder, 1977; Werry, Sprague, & Cohen, 1975). As discussed in Chapters 1, 5, and 6, females are also less likely than males to be diagnosed hyperactive. But what do we know about those girls who *are* launched into the clinical process? Do their difficulties match those of their male counterparts? How similar is the developmental course, and what environmental and behavioral characteristics are associated with female hyperactivity at various developmental levels? Perhaps female behaviors that generate the diagnostic label are more or less extreme than those of males, or perhaps they differ along qualitative rather than quantitative dimensions. There are some suggestions in the literature that the antecedents and concomitants of male and female hyperactivity may differ (Battle & Lacey, 1972; Prinz & Loney, 1974), and data presented by Preis and Huessy (1979) suggest that hyperactive girls may have a better prognosis than their male counterparts. At this point, however, the data are too sparse to allow more than speculation. Given the potential information yield, studies of female hyperactive children seem well worth the practical and economic costs.

Both of the epidemiological studies reported in this volume (Chapters 5 and 6) identified children who were perceived as displaying as much undesirable or "symptomatic" behavior as the hyperactive group, but who had never been diagnosed or treated. The existence of these subgroups underscores the need for caution in the use of cut-off scores as the primary criterion of hyperactivity. According to the data presented in Chapters 5 and 6, such a practice could lead to the labeling of between 3 and 8% of school-aged youngsters as hyperactive, even though they had not (yet) come to professional attention.

In addition to the diagnostic questions raised by these subgroups, there are intriguing research issues. Do these children have personal strengths that counteract their dysfunctional behaviors? Are there specific circumstances or situational factors that help them escape the labeling process? Is it more a matter of delay than of escape? Perhaps these children are just beginning to have difficulties and are soon to be referred for professional evaluation. Or, are the negative ratings for this subgroup more a function of parent and teacher characteristics than of child characteristics? Answers to these questions could help unravel the complex chain of events that leads to diagnosis and treatment. There are fundamental ethical issues involved in studies of unidentified children, however, and investigators will need to insure that research efforts do not in themselves lead to clinical labels or expectations that particular children are slated for difficulty.

Parents as Protagonists

As a group, parents have what might be called an "image problem" in the child health and education arena. It is often assumed that parents cannot (or will not) give accurate historical reports about their child or valid information about current difficulties. In many instances it is also assumed that parents can understand neither the complexities of possible problem causes nor the pros and cons of treatment alternatives. One common view is that parents are a necessary evil to be "managed" in the least obstructive and time-consuming manner. A related view is that parents are prime contributors to their child's problems and thus their impact must be either minimized or rectified. In a critique of the way professionals often treat parents of autistic children, Schopler (1971) describes the notion of "parentectomy," that is, the view that the child's best interests require complete and permanent separation from parents. Fortunately, physical separation of parent and child is not a common intervention for either hyperactive or autistic children. The point is that the implicit assumptions underlying such a view pervade many offices and agencies and contribute to what might be called the mismanagement of parents of atypical youngsters.

Indeed, parents do pose many problems for child specialists. Validity studies have documented inaccuracies in information obtained from parents about a child's family and medical history. Multivariate assessments demonstrate that checklist and observational data obtained from parents about their child's current functioning often correlate only marginally, or not at all, with data obtained from other, presumably more objective sources. Other research has delineated ways in which faulty parenting behaviors can interfere with healthy child development. Such findings have important implications for the prevention and amelioration of atypical behavior in children. The problem, however, is that the facts are overgeneralized to the point that parents are often viewed as falling somewhere on a truncated continuum that runs from "useless or irrelevant" through "minor irritant" to "pernicious influence." In addition to the obvious humanitarian and practical problems inherent in such views, these dysfunctional fictions seriously constrain the accumulation of research evidence on the causes and treatment of childhood disorders. It seems clear that some "image reparation" is in order.

In their multifaceted commerce with child specialists, parents serve—or should serve—in at least three important capacities, each in need of empirical investigation.

PARENTS AS INFORMATION PROVIDERS

Parents are a rich and often untapped source of data about atypical child development and family coping strategies. It is true that the information they provide is often imperfect and misleading, but such a criticism can also be leveled at most other measurement sources, even those considered well-standardized and highly objective. Problems with teacher checklists, mechanical devices for recording activity levels, autonomic nervous system indexes, etc., have *not* led investigators to discard these potentially important indicators, and it seems ironic that parent report—one of the richest data sources—is so frequently discounted.

PARENTS AS INFORMATION RECIPIENTS

When it comes to assessing and treating children, parents are the ones who are on the firing line, those most responsible for the child's welfare. Despite this obvious fact, it is still quite common to provide only minimal amounts of information about the results of diagnostic tests, the limitations and possible side effects of various treatment programs, etc. It is often assumed that parents are incapable of understanding clinical complexities and likely to misuse any information they glean. As Schopler (1976) notes, there are also serious role conflicts between parental responsibility and professional authority. Many professionals do not want to disclose the limits in their knowledge, nor do they want to be held accountable to parents. Traditionally, the role structure has been hierarchical, with the authoritative professionals at the top and in complete control. But changes are accruing as the result of new legislation and litigation. The Freedom of Information Act, the Buckley Amendment, mandated due process hearings for educational placement decisions, new guidelines for informed consent in clinical research with human subjects—all are opening up the information conduits for parents.

PARENTS AS CONSULTANTS FOR CHILD SPECIALISTS AND POLICYMAKERS

In addition to being in the best position to provide information about and implement intervention programs for their own children, parents of hyperactive and other atypical youngsters have had unique experiences and have evolved intriguing coping strategies that are worthy of study in their own right.

As Eisenpreis (1979) so aptly notes, "Living with some of these children is a feat that should not be discounted [p. 126]." Parents have developed creative lifestyle adjustments compatible with the needs of a hyperactive child, as well as with the needs and desires of other family members. Whereas some parents achieve remarkable success in these realms, others are unable to cope with the additional stresses engendered by living with a hyperactive child. There are signs of disproportionately high rates of psychopathology, marital discord, and divorce in families with hyperactive youngsters (e.g., Barkley, 1978; Stewart & Morrison, 1973), but it is not yet possible to assess direction of effect. The impressionistic and anecdotal data provided in clinical interviews and written parental accounts stand as vivid testimony to the importance of parental characteristics, environmental variables, and institutional parameters in determining specific outcomes for individual children (e.g., Bittinger, 1977; Gorham, des Jardins, Page, Pettis, & Scheiber, 1975; Henker & Whalen, in press).

On a more macrocosmic level, some parents have evolved productive conceptualizations of social and institutional networks and functional strategies for negotiating bureaucratic leviathans in the pursuit of their child's best interests. Parent interest groups have been spawned, and "parent power" has assumed a recognized role in political arenas. The ramifications of these phenomena are far reaching and poorly understood.

There are important research questions that need to be addressed, many of which stem directly from the three preceding parent role descriptions. For example, how can we improve the accuracy and utility of clinical information obtained *from* parents? How can we demystify professional practices and best communicate *to* parents the meaning of intelligence tests and other diagnostic indicators, the probabilistic nature of treatment outcomes, the cost–risk–benefit trade-offs involved in any form of treatment, and the limitations of scientific knowledge? Needed also are studies of the different coping mechanisms and lifestyle changes that unfold in families with hyperactive children, and the complex interrelationships among diverse family variables, environmental factors, and child outcomes. Another fruitful research arena is the natural careers of parents of atypical youngsters as they learn to negotiate complex social institutions and bureaucratic practices. The evolving roles and functions of parent coalitions and interest groups are also worthy areas for empirical investigation. Studies of this type will not only contribute to knowledge about hyperactivity, but will also provide much needed information about the complex interplay among individuals, families, health and education professions, and social institutions.

Nonpharmacologic Treatment Modalities

Behavioral approaches (including cognitive behavior modification and self-control training) are the most commonly used nonpharmacologic interventions for hyperactive youngsters. Unlike psychostimulant treatments, these alternative interventions were not developed specifically for the academic and behavior problems of hyperactive children. Token economies in the schools, parent management training, self-instructional programs—all were developed and tested on diverse adult and child populations prior to their specific applications with hyperactive children. Burgeoning concerns about the risks and limitations of psychostimulant treatment have spurred ambitious attempts to tailor these "tried and true" behavioral approaches to the specific needs and characteristics of hyperactive children and their families.

In many ways, the developmental course of behavioral approaches to hyperactivity mirrors the history of stimulant drug treatment. Early enthusiasm has been tempered substantially by limited results; long-term effects are either unknown or discouraging; and situational parameters are assuming a progressively central role. The research is plagued by the same problems found in stimulant drug studies, including heterogeneity of samples, problems of measurement, lack of generalization, and confounding of treatments. Despite the numerous conceptual, methodological, and logistic hurdles, many promising results are emerging from behavioral intervention programs. For critical reviews of these studies, the reader is referred to Backman and Firestone (1979), Craighead, Wilcoxon-Craighead, and Meyers (1978), Lahey (1978), Mash and Dalby (1979), Meichenbaum (1978),

Pelham (1978), and Rosenbaum and Drabman (1979). Details about specific treatment programs appear in Chapters 7, 8, and 11.

The current trend seems clear: Cost–risk–benefit analyses and omnibus treatment packages are becoming more common as clinical investigators recognize the risks and limitations of *any* single intervention approach. At the present time, however, such multimodal treatment programs are limited primarily to research settings. Stimulant treatment imposes fewer demands on a child, a teacher, and a family than any behavioral approach, and there is evidence suggesting that nonpharmacologic interventions are rarely implemented, even when they are recommended as adjuncts to medication (Sandoval, Lambert, & Yandell, 1976). A major need at the present time is research on the "palatability" of various treatment modalities and the logistics of implementation; as Kazdin and Wilson (1978) observe, "consumer evaluation" of treatment is a neglected area of therapy research.

The risks and hazards of alternate treatments, including the whole array of educational interventions and psychological therapies, have received far less attention than the side effects of psychoactive medication. It is commonly assumed that nonpharmacologic therapies carry no risks—almost by definition—but the requisite empirical studies have not yet been conducted.

Another research need is the delineation of optimal combinations of specific treatment techniques, child (and family) characteristics, environmental settings, and behavioral outcomes. For example, what is the best method for decreasing impulsive social behavior at school in a normally achieving, 10-year-old boy from a low-income family? Would the recommended approach vary for an underachiever, a middle-income family, an older child, a neighborhood setting? Empirical questions focused on interactions of this type are much more likely to yield functional answers than are attempts to determine, for example, whether drug treatment is superior to operant behavior modification or whether either of these approaches surpasses cognitive self-instructional training in a global sense (Bugental, Whalen, & Henker, 1977; Mash & Dalby, 1979.)

LEGISLATION AND LITIGATION: THE LEGACY OF THE 1970s

Judicial and Legislative Influences on Health and Education Practices

This is an era of concern about human rights, particularly those of children. Unprecedented legal actions are mandating immediate changes in the ways we teach and treat children. Public consciousness of individual rights and protections is increasing rapidly, and concerned parents, consumer action groups, the courts, and the legislatures are altering health care and educational institutions with an impact not seen for decades. These contemporary developments have both immediate and long-term implications for the identification and treatment of hyperactive children.

Perhaps the best known example of influential legislation is the Education for All Handicapped Children Act of 1975, typically referred to by its Public Law (PL) number as "94-142." This act has been billed as "the most significant federal legislation to affect education in the last decade [Ryor, 1978, p. 6]." Under the provisions of 94-142, all children are now guaranteed a free and appropriate public education. A multidisciplinary team must evaluate any child thought to be handicapped and prepare an individualized education program (IEP); a target subgroup or a diagnostic classification can no longer be the unit of analysis or application. Another major focus of this bill is on the assurance of due process procedures including provisions for parental participation in the planning and decision-making for their child.

The most provocative stipulation of 94-142 is that education be provided to all children in the *least restrictive environment,* a concept interpreted in this act to mean inclusion in regular classrooms to the maximum extent appropriate. While this bill does not directly mandate mainstreaming, the intent of the legislation is clear and each IEP must contain a statement of the extent to which the child will be able to participate in regular educational programs [Section 4(a)(17) of PL 94-142].

One immediate question concerns the extent to which hyperactive children are covered by the provisions of PL 94-142. Are they handicapped? The legal answer is a qualified "yes"; they would be eligible, under the act, to the extent that they have specific learning disabilities *and* their disabilities require specially designed instruction. The federal definition of learning disabilities includes perceptual handicaps, *minimal brain dysfunction* (emphasis ours), and dyslexia as well as brain injury or a language disorder that "may manifest itself in imperfect ability to listen, think, speak, read, write, spell, or do mathematical calculations [Section 5(b)(4) of PL 94-142]." At the same time, the definition specifically *excludes* learning problems that result from emotional disturbance or from environmental, cultural or economic disadvantage. (The pros and cons of trying to distinguish among learning problems on the basis of presumed etiology is, of course, another matter.)

The one feature that ensures substantial impact for 94-142 is that it carries a large degree of fiscal clout. From 1982 onward, each participating state is slated to receive a supplement of 40% of the national average per pupil expenditure for each student being served. (Smaller, escalating supplements are in effect prior to 1982.) There is a ceiling of 12% on the number of students who can be counted as handicapped and, currently, children with learning disabilities cannot exceed one-sixth of the total. If

Congress appropriates the full funding authorized, over 3 billion added dollars may go to special education in 1982. Congress has not yet, however, given full funding. For fiscal year 1980–81, the projected appropriation is $804 million, although the full authorization would be $2.3 billion. Even with this reduction, however, the immediate future will see many added dollars available for special education and related services (Where Are the Children, 1978).

Although PL 94-142 is being used here as the foremost example of influential legislation, its provisions are by no means unique. As noted by Ballard (1977), PL 93-380 carried similar guarantees of due process and of education in the least restrictive environment. Moreover, Section 504 of the Rehabilitation Act of 1973 (PL 93-112) anticipated most of the provisions of 94-142 and clearly affirmed the principle of meeting needs on an individual basis (as contrasted to group or type of disability).

It should be noted that the protections of the federal legislation extend to every qualifying child *whether or not* that child is counted for fiscal purposes. As Ballard (1977) points out, even if a given state refuses to participate under 94-142, that state must still meet the nearly identical requirements of Section 504.

The enactments of these federal protections in the middle 1970s were far from isolated events. One example of both legal precedent and public demand was seen in earlier lawsuits involving "classification challenges" (appropriate testing, labeling, and classification of children). The California public had recognized that racial and ethnic minorities are "overrepresented" in special classes for the educable mentally retarded (EMR). Board of Education statistics indicated that black children represented only 6% of the school-age population, yet they represented 24% of those enrolled in EMR classes. The analogous figures for Chicanos were 9% and 27% (Gilhool, 1976). Raising grave concerns about the discriminatory use of stigmatic labels, this information spurred both judicial and legislative action. Two landmark cases are particularly noteworthy, thc first involving Chicano youth (Diana v. Board of Education, 1970) and the second involving black youth (Larry P. v. Riles, 1972). These court cases, along with recent legislative acts, have led to wholesale changes in California educational policy. As Keogh and Barkett (1978) indicate, "The California Education Code (6902.085) now requires that testing can be conducted only with parental consent, that assessment include evidence relative to the pupil's developmental history and academic achievement, and that the child be tested in his native language [p. 91]. For additional details, see the trenchant analysis by Kirp, Kuriloff, and Buss (1975).

Moreover, the classification challenges and "rights to education" legislation have their close parallels in the body of case law building around the "rights to treatment" decisions. The past few years have witnessed judicial decisions that have far-reaching implications for the treatment of those deemed mentally ill or retarded. One of the most influential court cases involved an Alabama state institution for mentally retarded people. In the now classic *Wyatt* v. *Stickney* (1972) decision, the court not only affirmed the constitutional right to treatment, but also ordered implementation of an extensive set of minimal standards for habilitation. The themes are similar to those underlying the educational policy changes summarized above. *Wyatt* and progeny mandate individualized treatment plans designed to maximize each person's capabilities. Moreover, the treatment must be provided in the least restrictive setting (Gilhool, 1976).

The *Wyatt* decision also considers medication practices, articulating the right "to be free from unnecessary or excessive medication" and stipulating that "medication shall not be used as punishment, for the convenience of the staff, as a substitute for a habilitation program, or in quantities that interfere with the resident's habilitation program [Sprague & Baxley, 1978]." Although this particular case involved mentally retarded individuals confined to institutions, the implications are much broader. There is little question that the use of psychoactive medication will be more carefully monitored and more tightly regulated in the near future. In their excellent review, Sprague and Baxley (1978) chronicle the right to treatment litigation and detail the emergent "minimal standards" for habilitation.

In summary, there are several major themes and concepts that form the crest of the advancing legal wave: right to education, right to treatment, individualized programs, nondiscriminatory testing, parental participation, and due process guarantees. Of these leading concepts, the one with the most pervasive influence is clearly that of the "least restrictive alternative." Children are to be educated—and cared for—in the least restrictive environment, their status is to be evaluated using the least restrictive techniques, and they are to be given treatment using the least restrictive methods. It is this single theme of "least restrictiveness" that both creates the widest opportunities and raises the most difficult scientific, procedural, and ethical questions for society.

Implementation: The Impediments and Implications

The 1980s will see major advances in the implementation of the new legal stipulations. The pace is already a rapid one as, for example, PL 94-142 is scheduled to reach its full and permanent funding level on October 1, 1982. Although the Congress and the courts have already mandated the changes, many questions of both practicality and impact remain unanswered.

SCIENTIFIC FEASIBILITY

One immediate question is whether we have the actual knowledge and technology required to follow the legal dictates. In a concerned disquisition on children's rights, Mnookin (1978) observes that, "in many areas what is best for an individual child or for children in general is usually indeterminate or speculative, and is not demonstrable by scientific proof, but is instead fundamentally a matter of values [p. 163]." Has science produced any definitive answers, for instance, on which classroom environments are the least restrictive? The simplest route, conceptually, is to define this term on the basis of temporal and spatial considerations: The least restrictive educational setting is one in which the target child spends the largest amount of time possible in closest possible proximity to unlabeled children. However, this type of nonrestrictiveness may not enhance an atypical child's intellectual and interpersonal competencies. Inadequate academic background, inappropriate curricular materials, insensitive or impatient peers, undertrained and overworked teachers—all could seriously truncate educational progress for handicapped youngsters in regular classrooms. There has been no research on restrictiveness of educational settings, and we know very little about how to optimize learning environments for individual youngsters (Cruickshank, 1977; Keogh & Levitt, 1976).

Issues of scientific feasibility also emerge in outcome studies of educational programs and treatment modalities. Comparisons of alternative "mainstreaming" programs have been hampered by inadequate evaluation systems (Keogh & Levitt, 1976), as have attempts to implement legal decisions in the right to treatment cases. One recent judicial dictate, for example, is that the effects of drugs and other treatments must be monitored regularly and that treatment plans must be guided and modified on the basis of systematic outcome data. As Sprague and Baxley (1978) explicate, there is no well-accepted, standardized technique for evaluating treatment responsiveness. At present, these treatment issues are being rapidly extended beyond institutionalized populations. Already, there are trends in ongoing litigation to require physicians to obtain data from teachers when evaluating the effects of psychostimulants on hyperactive youngsters. The legal system is requiring the monitoring of progress, yet the technology for doing so is simply unavailable.

ADMINISTRATIVE AND FISCAL FEASIBILITY

A distinct but related problem concerns the pool of available talent. Regular classroom teachers have not been trained in special education, and many are worrying about their competence to design and implement IEPs (Ryor, 1978). Analogously, school and medical personnel who received no training in individual assessment or program evaluation are now being asked to collect systematic outcome data. In a review intended primarily for the medical profession, Palfrey, Mervis, and Butler (1978) maintain that PL 94-142 "assumes a sophistication of diagnostic ability and curriculum design that does not yet exist, and therefore places a special burden upon physicians [p.

819]." In addition to concerns over lack of preparation and inadequate methodology, there are real-life time and energy constraints, since these new responsibilities are often unaccompanied by sufficient resources.

In this time of limited resources, economic issues are paramount in the implementation process. Inevitably, the new legislation and litigation present additional, and often conflicting, demands on the public purse. Kirp *et al.* (1975) report that the cost of a due process hearing regarding a child's educational program in Pennsylvania in 1973 was about $500—an amount equal to half the annual cost of school for a typical child. Although federal funding is an important component of PL 94-142, there are still numerous financial obligations for state and local agencies. There are also many policy decisions to be made. Will class size be reduced when students with special needs are placed in regular classrooms? How about funding for inservice training or release time for teachers to participate in the IEP process? In brief, how will the priorities be established for the mandated changes, and by whom?

Ripples and Ramifications: A Journey into the Unknown

All of these developments are new, and it is too soon to predict their full impact. One thing seems certain: We are living in a litigation prone era, and the 1980s are sure to bring added courtroom settlements and legislative mandates intended to protect the rights of children—or of specific subgroups of children. Considered in isolation, each new shift in policy or practice would probably be widely accepted by professionals, policymakers, and the public. The intentions and basic philosophies are sound. The problem is that these changes cannot be considered in isolation; each modification creates reverberations throughout the health and education sectors. Thus we return to a discussion of unintended emanative effects, not of pharmacotherapy, as in Chapter 1 of this volume, but of the new legal mandates. The concentric circle model presented in the opening chapter will be used as an organizing schema for this discussion.

EFFECTS ON THE CHILD AND FAMILY (CIRCLES 1 AND 2)

Many of the current reforms touch directly on the hyperactive child. One major issue is medication. Whereas requirements for outcome monitoring are presently focused on children placed outside their own homes, many authorities believe it will be a very short time until regular monitoring will be in practice for every medicated child. To the extent that it is practical, such monitoring can have a salutary impact on hyperactive children through enhancement of physician–teacher communication and early recognition and continued assessment of the effects, and noneffects, of psychoactive medication. There are also certain hazards inherent in this trend, however, such as the threats to confidentiality and personal privacy always posed by systematic monitoring mechanisms.

Families are going to have a greater voice—and schools or physicians a lesser voice—in whether or not a child takes medication at all. Gone are the days when a child can be sent home from school with the proviso that he cannot return until he is on medication or, conversely, be barred from admission if he *is* taking stimulants. Children's rights to treatment are being strongly upheld in the courts, as are their parallel rights to refuse treatment (see discussions by Gilhool, 1976; Weithorn, 1979; Wells, 1973). A related issue that is receiving increased attention is the question of "who decides" when parent and child disagree about an intervention or treatment program, particularly in instances where the parent may have a potential conflict of interest (Mnookin, 1978). Padway (1978), for example, speculates that, "The parent may face conflicting interests as a decision-maker on behalf of the child, since the child's interests may best be served by substantial environmental changes in lieu of drug treatment, while the parent may be discomfited by those changes [p. 459]."

EFFECTS ON PROFESSIONAL PRACTICES AND SOCIAL INSTITUTIONS (CIRCLES 3 and 4)

Schools have considerable discretion in initiating referrals for evaluation and specialized programming. In the best of possible worlds, such decisions would be based primarily on the needs and competencies of the individual child. The burgeoning policy changes dictated by courts and legislatures, however, have been followed by disconcerting reports that these decisions are being made on the basis of fiscal fears, administrative exigencies, or professional self-interest. One psychiatrist told us that there has been a substantial decrease in school referrals for psychiatric evaluation since the passage of PL 94-142. His interpretation is that the schools fear additional budgetary burdens. If the psychiatric evaluation includes a recommendation for a program not currently available in the public education sector, the school system may have to arrange—and foot the bill—for an expensive private program. Another interpretation of such a decrease is that the new federal legislation has enhanced the assessment and intervention capacities of local school districts to such an extent that psychiatric referrals are not as often required. This interpretation seems unlikely, however, given the short amount of time since the passage of PL 94-142.

There are also concerns about due process hearings. Professionals fear unpleasant confrontations and administrators fear lawsuits from irate parents (Keogh & Barkett, 1978; Kirp *et al.*, 1975). An easy way to alleviate these fears is to refrain from referring youngsters with problems. Thus,there are systemic and bureaucratic forces that might prevent children with special needs from receiving mandated services.

The net effects of such an outcome cannot be predicted at the present time. Some teachers may be encouraged by these changes to focus on identifying each child's specific learning styles and tailoring pedagogical approaches to individual children rather than to diagnostic labels. Without individualized programming, however, maintaining youngsters in regular classrooms may have negative consequences not only for the atypical child, but also for classmates and teachers. A related concern is that the new policies for handicapped children may be a disservice to normal youngsters, as disproportionate amounts of scarce teacher time and energy are consumed by one or two atypical children.

Another mixed blessing can be seen in the fact that, in order to qualify under much of the legislation, a child must be considered "handicapped." An IEP is not written for a nonlabeled child, and special educational services are not available unless a child is identified. Many children who show hyperactive behavior patterns have nonetheless avoided formal diagnosis or else they are considered only "slightly hyperactive." Now there will be clear fiscal incentives to identify these children as having a learning disability or, perhaps, minimal cerebral dysfunction.

There are yet other features of 94-142 that may encourage labeling. Under Section 619 of the bill, states receive special incentive grants for providing special educational services to children in the preschool age group. Once again, special monies are available contingent upon early diagnosis of the individual. The regulations also specify that priority considerations be given to the most severely handicapped children. These fiscal incentives for labeling may, in the long run, create far more benefit than harm to the child. Nonetheless, such regulations are double-edged swords, increasing the probability that some children will be labeled inappropriately or unnecessarily.

The emerging legislative and judicial mandates for educational reforms are not, ipso facto, either salutary or deleterious. Rather, they have weighty yet uncharted consequences. Recent policy shifts have resulted in what might be termed "natural experiments," and it is not too soon to start analyzing outcomes. For example, Keogh and Barkett (1978) note that the California moratorium on intelligence testing has resulted in virtually no placement in EMR classes, and it is imperative to track the careers of those students who would have been placed in EMR classes if testing policies had continued unchanged. How many of them are functioning well and, perhaps more importantly, what are the personal, environmental, and programmatic correlates of good versus poor outcomes? Current ethical constraints regarding research with children may severely shackle researchers seeking these data, but the questions are important ones to answer if policymakers are to be guided by facts in addition to intentions and intuitions.

Without careful monitoring, the new legal compulsions may insure procedural but not substantive due process (Keogh & Barkett, 1978). Diagnosed handicapped children may indeed remain in physical proximity to their normal peers, and others may escape formal diagnosis and classification. Although these changes satisfy many, they do nothing to guarantee optimal educational and social achievements for individual children. Under which conditions do such changes enhance individual competencies, and under which conditions do they interfere with long-term adaptations?

Furthermore, PL 94-142 places added stresses and strains on an educational system already struggling to meet overwhelming commitments. In better times, this act would have been met with open arms by child specialists and educators. The mandate to individualize curriculum planning and to involve parents in their children's education would have been welcomed with little ambivalence. It would have provided a golden opportunity to enhance professional competencies, to improve communication, and to conduct basic research on learning.

Undoubtedly, some of these lofty goals will be realized. Yet 94-142 occurs in the midst of other social movements, not always mutually compatible. The so-called taxpayers' revolt and the antiresearch efforts are among the leading contenders. How can we explain the fact that Massachusetts, long considered one of the most enlightened states in terms of mental health care, was also the first state to formally block needed research on child interventions? If the public purse constricts with the taxpayers' revolt, how readily will expensive individualized interventions be funded for children who can be maintained on inexpensive medication or group programs?

The dynamic interplay among these social movements is highly complex and not well understood. In studying this interplay, we also need to look at the entire process of social and political agenda setting. That new rights for children have achieved a secure niche on the public agenda is now undeniable. The will of parents and advocates has been translated into effective power. It is indeed regrettable that these events have placed child specialists in a reactive (and sometimes defensive) mode. Given the special expertise of professionals in guiding the needed changes, the reactive stance is neither appropriate nor cost-effective. This seems a propitious time to consider ways to reverse the directional arrow so that child specialists' *actions* may come to generate legal *reactions* in the common pursuit of children's rights.

EPILOGUE

In the next few years we can expect that hyperactivity, as a label or diagnosis, is going to receive less usage. Most of the dissatisfactions with the diagnostic term stem as much from the fact that it is a misnomer as from the fact that the syndrome it supposedly represents is neither unitary nor cohesive. It is unquestionably true that excessive or *hyper*-activity levels are seldom the major problem in the children who receive this diagnosis; many such children show unremarkable levels of general activity. As mentioned earlier, the American Psychiatric Association is proposing a nomenclature revision that would change the main descriptor to Attention Deficit Disorder. Also previously noted were the new federal provisions for special education, provisions that are likely to revitalize the term Minimal Cerebral Dysfunction, as well as bring increasingly specific and descriptive labeling of problems in school learning. Terminology changes will almost certainly occur, although it is too early to predict with any confidence whether the psychiatric or the legal–educational classification will prevail.

Still, before the term hyperactivity goes away, one can argue, wistfully if not scientifically, that although it may indeed be a misnomer, it has been a fairly benevolent misnomer. It does not carry the connotation of defect or deficit, and it does not imply a lifelong condition or trait. The term can appear on a cumulative record or in a medical summary without conveying a host of pejorative expectations. In the eyes of the public, as well as most practicing professionals, hyperactivity is something that will be outgrown. Whether its replacements will be so benign remains to be seen.

One thing seems certain—whether or not the term is disappearing, the children are most assuredly still here. Research in the area of hyperactivity is growing in quantity, creativity, and methodological sophistication. Although there is still a long way to go, we can pronounce the state of research at the moment as healthy. Yet, we have been painfully slow in putting research into practice, in translating the findings from major studies into clinically and educationally useful innovations. Even a cursory or informal survey of any community in the country will show that the average hyperactive child is receiving no special help or treatment beyond that which the intuitions of parents and teacher can provide. For the relatively small group of children who are on medication and who are showing successful responses to it, the situation is not much better, if any. Although medication ought to be an *adjunctive* therapy, it is all too often the primary or even the sole intervention, as discussed previously. And just as surely as it makes little sense to rely solely on treatment by medication, it makes equally little sense to rely solely on any single mode of psychological intervention, be it family therapy, classroom engineering, or self-regulation training for the child.

The gap between research and practice poses a complex challenge concerning the dissemination of empirical findings that have direct and weighty implications for clinical practice. What are the optimal means of facilitating the impact of valid research results, without encouraging premature applications of tentative findings? Stated alternatively, how can we increase the bidirectional flow of information between practitioner and researcher?

One useful step toward meeting this challenge is increased integration of research and clinical settings. Much of the most consequential information now available on hyperactivity has been generated in combined research–treatment facilities. There are, however, a large number of private practitioners, small group practices, and independent clinics that treat numerous hyperactive children without systematic documentation of any type. To continue to ignore these fertile research arenas is a luxury society can no longer afford. Practitioners who see dozens of children each day have little time to mount systematic data collection efforts. Even the addition of a single, part-time research investigator to a clinic facility would significantly enhance the accumulation of the empirical information needed to optimize diagnostic and intervention efforts.

Even greater gains could be made if such an approach were launched directly in the schools. Right now, virtually all of the useful data on the daily response styles and performances of these youngsters are lost because no functional guidance is available to the people in a position to collect these data.

An analysis of the current picture shows two very major and global areas of need. What is needed most at the micro level—the level of the individual child—is a more clinically useful model of treatment. At the macro level, the need is for sweeping revisions in the current system for delivering services to children.

A clinically useful model is one that involves functional assessment and task analysis, and matches the steps taken during assessment phases to those taken during treatment phases. There are two unfortunate aspects of the typical assessment–treatment disjunction. The first is that children are often subjected to numerous medical and psychological tests, despite the fact that the results of such tests, given the current state of knowledge, have no bearing on treatment recommendations. The second is that even when clinical assessments could and probably should have direct implications for treatment, the interface is rarely achieved. Very few children given the diagnosis "Attention Deficit Disorder" are enrolled in treatment programs designed to enhance attentional skills, and youngsters labeled "interpersonally incompetent" are unlikely to receive social skills training. Given recent developments in treatment–training programs of this type—as discussed throughout this volume—it is now possible to create the needed links between assessment and intervention.

The major need at the macro level concerns service delivery. Outside the family, the educational system and the medical system are the two major social institutions charged with guiding the growth and development of every child. At times, the service responsibilities of these two systems articulate well, as when both participate in a vaccination program. More often, a given group of children presents special problems that are not clearly within the province of either system. Such seems to be the case with hyperactivity. Education is on one side, medicine on the other, and the most salient problems of the hyperactive child fall squarely into the void between the two. The family pediatrician may be the final authority on the child's "hyperactivity," but that same pediatrician is not in a good position to be of any direct help with the child's poor peer relationships, failure to remember long division, or incessant practice with bird calls at the dinner table. The teacher is in a much better position to exercise day-to-day responsibility, but that same teacher has had no special training in the remediation of attention and memory problems, in the teaching of social skills, or in the management of classroom behavior. The physician can write a prescription and the teacher can provide individual attention, but neither of them has the time or expertise to help the child get through the lunch hour without a tussle, or to train the parent in setting up a system to make the household more livable.

In concluding their excellent book on hyperactivity, Ross and Ross (1976) noted many of these same themes. Their suggestion was for the establishment of interdisciplinary teams, each member with a high level of training, who would guide the management of each youngster and also work directly with parents. These teams would contain not only the teacher and the physician, but also a social worker, school nurse, and psychologist. The latter, preferably a pediatric psychologist, would be the team's coordinator and also be responsible for evaluating their procedures.

We would strongly agree with Ross and Ross and even suggest that perhaps what is needed is a third major system, one charged with responsibility for the behavioral, social, and mental health of children and families. Members of this system would include the psychologists, the nurses, and the social workers—all three professions that have vital skills to offer but whose contributions have been severely limited by the existing structure of service delivery. To establish a delivery system oriented toward behavioral health will not be a simple task. Entrenched interests and bureaucracies do not easily bend to innovation. The required changes will take several years, much re-education, and, beyond that, a large number of scarce and shrinking dollars.

But there is also a much brighter side to the picture. The multifaceted problem called hyperactivity is a tough but not intractable one. Whether one speaks of the 1–2% of children who are medically identified and treated or of the 5–10% who are socially or educationally defined, included are many children whose prognosis is one of relative optimism. Although some will go on to careers of school failure, later delinquency, or adult maladjustment, a great many more will go on to negotiate successfully the major hurdles of growing up and becoming productive members of society.

In this very important way, the outlook for the hyperactive child differs from that for a child with almost any other enduring problem of psychological health. In the last analysis, hyperactivity is just another degree of normality; the potential for change, in either direction, is high. These are challenging children who create, in turn, a challenging arena for new interventions and for the continued and conjoint study of both individual development and contextual influences. Because of the potential and the challenge, this area seems an excellent one in which to invest the best of our clinical thinking as well as the necessary time, funding, and effort.

References

Abelson, H., & Fishburne, P. *Nonmedical use of psychoactive substances: 1975/6 nationwide study among youth and adults.* Princeton: Response Analysis Corporation, 1976.

Abikoff, H., Gittelman-Klein, R., & Klein, D. F. Validation of a classroom observation code for hyperactive children. *Journal of Consulting and Clinical Psychology,* 1977, *45,* 772–783.

Ackerman, P. T., Dykman, R. A., & Peters, J. E. Teenage status of hyperactive and nonhyperactive learning disabled boys. *American Journal of Orthopsychiatry,* 1977, *47,* 577–596.

Adler, S. *Your overactive child: Normal or not?* New York: Medcom Press, 1972.

Ainsworth, M. D. Patterns of attachment behavior shown by the infant in interaction with his mother. *Merrill-Palmer Quarterly,* 1964, *10,* 51–58.

Alabiso, F. Inhibitory functions of attention in reducing hyperactive behavior. *American Journal of Mental Deficiency,* 1972, *77,* 259–282.

Allen, K. E., Henke, L. B., Harris, F. R., Baer, D. M., & Reynolds, N. J. Control of hyperactivity by social reinforcement of attending behavior. *Journal of Educational Psychology,* 1967, *58,* 231–237.

Allen, R. P., & Safer, D. Long term effects of stimulant therapy for HA children: Risk benefits analysis. In M. J. Cohen (Ed.), *Drugs and the special child.* New York: Gardner Press, 1979.

Allen, R. P., Safer, D., & Covi, L. Effects of psychostimulants on aggression. *Journal of Nervous and Mental Disease,* 1975, *160,* 138–145.

Aman, M. G. Drugs, learning and the psychotherapies. In J. S. Werry (Ed.), *Pediatric psychopharmacology: The use of behavior modifying drugs in children.* New York: Brunner/Mazel, 1978.

Aman, M. G., & Sprague, R. L. The state-dependent effects of methylphenidate and dextroamphetamine. *Journal of Nervous and Mental Disease,* 1974, *158,* 268–279.

Aman, M. G., & Werry, J. S. Methylphenidate in children: Effects upon cardiorespiratory function on exertion. *International Journal of Mental Health,* 1975, *4,* 119–131.

American Psychiatric Association, Committee on Nomenclature and Statistics. *Diagnostic and statistical manual of mental disorders* (2nd ed.). Washington, D. C.: American Psychiatric Association, 1968.

American Psychiatric Association, Task Force on Nomenclature and Statistics. *Diagnostic and statistical manual of mental disorders* (3rd ed., Draft version of January 15, 1978).

Anders, T. F., & Ciaranello, R. D. Pharmacological treatment of the minimal brain dysfunction syndrome. In J. D. Barchas, P. A. Berger, R. D. Ciaranello, & G. R. Elliott (Eds.), *Psychopharmacology: From theory to practice.* New York: Oxford University Press, 1977.

Anderson, D. R., & Levin, S. R. Young children's attention to "Sesame Street." *Child Development, 1976, 47,* 806–811.

Anderson, R. P., Halcomb, C. G., & Doyle, R. B. The measurement of attentional deficits. *Exceptional Children,* 1973, *39,* 534–539.

Anisman, H. Time-dependent variations in aversively motivated behaviors: Nonassociative effects of cholinergic and catecholaminergic activity. *Psychological Review,* 1975, *82,* 357–385.

Arnold, L. E. The art of medicating hyperkinetic children. A number of practical suggestions. *Clinical Pediatrics,* 1973, *12,* 35–41. (a)

Arnold, L. E. Is this label necessary? *Journal of School Health,* 1973, *23,* 510–514. (b)

Arnold, L. E., Huestis, R. D., Smeltzer, D. J., Scheib, J., Wemmer, D., & Colner, G. Levoamphetamine versus dextroamphetamine in minimal brain dysfunction. *Archives of General Psychiatry,* 1976, *33,* 292–301.

Arnold, L. E., Strobl, D., & Weisenberg, A. Hyperkinetic adult: Study of the "paradoxical" amphetamine response. *Journal of the American Medical Association,* 1972, *222,* 693–694.

Arnold, L. E., & Wender, P. H. Levoamphetamine's changing place in the treatment of children with behavior disorders. In C. K. Conners (Ed.), *Clinical use of stimulant drugs in children.* New York: American Elsevier, 1974.

Ayllon, T., Layman, D., & Burke, S. Disruptive behavior and reinforcement of academic performance. *Psychological Record,* 1972, *22,* 315–323.

Ayllon, T., Layman, D., & Kandel, H. J. A behavioral–educational alternative to drug control of hyperactive children. *Journal of Applied Behavior Analysis,* 1975, *8,* 137–146.

Ayllon, T., & Roberts, M. D. Eliminating discipline problems by strengthening academic performance. *Journal of Applied Behavior Analysis,* 1974, *7,* 71–76.

Backman, J. E., & Firestone, P. A review of psychopharmacological and behavioral approaches to the treatment of hyperactive children. *American Journal of Orthopsychiatry,* 1979, *49,* 500–504.

Bakwin, H. Cerebral damage and behavior disorders in children. *Journal of Pediatrics,* 1949, *34,* 371–382.

Ballard, J. E. *Public Law 94–142 and Section 504—Understanding what they are and are not.* Reston, VA: Council for Exceptional Children, 1977.

Ballard, J. E., Boileau, R. A., Sleator, E. K., Massey, B. H., & Sprague, R. L. Cardiovascular responses of hyperactive children to methylphenidate. *Journal of the American Medical Association,* 1976, *236,* 2870–2874.

Ballard, K. D., & Glynn, T. Behavioral self-management in story writing with elementary school children. *Journal of Applied Behavior Analysis,* 1975, *8,* 387–398.

Bandura, A. *Aggression: A social learning analysis.* Englewood Cliffs, NJ: Prentice-Hall, 1973.

Bandura, A., Jeffery, R. W., & Gajdos, E. Generalizing changes through participant modeling with self-directed mastery. *Behaviour Research and Therapy,* 1975, *13,* 141–152.

Banks, W. Drugs, hyperactivity, and black schoolchildren. *Journal of Negro Education,* 1976, *45,* 150–160.

Barker, P. Haloperidol. *Journal of Child Psychology and Psychiatry,* 1975, *16,* 169–172.

Barkley, R. A. Predicting the response of hyperkinetic children to stimulant drugs: A review. *Journal of Abnormal Child Psychology,* 1976, *4,* 327–348.

Barkley, R. A. The effects of methylphenidate on various types of activity level and attention in hyperkinetic children. *Journal of Abnormal Child Psychology,* 1977, *5,* 351–369. (a)

Barkley, R. A. A review of stimulant drug research with hyperactive children. *Journal of Child Psychology and Psychiatry,* 1977, *18,* 137–165. (b)

Barkley, R. A. Recent developments in research on hyperactive children. *Journal of Pediatric Psychology,* 1978, *3,* 158–163.

Barkley, R. A., & Cunningham, C. E. Do stimulant drugs improve the academic performance of hyperkinetic children? *Clinical Pediatrics,* 1978, *17,* 85–92.

Barkley, R. A., & Cunningham, C. The effects of Ritalin on the mother–child interactions of hyperactive children. *Archives of General Psychiatry,* 1979, *36,* 201–208.

Barkley, R. A., & Jackson, T. L., Jr. Hyperkinesis, autonomic nervous system activity, and stimulant drug effects. *Journal of Child Psychology and Psychiatry,* 1977, *18,* 347–357.

Barkley, R. A., & Routh, D. K. Reduction of children's locomotor activity by modeling and the promise of contingent reward. *Journal of Abnormal Child Psychology,* 1974, *2,* 117–131.

Barkley, R. A., & Ullman, D. C. A comparison of objective measures of activity and distractibility in hyperactive and nonhyperactive children. *Journal of Abnormal Child Psychology,* 1975, *3,* 231–244.

Barnard, J. D., Christophersen, E. R., & Wolf, M. M. Teaching children appropriate shopping behavior through parent training in the supermarket setting. *Journal of Applied Behavior Analysis,* 1977, *10,* 49–59.

Barrish, H. H., Saunders, M., & Wolf, M. M. Good behavior game: Effects of individual contingencies for group consequences on disruptive behavior in a classroom. *Journal of Applied Behavior Analysis,* 1969, *2,* 119–124.

Battle, E. S., & Lacey, B. A context for hyperactivity in children, over time. *Child Development,* 1972, *43,* 757–773.

Baxley, G. B., & LeBlanc, J. M. The hyperactive child: Characteristics, treatment, and evaluation of research design. In H. W. Reese (Ed.), *Advances in child development and behavior* (Vol. 11). New York: Academic Press, 1976.

Beck, L., Langford, W. S., Mackay, M., & Sum, G. Childhood chemotherapy and later drug abuse and growth curve: A follow-up study. *American Journal of Psychiatry,* 1975, *4,* 436–438.

Becker, L. D. Conceptual tempo and the early detection of learning problems. *Journal of Learning Disabilities,* 1976, *9,* 38–47.

Becker, W. C. *Parents are teachers: A child management program.* Champaign, IL: Research Press, 1971.

Becker, W. C., & Krug, R. S. The parent attitude research instrument: A research review. *Child Development,* 1965, *36,* 329–365.

Becker, W. C., Madsen, C. H., Jr., Arnold, C. R., & Thomas, D. R. The contingent use of teacher attention and praise in reducing classroom behavior problems. *Journal of Special Education,* 1967, *1,* 287–307.

Belkin, E. P., & Routh, D. K. Effects of presence of mother versus stranger on the behavior of three-year-old children in a novel situation. *Developmental Psychology,* 1975, *11,* 400.

Bell, R. Q. A reinterpretation of the direction of effects in studies of socialization. *Psychological Review,* 1968, *75,* 81–95.

Bell, R. Q., & Harper, L. V. *Child effects on adults.* Hillsdale, NJ: Erlbaum, 1977.

Bell, R. Q., & Hertz, T. W. Toward more comparability and generalizability of developmental research. *Child Development,* 1976, *47,* 6–13.

Bem, S. L. Verbal self-control: The establishment of effective self-instruction. *Journal of Experimental Psychology,* 1967, *74,* 485–491.
Bender, N. N. Self-verbalization versus tutor verbalization in modifying impulsivity. *Journal of Educational Psychology,* 1976, *68,* 347–354.
Bendix, S. Drug modification of behavior: A form of chemical violence against children? *Journal of Clinical Child Psychology,* 1973, *2,* 17–19.
Benezra, E. *Learning and memory in hyperactive, reading disabled, and normal children.* Unpublished manuscript, Department of Psychology, McGill University, 1978.
Bentler, P. M., & McClain, J. A multitrait-multimethod analysis of reflection–impulsivity. *Child Development,* 1976, *47,* 218–226.
Bergin, A. E., & Strupp, H. H. *Changing frontiers in the science of psychotherapy.* New York: Aldine-Atherton, 1972.
Berlyne, D. E. *Conflict, arousal, and curiosity.* New York: McGraw-Hill, 1960.
Bierman, C. W., & Furukawa, C. T. Food additives and hyperkinesis: Are there nuts among the berries? *Pediatrics,* 1978, *61,* 932–934.
Bindra, D. *A Theory of intelligent behavior.* New York: Wiley, 1976.
Bittinger, M. L. (Ed.). *Living with our hyperactive children.* New York: Two Continents Publishing Group, 1977.
Block, J., Block, H. J., & Harrington, D. M. Some misgivings about the Matching Familiar Figures Test as a measure of reflection–impulsivity. *Developmental Psychology,* 1974, *10,* 611–632.
Blumenthal, D. S., Burke, R., & Shapiro, A. K. The validity of "identical matching placebos." *Archives of General Psychiatry,* 1974, *31,* 214–215.
Blunden, D., Spring, C., & Greenberg, L. M. Validation of the Classroom Behavior Inventory. *Journal of Consulting and Clinical Psychology,* 1974, *42,* 84–88.
Bok, S. The ethics of giving placebos. *Scientific American,* 1974, *231,* 17–23.
Bolstad, O. D., & Johnson, S. M. Self-regulation in the modification of disruptive classroom behavior. *Journal of Applied Behavior Analysis,* 1972, *5,* 443–454.
Borland, B. L., & Heckman, H. K. Hyperactive boys and their brothers: A 25-year follow-up study. *Archives of General Psychiatry,* 1976, *33,* 669–675.
Bosco, J. J., & Robin, S. S. Ritalin usage: A challenge to teacher education. *Peabody Journal of Education,* 1976, *53,* 187–193.
Bower, K., & Mercer, C. D. Hyperactivity: Etiology and intervention techniques. *Journal of School Health,* 1975, *45,* 195–202.
Boydstun, J. A., Ackerman, P. T., Stevens, D. A., Clements, S. D., Peters, J. E., & Dykman, R. A. Physiological and motor conditioning and generalization in children with minimal brain dysfunction. *Conditional Reflex,* 1968, *3,* 81–104.
Bradley, C. The behavior of children receiving benzedrine. *American Journal of Psychiatry,* 1937, *94,* 577–585.
Brandon, S. Overactivity in childhood. *Journal of Psychosomatic Research,* 1971, *15,* 411–415.
Brecher, E. M., & the Editors of *Consumer Reports. Licit and illicit drugs.* Boston: Little, Brown, 1972.
Bremer, D. A., & Stern, J. A. Attention and distractibility during reading in hyperactive boys. *Journal of Abnormal Child Psychology,* 1976, *4,* 381–387.
Brent, D. E., & Routh, D. K. Response cost and impulsive word recognition errors in reading disabled children. *Journal of Abnormal Child Psychology,* 1978, *6,* 211–219.
Brim, O. G. Macro-structural influences on child development and the need for childhood social indicators. *American Journal of Orthopsychiatry,* 1975, *45,* 516–524.
Broadbent, D. E. *Decision and stress.* New York: Academic Press, 1971.

Bronfenbrenner, U. Developmental research, public policy and the ecology of childhood. *Child Development,* 1974, *45,* 1–5. (a)

Bronfenbrenner, U. *A report on longitudinal evaluations of preschool programs: Is early intervention effective?* (Vol. 2) (DHEW Publication No. OHD-74-25). Washington, D. C.: U. S. Government Printing Office, 1974. (b)

Bronfenbrenner, U. Toward an experimental ecology of human development. *American Psychologist,* 1977, *32,* 513–531.

Brook, J. S., Whiteman, M., Peisach, E., & Deutsch, M. Aspiration levels of and for children: Age, sex, race, and socioeconomic correlates. *Journal of Genetic Psychology,* 1974, *124,* 3–16.

Broudy, H. S. Ideological, political, and moral considerations in the use of drugs in hyperkinetic therapy. *School Review,* 1976, *85,* 43–60.

Browder, J. A. Appropriate use of psychic drugs in school children. *American Journal of Diseases in Children,* 1972, *124,* 606–607.

Brown, A. L. The development of memory: Knowing, knowing about knowing, and knowing how to know. In H. W. Reese (Ed.), *Advances in child development and behavior* (Vol. 10). New York: Academic Press, 1975.

Brown, A. L., Campione, J. C., & Barclay, C. R. Training self-checking routines for estimating test readiness: Generalization from list learning to prose recall. *Child Development,* 1979, *50,* 501–512.

Brown, D., Winsberg, B. C., Bialer, I., & Press, M. Imipramine therapy and seizures. Three children treated for hyperactive behavior disorders. *American Journal of Psychiatry,* 1973, *130,* 210–212.

Brown, J. L., & Bing, S. R. Drugging children: Child abuse by professionals. In G. P. Koocher (Ed.), *Children's rights and the mental health professions.* New York: Wiley, 1976.

Browning, R. B. Hypo-responsiveness as a behavioral correlate of brain damage in children. *Psychological Reports,* 1967, *20,* 251–259.

Bruck, C. Battle lines in the Ritalin war. *Human Behavior,* 1976, *5,* 25–33.

Buchsbaum, M., & Wender, P. Average evoked responses in normal and minimally brain dysfunctioned children treated with amphetamine. *Archives of General Psychiatry,* 1973, *29,* 764–770.

Buddenhagen, R. G., & Sickler, P. Hyperactivity: A forty-eight hour sample plus a note on etiology. *American Journal of Mental Deficiency,* 1969, *73,* 580–589.

Bugental, D. B., Whalen, C., & Henker, B. Causal attributions of hyperactive children and motivational assumptions of two behavior change approaches: Evidence for an interactionist position. *Child Development,* 1977, *48,* 874–884.

Burk, H. The hyperkinetic child. *Exceptional Children,* 1960, *27,* 18–26.

Buss, A. H., & Plomin, R. *A temperament theory of personality development.* New York: Wiley, 1975.

Camp, B. W. WISC performance in acting-out and delinquent children with and without EEG abnormality. *Journal of Consulting Psychology,* 1966, *30,* 350–353.

Camp, B. W. Research with the SMART reading program. In R. P. Anderson & C. G. Halcomb (Eds.), *Learning disability–minimal brain dysfunction syndrome.* Springfield, IL: Charles C Thomas, 1976. (a)

Camp, B. W. Stability of behavior ratings. *Perceptual and Motor Skills,* 1976, *43,* 1065–1066. (b)

Camp, B. W., *A pilot study of verbal learning in young aggressive boys. Final report.* Denver, CO: University of Colorado Medical Center, 1977. (ERIC Document Reproduction Service No. ED 142 023) (a)

Camp, B. W. Verbal mediation in young aggressive boys. *Journal of Abnormal Psychology,* 1977, *86,* 145–153. (b)

Camp, B. W., & Bash, M. A. Think aloud program manual. In B. W. Camp (Ed.), *A pilot study of verbal learning in young aggressive boys. Appendix H.* Denver, CO: University of Colorado Medical Center, 1977. (ERIC Document Reproduction Service No. ED 142 024)

Camp, B. W., Blom, G. E., Hebert, F., & van Doorninck, W. J. "Think Aloud": A program for developing self-control in young aggressive boys. *Journal of Abnormal Child Psychology,* 1977, *5,* 157–169.

Camp, B. W., & Dolcourt, J. L. Reading and spelling in good and poor readers. *Journal of Learning Disabilities,* 1977, *10,* 300–307.

Camp, B. W., & Simmons, M. Great expectations program manual. In B. W. Camp (Ed.), *A pilot study of verbal learning in young agressive boys. Final report.* Denver, CO: University of Colorado Medical Center, 1977. (ERIC Document Reproduction Service No. ED 142 023)

Camp, B. W., & Zimet, S. G. The relationship of teacher rating scales to behavior observations and reading achievement of first-grade children. *Journal of Special Education,* 1974, *8,* 353–359.

Camp, B. W., Zimet, S. G., van Doorninck, W. J., & Dahlem, N. W. Verbal abilities in young aggressive boys. *Journal of Educational Psychology,* 1977, *69,* 129–135.

Campbell, B. A., & Jaynes, J. Reinstatement. *Psychological Review,* 1966, *73,* 478–480.

Campbell, D. T., & Stanley, J. C. *Experimental and quasi-experimental designs for research.* Chicago: Rand McNally, 1966.

Campbell, S. B. Mother–child interaction: A comparison of hyperactive, learning disabled, and normal boys. *American Journal of Orthopsychiatry,* 1975, *45,* 51–57.

Campbell, S. B. Hyperactivity: Course and treatment. In A. Davids (Ed.), *Child personality and psychopathology: Current topics* (Vol. 3). New York: Wiley, 1976.

Campbell, S. B., Douglas, V. I., & Morgenstern, G. Cognitive styles in hyperactive children and the effect of methylphenidate. *Journal of Child Psychology and Psychiatry,* 1971, *12,* 55–67.

Campbell, S. B., Endman, M. W., & Bernfeld, G. A three-year follow-up of hyperactive preschoolers into elementary school. *Journal of Child Psychology and Psychiatry,* 1977, *18,* 239–249.

Campbell, S. B., Schleifer, M., Weiss, G., & Perlman, T. A two-year follow-up of hyperactive preschoolers. *American Journal of Orthopsychiatry,* 1977, *47,* 149–162.

Cantwell, D. P. Psychiatric illness in the families of hyperactive children. *Archives of General Psychiatry,* 1972, *27,* 414–417.

Cantwell, D. P. A critical review of therapeutic modalities with hyperactive children. In D. P. Cantwell (Ed.), *The hyperactive child: Diagnosis, management, current research.* New York: Spectrum, 1975. (a)

Cantwell, D. P. Familial–genetic research with hyperactive children. In D. P. Cantwell (Ed.), *The hyperactive child: Diagnosis, management, current research.* New York: Spectrum, 1975. (b)

Cantwell, D. P. (Ed.). *The hyperactive child: Diagnosis, management, current research.* New York: Spectrum, 1975. (c)

Cantwell, D. P. Psychopharmacologic treatment of the minimal brain dysfunction syndrome. In J. M. Wiener (Ed.), *Psychopharmacology in childhood and adolescence.* New York: Basic Books, 1977.

Cantwell, D. P., & Carlson, G. A. Stimulants. In J. S. Werry (Ed.), *Pediatric psychopharmacology: The use of behavior modifying drugs in children.* New York: Brunner/Mazel, 1978.

Castner, M. H., Della-Piana, G., Hogben, M., & Allen, J. E. *Granite School District first grade reading study.* Salt Lake City, UT: Exemplary Center for Reading Instruction, 1968.

Chambers, C. D., Inciardi, J. A., & Siegal, H. A. *Chemical coping: A report on legal drug use in the United States.* New York: Spectrum, 1975.

Chess, G. F., Tam, M. K., & Calaresu, F. R. Influence of cardiac neutral inputs on rhythmic variations of heart period in the cat. *American Journal of Physiology,* 1975, *228,* 775–780.

Chess, S. Neurological dysfunction and childhood behavioral pathology. *Journal of Autism and Childhood Schizophrenia,* 1972, *2,* 299–311.

Cheung, M. N. *Cardiac responses as measures of the orienting reflex: A factor analytic approach.* Unpublished master's thesis, West Virginia University, 1973.

Chisolm, J. J. *Models of neurotoxicity of lead.* Paper presented at the meetings of the American Psychological Association, San Francisco, August 1977.

Christensen, D. E. Effects of combining methylphenidate and a classroom token system in modifying hyperactive behavior. *American Journal of Mental Deficiency,* 1975, *80,* 266–276.

Christensen, D. E., & Sprague, R. L. Reduction of hyperactive behavior by conditioning procedures alone and combined with methylphenidate. *Behavior Research and Therapy,* 1973, *11,* 331–334.

Clements, S. D. *Minimal brain dysfunction in children—terminology and identification* (USPHS Publication No. 1415). Washington, D. C.: U. S. Government Printing Office, 1966.

Clements, S. D., & Peters, J. Minimal brain dysfunction in the school-age child. *Archives of General Psychiatry,* 1962, *6,* 185–197.

Cohen, J. The factorial structure of the WISC at ages 7–6, 10–6, and 13–6. *Journal of Consulting Psychology,* 1959, *23,* 285–299.

Cohen, N. J. *Psychophysiological concomitants of attention in hyperactive children.* Unpublished doctoral dissertation, McGill University, 1970.

Cohen, N. J., & Douglas, V. I. Characteristics of the orienting response in hyperactive and normal children. *Psychophysiology,* 1972, *9,* 238–245.

Cohen, N. J., Douglas, V. I., & Morgenstern, G. The effect of methylphenidate on attentive behavior and autonomic activity in hyperactive children. *Psychopharmacologia,* 1971, *22,* 282–294.

Cohen, N. J., Weiss, G., & Minde, K. Cognitive styles in adolescents previously diagnosed as hyperactive. *Journal of Child Psychology and Psychiatry,* 1972, *13,* 203–209.

Cohen, S., & Przybycien, C. A. Some effects of sociometrically selected peer models on the cognitive styles of impulsive children. *Journal of Genetic Psychology,* 1974, *124,* 213–220.

Coleman, N., Dexheimer, P., DiMascio, A., Redman, W., & Finnerty, R. Deanol in the treatment of hyperkinetic children. *Psychosomatics,* 1976, *17,* 68–72.

Colman, R. S., Frankel, F., Ritvo, E., & Freeman, B. J. The effects of fluorescent and incandescent illumination upon repetitive behaviors in autistic children. *Journal of Autism and Childhood Schizophrenia,* 1976, *6,* 157–162.

Conger, J. J., & Miller, W. C. *Personality, social class, and delinquency,* New York: Wiley, 1966.

Conners, C. K. A teacher rating scale for use in drug studies with children. *American Journal of Psychiatry,* 1969, *126,* 884–888.

Conners, C. K. Symptom patterns in hyperkinetic, neurotic, and normal children. *Child Development,* 1970, *41,* 667–682.

Conners, C. K. Pharmacotherapy of psychopathology in children. In H. C. Quay & J. S. Werry (Eds.), *Psychopathological disorders of childhood.* New York: Wiley, 1972 (a)

Conners, C. K. Stimulant drugs and cortical evoked responses in learning and behavior disorders in children. In W. L. Smith (Ed.), *Drugs, development, and cerebral function.* New York: Charles C Thomas, 1972. (b)

Conners, C. K. Symposium: Behavior modification by drugs. II. Psychological effects of stimulant drugs in children with minimal brain dysfunction. *Pediatrics,* 1972, *49,* 702–708. (c)

Conners, C. K. Deanol and behavior disorders in children: A critical review of the literature and recommended future studies for determining efficacy. *Psychopharmacology Bulletin* (Special issue: Pharmacotherapy of Children), 1973, 188–195. (a)

Conners, C. K. Psychological assessment of children with minimal brain dysfunction. *Annals of the New York Academy of Sciences,* 1973, *205,* 283–302. (b)

Conners, C. K. Rating scales for use in drug studies with children. *Psychopharmacology Bulletin* (Special issue: Pharmacotherapy of children), 1973, 24–84. (c)

Conners, C. K. Controlled trial of methylphenidate in preschool children with minimal brain dysfunction. *International Journal of Mental Health,* 1975, *4,* 61–75. (a)

Conners, C. K. Minimal brain dysfunction and psychopathology in children. In A. Davids (Ed.), *Child personality and psychopathology: Current topics* (Vol. 2). New York: Wiley, 1975. (b)

Conners, C. K. A placebo-crossover study of caffeine treatment of hyperkinetic children. *International Journal of Mental Health,* 1975, *4,* 132–143. (c)

Conners, C. K. Learning disabilities and stimulant drugs in children: Theoretical implications. In R. M. Knights & D. J. Bakker (Eds.), *The neuropsychology of learning disorders. Theoretical approaches.* Baltimore: University Park Press, 1976.

Conners, C. K. Methodological considerations in drug research with children. In J. M. Wiener (Ed.), *Psychopharmacology in childhood and adolescence.* New York: Basic Books, 1977.

Conners, C. K., Goyette, C. H., Southwick, D. A., Lees, J. M., & Andrulonis, P. A. Food additives and hyperkinesis: A controlled double-blind experiment. *Pediatrics,* 1976, *58,* 154–166.

Conners, C. K., & Rothschild, G. Drugs and learning in children. In J. Hellmuth (Ed.), *Learning disorders* (Vol. 3). Seattle: Special Child Publications, 1968.

Conners, C. K., & Rothschild, G. H. The effects of dextroamphetamine on habituation of peripheral vascular response in children. *Journal of Abnormal Child Psychology,* 1973, *1,* 16–25.

Conners, C. K., Taylor, E., Meo, G., Kurtz, M. A., & Fournier, M. Magnesium pemoline and dextroamphetamine: A controlled study in children with minimal brain dysfunction. *Psychopharmacologia,* 1972, *26,* 321–336.

Conrad, P. The discovery of hyperkinesis: Notes on the medicalization of deviant behavior. *Social Problems,* 1975, *23,* 12–21.

Conrad, W., & Insel, J. Anticipating the response to amphetamine therapy in the treatment of hyperkinetic children. *Pediatrics,* 1967, *40,* 96–98.

Conway, A. An evaluation of drugs in the elementary schools: Some geographic considerations. *Journal of Psychology in the Schools,* 1976, *13,* 442–444.

Cook, T. D., & Campbell, D. T. The design and conduct of quasi-experiments in field settings. In M. D. Dunnette (Ed.), *Handbook of industrial and organizational psychology.* Chicago: Rand McNally, 1975.

Copeland, A. P., & Weissbrod, C. S. Behavioral correlates of the hyperactivity factor of the Conners Teacher Questionnaire. *Journal of Abnormal Child Psychology,* 1978, *6,* 339–343.

Coquery, J. M., & Lacey, J. I. *The effect of foreperiod duration on the components of the cardiac response during the foreperiod of a reaction time experiment.* Paper presented at the annual meeting of the Society for Psychophysiological Research, Denver, Colorado, 1966.

Craighead, W. E., Wilcoxon-Craighead, L., & Meyers, A. W. New directions in behavior modification with children. In M. Hersen, R. M. Eisler, & P. M. Miller (Eds.), *Progress in behavior modification* (Vol. 6). New York: Academic Press, 1978.

Creak, M. Schizophrenic syndrome in childhood: Further progress report of a working party (April, 1964). *Developmental Medicine and Child Neurology,* 1964, *6,* 530–535.

Cruickshank, W. M. *The brain-injured child in home, school and community.* Syracuse: Syracuse University Press, 1967. (Revised as *Learning disabilities in home, school and community.* Syracuse: Syracuse University Press, 1977.)

Cruickshank, W. M. Least-restrictive placement: Administrative wishful thinking. *Journal of Learning Disabilities,* 1977, *10,* 193–194.

Cruickshank, W. M., Bentzen, F., Ratzeburg, F., & Tannhauser, M. *A teaching method for brain-injured and hyperactive children: A demonstration pilot study.* Syracuse: Syracuse University Press, 1961.

Dalby, J. T., Kinsbourne, M., Swanson, J. M., & Sobol, M. P. Hyperactive children's under-use of learning time: Corrections by stimulant treatment. *Child Development,* 1977, *48,* 1448–1453.

David, O. J. Association between lower level lead concentrations and hyperactivity in children. *Environmental Health Perspectives,* 1974, 17–25.

David, O. J., Hoffman, S., & Koltun, A. Threshold levels and lead toxicity. *Psychopharmacology Bulletin,* 1978, *14,* 50–53.

David, O. J., Hoffman, S. P., Sverd, J., & Clark, J. Lead and hyperactivity: Lead levels among hyperactive children. *Journal of Abnormal Child Psychology,* 1977, *5,* 405–416.

David, O. J., Hoffman, S. P., Sverd, J., Clark, J., & Voeller, K. Lead and hyperactivity. Behavioral response to chelation: A pilot study. *American Journal of Psychiatry,* 1976, *133,* 1155–1158.

Davis, J. M., Gosenfield, L., & Tsai, C. C. Maintenance antipsychotic drugs do prevent relapse: A reply to Tobias and MacDonald. *Psychological Bulletin,* 1976, *83,* 431–447.

Davison, G. C., Tsujimoto, R. N., & Glaros, A. G. Attribution and the maintenance of behavior change in falling asleep. *Journal of Abnormal Psychology,* 1973, *82,* 124–133.

de la Burdé, B., & Choate, M. S. Early asymptomatic lead exposure and development at school age. *Journal of Pediatrics,* 1975, *87,* 638–642.

Denhoff, E. The natural life history of children with minimal brain dysfunction. *Annals of the New York Academy of Sciences,* 1973, *205,* 188–205.

Denson, R., Nanson, J. L., & McWatters, M. A. Hyperkinesis and maternal smoking. *Canadian Psychiatric Association Journal,* 1975, *20,* 183–187.

Deutsch, C. P. Social class and child development. In B. M. Caldwell & H. N. Ricciuti (Eds.), *Review of child development research: Child development and social policy.* Chicago: University of Chicago Press, 1973.

Deutsch, J. A., & Deutsch, D. Attention: Some theoretical considerations. *Psychological Review,* 1963, *70,* 80–90.

Diana v. *State Board of Education.*, No. C-70-37 (N. D. Cal. 1970).

DiMascio, A., Soltys, J. J., & Shader, R. I. Psychotropic drug side effects in children. In R. I. Shader & A. DiMascio (Eds.), *Psychotropic drug side effects: Clinical and theoretical perspectives.* Baltimore: Williams & Wilkins, 1970.

Dimond, S. J. Drugs to improve learning in man: Implications and neuropsychological analysis. In R. M. Knights & D. J. Bakker (Eds.), *The neuropsychology of learning disorders. Theoretical approaches.* Baltimore: University Park Press, 1976.

Doster, J. T. *Differential base rates of hyperactive behavior in open and closed classrooms.* Paper presented at the meeting of the American Psychological Association, San Francisco, August 1977.

Doubros, S. G., & Daniels, G. J. An experimental approach to the reduction of overactive behavior. *Behaviour Research and Therapy,* 1966, *4,* 251–258.

Douglas, V. I. Stop, look and listen: The problem of sustained attention and impulse control in hyperactive and normal children. *Canadian Journal of Behavioral Science,* 1972, *4,* 259–282.

Douglas, V. I. Sustained attention and impulse control: Implications for the handicapped child. In J. A. Swets & L. L. Elliott (Eds.), *Psychology and the handicapped child.* (DHEW Publication No. [OE] 73–05000) Washington, D. C.: U. S. Government Printing Office, 1974.

Douglas, V. I. Are drugs enough? To treat or train the hyperactive child. *International Journal of Mental Health,* 1975, *4,* 199–212.

Douglas, V. I. Effects of medication on learning efficiency. Research findings review and synthesis. In R. P. Anderson & C. G. Halcomb (Eds.), *Learning disability/minimal brain dysfunction syndrome.* Springfield, IL: Charles C Thomas, 1976. (a)

Douglas, V. I. Perceptual and cognitive factors as determinants of learning disabilities: A review chapter with special emphasis on attentional factors. In R. M. Knights & D. J. Bakker (Eds.), *The neuropsychology of learning disorders. Theoretical approaches.* Baltimore: University Park Press, 1976. (b)

Douglas, V. I. Research on hyperactivity: Stage two. *Journal of Abnormal Child Psychology,* 1976, *4,* 307–308. (c)

Douglas, V. I. Higher mental processes in hyperactive children: Implications for training. In R. M. Knights and D. J. Bakker (Eds.), *Rehabilitation, treatment and management of learning disorders.* Baltimore: University Park Press, in press.

Douglas, V. I., Parry, P., Marton, P., & Garson, C. Assessment of a cognitive training program for hyperactive children. *Journal of Abnormal Child Psychology,* 1976, *4,* 389–410.

Douglas, V. I., & Peters, K. G. Toward a clearer definition of the attentional deficit of hyperactive children. In G. A. Hale & M. Lewis (Eds.), *Attention and the development of cognitive skills.* New York: Plenum, 1979, 173–247.

Doyle, R. B., Anderson, R. P., & Halcomb, C. G. Attention deficits and the effects of visual distraction. *Journal of Learning Disabilities,* 1976, *9,* 48–54.

Drabman, R. S., Spitalnik, R., & O'Leary, K. D. Teaching self-control to disruptive children. *Journal of Abnormal Psychology,* 1973, *82,* 10–16.

Dreger, R. A progress report on a factor analytic approach to classification in child psychiatry. In J. Jenkins & J. Cole (Eds), *Research report No. 18.* Washington, D. C.: American Psychiatric Association, 1964.

Dubey, D. R. Organic factors in hyperkinesis: A critical evaluation. *American Journal of Orthopsychiatry,* 1976, *46,* 353–366.

Duncan, O. D. A socioeconomic index for all occupations. In A. Reiss, Jr., O. D. Duncan, P. K. Hatt, & C. North (Eds.), *Occupations and social status.* New York: Free Press, 1961.

Dykman, R. A., & Ackerman, P. T. Hyperactive boys as adolescents. In W. Farrar (Chair), *Hyperactive children: Assessment, treatment, and outcome.* Symposium presented at the annual meeting of the American Psychological Association, Chicago, September 1975.

Dykman, R. A., Ackerman, P. T., Clements, S. D., & Peters, J. E. Specific learning disabilities: An attentional deficit syndrome. In H. R. Myklebust (Ed.), *Progress in learning disabilities* (Vol. 2). New York: Grune & Stratton, 1971.

Dykman, R. A., McGrew, J., & Ackerman, P. T. A double-blind clinical study of pemoline in MBD children: Comments on the psychological test results. In C. K. Conners (Ed.), *Clinical use of stimulant drugs in children.* New York: American Elsevier, 1974.

Dykman, R. A., McGrew, J., Harris, T. S., Peters, J. E., & Ackerman, P. T. Two blinded studies of the effects of stimulant drugs on children: Pemoline, methylphenidate, and placebo. In R.

P. Anderson & C. G. Halcomb (Eds.), *Learning disability–minimal brain dysfunction syndrome.* Springfield, IL: Charles C Thomas, 1976.

Dykman, R. A., Peters, J. E., & Ackerman, P. T. Experimental approaches to the study of minimal brain dysfunction: A follow-up study. *Annals of the New York Academy of Sciences,* 1973, *205,* 93–108.

Eaton, M., Sells, C. J., & Lucas, B. Psychoactive medication and learning disabilities. *Journal of Learning Disabilities,* 1977, *10,* 403–410.

Ebaugh, F. G. Neuropsychiatric sequelae of acute epidemic encephalitis in children. *American Journal of Diseases in Children,* 1923, *25,* 89–97.

Eckoldt, K., & Schubert, E. The influence of the tidal volume on the sinus arrhythmia of the heart. *Acta Biologica et Medica Germanica,* 1975, *34,* 767–771.

Egeland, B. Training impulsive children in the use of more efficient scanning techniques. *Child Development,* 1974, *45,* 165–171.

Eisenberg, L. The management of the hyperkinetic child. *Developmental Medicine and Child Neurology,* 1966, *8,* 593–598.

Eisenberg, L. The clinical use of stimulant drugs in children. *Pediatrics,* 1972, *49,* 709–715.

Eisenberg, L. Future threats or clear and present dangers? *School Review,* 1976, *85,* 155–165.

Eisenpreis, B. Drugs and the family. In M. J. Cohen (Ed.), *Drugs and the special child.* New York: Gardner Press, 1979.

Ellis, M. J., Witt, P. A., Reynolds, R., & Sprague, R. L. Methylphenidate and the activity of hyperactives in the informal setting. *Child Development,* 1974, *45,* 217–220.

Ellis, N. R., & Pryer, R. S. Quantification of gross bodily activity in children with severe neuropathology. *American Journal of Mental Deficiency,* 1959, *63,* 1034–1037.

Endler, N. S., & Magnusson, D. Toward an interactional psychology of personality. *Psychological Bulletin,* 1976, *83,* 956–974.

Engelman, S., & Bruner, E. C. *Direct instructional system for teaching arithmetic and reading (DISTAR).* Chicago: Science Research Associates, 1969.

Eron, L. D., Walder, L. O., & Lefkowitz, M. M. *Learning of aggression in children.* Boston: Little, Brown, 1971.

Errickson, E. A., Wyne, M. D., & Routh, D. K. A response–cost procedure for reduction of impulsive behavior of academically handicapped children. *Journal of Abnormal Child Psychology,* 1973, *1,* 350–357.

Estes, W. K. Learning theory and intelligence. *American Psychologist,* 1974, *29,* 740–749.

Eysenck, N. T., & Rachman, S. T. The application of learning theory to child psychiatry. In T. C. Howells (Ed.), *Modern perspectives in child psychiatry.* New York: Brunner/Mazel, 1971.

Farrington, D. P., & West, D. J. A comparison between early delinquents and young aggressives. *British Journal of Criminology,* 1971, *11,* 341–358.

Feingold, B. F. Food additives and child development. *Hospital Practice,* 1973, *8,* 11–12; 17–18; 21.

Feingold, B. F. *Why your child is hyperactive.* New York: Random House, 1975.

Feingold, B. F. Hyperkinesis and learning disabilities linked to the ingestion of artificial food colors and flavors. *Journal of Learning Disabilities,* 1976, *9,* 551–559.

Feldhusen, J. F., Thursten, J. F., & Benning, J. J. A longitudinal study of delinquency and other aspects of children's behavior. *International Journal of Criminology and Penology,* 1973, *1,* 341–351.

Ferritor, D. E., Buckholdt, D., Hamblin, R. L., & Smith, L. The noneffects of contingent reinforcement for attending behavior on work accomplished. *Journal of Applied Behavior Analysis,* 1972, *5,* 7–17.

Feshbach, N. D., & Feshbach, S. (Eds.). The changing status of children: Rights, roles, and responsibilities. *Journal of Social Issues,* 1978, *34,* 1–196.

Firestone, P., Davey, J., Goodman, J. T., & Peters, S. The effects of caffeine and methylphenidate on hyperactive children. *Journal of Child Psychiatry,* 1978, *17,* 445–456.

Firestone, P., & Douglas, V. I. The effects of reward and punishment on reaction times and autonomic activity in hyperactive and normal children. *Journal of Abnormal Child Psychology,* 1975, *3,* 201–215.

Firestone, P., & Martin, J. E. An analysis of the hyperactive syndrome: A comparison of hyperactive, behavior problem, asthmatic and normal children. *Journal of Abnormal Child Psychology,* 1979, *7,* 261–273.

Firestone, P., Wright, H. P., & Douglas, V. The effects of caffeine on hyperactive children. *Journal of Learning Disabilities,* 1978, *11,* 133–141.

Fish, B. The "one child, one drug" myth of stimulants in hyperkinesis. *Archives of General Psychiatry,* 1971, *25,* 193–203.

Fish, B. Stimulant drug treatment of hyperactive children. In D. P. Cantwell (Ed.), *The hyperactive child: Diagnosis, management, current research.* New York: Spectrum, 1975.

Fisher, M. A. Dextroamphetamine and placebo practice effects on selective attention in hyperactive children. *Journal of Abnormal Child Psychology,* 1978, *6,* 25–32.

Flavell, J. H., Beech, D. H., & Chinsky, J. M. Spontaneous verbal rehearsal in a memory task as a function of age. *Child Development,* 1966, *37,* 283–289.

Flynn, N. M., & Rapoport, J. L. Hyperactivity in open and traditional classroom environments. *Journal of Special Education,* 1976, *10,* 285–290.

Forness, S. *Classroom observation and potential special education children* (Technical Report SERP 1972-A3). Los Angeles: University of California, Graduate School of Education, 1972.

Forness, S. *Screening kindergarten children for early intervention through direct observation of classroom behavior* (Technical Report SERP 1973-A3). Los Angeles: University of California, Graduate School of Education, 1973.

Fowlie, B. A parent's guide to amphetamine treatment of hyperkinesis. *Journal of Learning Disabilities,* 1973, *6,* 352–355.

Frederiksen, N. Toward a taxonomy of situations. *American Psychologist,* 1972, *27,* 114–123.

Freedman, A. M. Drugs and society: An ecological approach. In J. O. Cole, A. M. Freeman, & A. J. Friedhoff (Eds.), *Psychopathology and psychopharmacology.* Baltimore: Johns Hopkins University Press, 1973.

Freeman, R. D. Drug effects on learning in children: A selective review of the past thirty years. *Journal of Special Education,* 1966, *1,* 17–44.

Freeman, R. D. Minimal brain dysfunction, hyperactivity, and learning disorders: Epidemic or episode? *School Review,* 1976, *85,* 5–30.

Freibergs, V., & Douglas, V. I. Concept learning in hyperactive and normal children. *Journal of Abnormal Psychology,* 1969, *74,* 388–395.

Fry, P. S. Affect and resistance to temptation. *Developmental Psychology,* 1975, *11,* 466–472.

Gadow, K. D. *Psychotropic and anticonvulsant drug usage in early childhood special education programs III. A preliminary report: Parent interviews about drug treatment.* Paper presented at the meeting of the Council for Exceptional Children, Atlanta, April 1977.

Gadow, K. D. *Psychotropic and antiepileptic drug treatment in early childhood special education* (Final report for HEW Research Grant No. 00–75–00–381). Urbana-Champaign: Institute for Child Behavior and Development, University of Illinois, 1977.

Gallagher, C. E. *Federal involvement in the use of behavior modification drugs on grammar school children* (Hearing before a subcommittee of the Committee of Government Oper-

ations, House of Representatives, September 29, 1970). Washington, D. C.: U. S. Government Printing Office, 1970.
Garbarino, J. A preliminary study of some ecological correlates of child abuse: The impact of socioeconomic stress on mothers. *Child Development,* 1976, *47,* 178–185.
Gardner, R. *MBD: The family book about minimal brain dysfunction.* New York: Aronson, 1973.
Garfinkel, B., Webster, C., & Sloman, L. Methylphenidate and caffeine in the treatment of children with minimal brain dysfunction. *American Journal of Psychiatry,* 1975, *132,* 723–728.
Garson, C. *Cognitive impulsivity in children and the effects of training.* Unpublished doctoral dissertation, McGill University, 1977.
Gelfand, D. M., & Hartmann, D. P. *Child behavior: Analysis and therapy.* New York: Pergamon Press, 1975.
Gibson, E. J. *Principles of perceptual learning and development.* New York: Prentice-Hall, 1969.
Gilhool, T. K. Changing public policies: Roots and forces. *Minnesota Education,* 1976, *2,* 8–14.
Giora, Z. *Psychopathology: A cognitive view.* New York: Gardner Press, 1975.
Gittelman-Klein, R. Review of clinical psychopharmacological treatment of hyperkinesis. In D. F. Klein & R. Gittelman-Klein (Eds.), *Progress in psychiatric drug treatment.* New York: Brunner/Mazel, 1975. (a)
Gittelman-Klein, R. *A preliminary report of the efficacy of methylphenidate and behavior therapy in hyperactive children.* Paper presented at the Annual Meeting of The American College of Neuropsychopharmacology, San Juan, Puerto Rico, December 1975. (b)
Gittelman-Klein, R., & Klein, D. F. School phobia: Diagnostic considerations in the light of imipramine effects. *Journal of Nervous and Mental Disease,* 1973, *156,* 199–215.
Gittelman-Klein, R., & Klein, D. F. Are behavioral and psychometric changes related in methylphenidate-treated, hyperactive children? *International Journal of Mental Health,* 1975, *4,* 182–198.
Gittelman-Klein, R., & Klein, D. F. Methylphenidate effects in learning disabilities: Psychometric changes. *Archives of General Psychiatry,* 1976, *33,* 655–664.
Gittelman-Klein, R., Klein, D. F., Abikoff, H., Katz, S., Gloisten, C., & Kates, W. Relative efficacy of methylphenidate and behavior modification in hyperkinetic children: An interim report. *Journal of Abnormal Child Psychology, 1976, 4,* 361–379.
Gittelman-Klein, R., Klein, D. F., Katz, S., Saraf, K., & Pollack, E. Comparative effects of methylphenidate and thioridazine in hyperkinetic children. I. Clinical results. *Archives of General Psychiatry,* 1976, *33,* 1217–1231.
Gittelman-Klein, R., Spitzer, R. L., & Cantwell, D. P. Diagnostic classifications and psychopharmacological indications. In J. S. Werry (Ed.), *Pediatric psychopharmacology: The use of behavior modifying drugs in children.* New York: Brunner/Mazel, 1978.
Glick, S. J. First follow-up study of Glueck Table to identify predelinquents at school entrance. In S. Glueck & E. Glueck (Eds.), *Identification of predelinquents.* New York: Intercontinental Medical Book Corporation, 1972.
Glock, C. Y., & Stark, R. *Christian beliefs and anti-semitism.* New York: Harper & Row, 1966.
Glueck, S., & Glueck, E. (Eds.), *Identification of predelinquents.* New York: Intercontinental Medical Book Corporation, 1972.
Goddard, J. L. The medical business. *Scientific American,* 1973, *229,* 161–166.
Goodman, J. F. The diagnostic fallacy: A critique of Jane Mercer's concept of mental retardation. *Journal of School Psychology,* 1977, *15,* 197–206.

Goodman, L. S., & Gilman, A. *The pharmacological basis of therapeutics* (5th ed.). New York: Macmillan, 1975.

Goodwin, D. W., Schulsinger, F., Hermansen, L., Guze, S. B., & Winokur, G. Alcoholism and the hyperactive child syndrome. *Journal of Nervous and Mental Disease,* 1975, *160,* 349–353.

Goodwin, S. E., & Mahoney, M. J. Modification of aggression through modeling: An experimental probe. *Journal of Behavioral Therapy and Experimental Psychiatry,* 1975, *6,* 200–202.

Gorham, K. A., des Jardins, C., Page, R., Pettis, E., & Scheiber, B. Effect on parents. In N. Hobbs (Ed.), *Issues in the classification of children* (Vol. 2). San Francisco: Jossey-Bass, 1975.

Gove, W. A. *The labeling of deviance: Evaluating a perspective.* New York: Wiley, 1975.

Goyette, C. H., Conners, C. K., & Ulrich, R. F. Normative data on revised Conners Parent and Teacher Rating Scales. *Journal of Abnormal Child Psychology,* 1978, *6,* 221–236.

Graham, E. E., & Kamano, D. Reading failure as a factor in the WAIS subtest pattern of youthful offenders. *Journal of Clinical Psychology,* 1958, *14,* 302–305.

Graham, F. K., & Clifton, R. K. Heart-rate change as a component of the orienting response. *Psychological Bulletin,* 1966, *65,* 305–360.

Greenberg, L. M., Deem, M. A., & McMahon, S. Effects of dextroamphetamine, chlorpromazine, and hydroxyzine on behavior and performance in hyperactive children. *American Journal of Psychiatry,* 1972, *129,* 532–539.

Greenberg, L. M., & Lipman, R. S. Pharmacotherapy of hyperactive children: Current practices. *Clinical Proceedings Children's Hospital,* 1971, *27,* 101–105.

Greenberg, L. M., & Lourie, R. S. Physiochemical treatment methods. In B. B. Wolman (Ed.), *Manual of child psychopathology.* New York: McGraw-Hill, 1972.

Greenberg, L. M., Yellin, A. M., Spring, C., & Metcalf, M. Clinical effects of imipramine and methylphenidate in hyperactive children. *International Journal of Mental Health,* 1975, *4,* 144–156.

Greenhill, L., Rieder, R., Wender, P., Buchsbaum, M., & Kahn, T. Lithium carbonate in the treatment of hyperactive children. *Archives of General Psychiatry,* 1973, *38,* 636–640.

Grinspoon, L., & Singer, S. B. Amphetamines in the treatment of hyperkinetic children. *Harvard Educational Review,* 1973, *43,* 515–555.

Gritz, E. R., & Jarvik, M. E. Psychoactive drugs and social behavior. In D. R. Hammond & C. R. B. Joyce (Eds.), *Psychoactive drugs and social judgment: Theory and research.* New York: Wiley, 1975.

Gross, B., & Gross, R. (Eds.), *The children's rights movement. Overcoming the oppression of young people.* Garden City, NY: Anchor, 1977.

Gross, M. D. Caffeine in the treatment of children with minimal brain dysfunction or hyperkinetic syndrome. *Psychosomatics,* 1975, *75,* 26–27.

Gross, M. D. Growth of hyperkinetic children taking methylphenidate, dextroamphetamine, or imipramine/desipramine. *Pediatrics,* 1976, *58,* 423–431.

Gualtieri, C. T. Imipramine and children: A review and some speculations about the mechanism of drug action. *Diseases of the Nervous System,* 1977, *38,* 368–375.

Guskin, S. L., Bartel, N. R., & MacMillan, D. L. Perspective of the labeled child. In N. Hobbs (Ed.), *Issues in the classification of children* (Vol. 2). San Francisco: Jossey-Bass, 1975.

Guy, W. *ECDEU assessment manual for psychopharmacology* (Rev.) (DHEW Publication No. [ADM] 76–338). Washington, D. C.: U. S. Government Printing Office, 1976.

Hagen, J. W. The effect of distraction on selective attention. *Child Development,* 1967, *38,* 685–694.

Hagen, J. W., & Hale, G. H. The development of attention in children. In A. D. Pick (Ed.), *Minnesota symposium on child psychology* (Vol. 7). Minneapolis: University of Minnesota Press, 1973.

Hall, R. A., Griffin, R. B., Moyer, D. L., Hopkins, K. H., & Rappaport, M. Evoked potential, stimulus intensity, and drug treatment in hyperkinesis. *Psychophysiology,* 1976, *13,* 405–418.

Hall, R. J., & Keogh, B. K. Qualitative characteristics of educationally high-risk children. *Learning Disability Quarterly,* 1978, *1,* 62–68.

Hall, R. V., Lund, D., & Jackson, D. Effects of teacher attention on study behavior. *Journal of Applied Behavior Analysis,* 1968, *1,* 1–12.

Hallahan, D. P., Kauffman, J. M., & Ball, D. W. Selective attention and cognitive tempo of low achieving and high achieving sixth grade males. *Perceptual and Motor Skills,* 1973, *36,* 579–583.

Halliday, R., Rosenthal, J. H., Naylor, H., & Callaway, E. Averaged evoked potential predictors of clinical improvement in hyperactive children treated with methylphenidate: An initial study and replication. *Psychophysiology,* 1976, *13,* 429–440.

Harley, J. P., Ray, R. S., Tomasi, L., Eichman, P. L., Matthews, C. G., Chun, R., Cleeland, C. S., & Traisman, E. Hyperkinesis and food additives: Testing the Feingold hypothesis. *Pediatrics,* 1978, *61,* 818–828.

Harlin, V. K. The hyperkinetic child: His management in the school environment. *School Health Review,* 1973, *4,* 9–13.

Harris, R. J. *A primer of multivariate statistics.* New York: Academic Press, 1975.

Harter, S. Effectance motivation reconsidered: Toward a developmental model. *Human Development,* 1978, *21,* 34–64.

Hastings, J. E., & Barkley, R. A. A review of psychophysiological research with hyperkinetic children. *Journal of Abnormal Child Psychology,* 1978, *6,* 413–447.

Hebb, D. O. Physîological learning theory. *Journal of Abnormal Child Psychology,* 1976, *4,* 309–314.

Henker, B., & Whalen, C. K. The many messages of medication: Hyperactive children's perceptions and attributions. In S. Salzinger, J. Antrobus, & J. Glick (Eds.), *The ecosystem of the "sick" kid.* New York: Academic Press, in press.

Henker, B., Whalen, C. K., Bugental, D. B., & Barker, C. Licit and illicit drug use patterns in stimulant treated children and their peers. In K. D. Gadow & J. Loney (Eds.), *Psychosocial aspects of drug treatment for hyperactivity.* Boulder, CO: Westview Press, in press.

Henker, B., Whalen, C. K., & Collins, B. E. Double-blind and triple-blind assessments of medication and placebo responses in hyperactive children. *Journal of Abnormal Child Psychology,* 1979, *7,* 1–13.

Herjanic, B., & Campbell, J. Differentiating psychiatrically disturbed children on the basis of a structured interview. *Journal of Abnormal Child Psychology,* 1977, *5,* 127–135.

Herjanic, B., Herjanic, M., Brown F., & Wheatt, T. Are children reliable reporters? *Journal of Abnormal Child Psychology,* 1975, *3,* 41–48.

Hersen, M., & Barlow, D. H. *Single case experimental designs: Strategies for studying behavior change.* New York: Pergamon Press, 1976.

Hershey, N., & Miller, R. D. *Human experimentation and the law.* Germantown, MD: Aspen Systems Corporation, 1976.

Herzog, E., & Lewis, H. Children in poor families: Myths and realities. *American Journal of Orthopsychiatry,* 1970, *40,* 375–387.

Hess, R. Social class and ethnic influences upon socialization. In P. Mussen (Ed.), *Carmichael's handbook of child psychology* (Vol. 2). New York: Wiley, 1970.

Hetherington, E. M., & Martin, B. Family interaction and psychopathology in children. In H. C. Quay & J. S. Werry (Eds.), *Psychopathological disorders of childhood.* New York: Wiley, 1972.

Hewett, F. M. *The emotionally disturbed child in the classroom: A developmental strategy for educating children with maladaptive behavior.* Boston: Allyn & Bacon, 1968.

Hirst, I. *Removal of a student on a methylphenidate (Ritalin) prescription in an open classroom condition.* Paper presented at the meeting of the Council for Exceptional Children, Chicago, April 1976.

Hollingshead, A. B. *Two factor index of social position.* New Haven: Yale Station, 1957.

Hollingshead, A. B., & Redlich, F. C. *Social class and mental illness.* New York: Wiley, 1958.

Holloway, F. A., & Parsons, O. A. Physiological concomitants of reaction time performance in normal and brain-damaged subjects. *Psychophysiology,* 1972, *9,* 189–198.

Horn, J. L. An empirical comparison of methods for estimating factor scores. *Educational and Psychological Measurement,* 1965, *25,* 313–322.

Hoy, E., Weiss, G., Minde, K., & Cohen, N. The hyperactive child at adolescence: Emotional, social, and cognitive functioning. *Journal of Abnormal Child Psychology,* 1978, *6,* 311–324.

Huessy, H. R. Study of the prevalence and therapy of the choreatiform syndrome or hyperkinesis in rural Vermont. *Acta Paedopsychiatrica,* 1967, *34,* 130–135.

Huessy, H. R. Hyperkinetic problems continue to teens. *Clinical Psychiatry News,* 1974, *2,* 5.

Huessy, H. R., & Cohen, A. H. Hyperkinetic behaviors and learning disabilities followed over seven years. *Pediatrics,* 1976, *57,* 4–10.

Huessy, H. R., Cohen, S. M., Blair, C. L., & Rood, P. *Clinical explorations in adult MBD.* Paper presented at the Conference on Minimal Brain Dysfunction in Adults, Scottsdale, Arizona, March 1978.

Huessy, H. R., & Gendron, R. Prevalence of the so-called hyperkinetic syndrome in public school children of Vermont. *Acta Paedopsychiatrica,* 1970, *37,* 243–248.

Huessy, H. R., Marshall, C., & Gendron, R. Five hundred children followed from 2nd–5th grade for the prevalence of behavior disorder. *Acta Paedopsychiatrica,* 1973, *39,* 301–309.

Huessy, H. R., Metoyer, M., & Townsend, M. 8–10 year follow-up of 84 children treated for behavioral disorder in rural Vermont. *Acta Paedopsychiatrica,* 1974, *40,* 230–235.

Huessy, H. R., & Wright, A. L. The use of imipramine in children's behavior disorders. *Acta Paedopsychiatrica,* 1970, *37,* 194–199.

Humphries, T., Kinsbourne, M., & Swanson, J. Stimulant effects on cooperation and social interaction between hyperactive children and their mothers. *Journal of Child Psychology and Psychiatry,* 1978, *19,* 13–22.

Hutt, S. J., & Hutt, C. Hyperactivity in a group of epileptic (and some nonepileptic) brain-damaged children. *Epilepsia,* 1964, *5,* 334–351.

Insel, P. M., & Moos, R. H. Psychological environment: Expanding the scope of human ecology. *American Psychologist,* 1974, *29,* 179–188.

Jackson, J. E. The coerced use of Ritalin for behavior control in public schools: Legal challenges. *Clearinghouse Review,* 1976, *10,* 181–193.

Jacob, R. G., O'Leary, K. D., & Rosenblad, C. Formal and informal classroom settings: Effects on hyperactivity. *Journal of Abnormal Child Psychology,* 1978, *6,* 47–59.

Jacobs, N. T. A comparison of hyperactive and normal boys in terms of reaction time, motor time, and decision-making time, under conditions of increasing task complexity. *Dissertation Abstracts International,* 1972, *33,* 1045.

Jacobson, J. M., Bushell, D., Jr., & Risley, T. Switching requirements in a Head Start classroom. *Journal of Applied Behavior Analysis,* 1969, *2,* 43–47.

James, W. *Principles of psychology.* New York: Holt, 1890.
Janowsky, D. S., & Davis, J. M. Methylphenidate, dextroamphetamine, and levamfetamine. *Archives of General Psychiatry,* 1976, *33,* 304–308.
Jenkins, R. L., & Stable, G. Special characteristics of retarded children rated as severely hyperactive. *Child Psychiatry and Human Development,* 1971, *2,* 26–31.
Jensen, A. R. Verbal mediation and educational potential. *Psychology in the Schools,* 1966, *3,* 99–109.
Jensen, A. R. Varieties of individual differences in learning. In R. M. Gagné (Ed.), *Learning and individual differences.* Columbus, OH: Merrill, 1967.
Johnson, R. A., Kenney, J. B., & Davis, J. B. Developing school policy for use of stimulant drugs for hyperactive children. *School Review,* 1976, *85,* 78–96.
Johnson, S. E. Hierarchical clustering schemes. *Psychometrika,* 1967, *32,* 241–254.
Jones, N. M., Loney, J., Weissenburger, F. E., & Fleischmann, D. J. The hyperkinetic child: What do teachers know? *Psychology in the Schools, 1975, 12,* 388–392.
Joyce, C. R. B., & Hammond, K. R. Future research. In K. R. Hammond & C. R. B. Joyce (Eds.), *Psychoactive drugs and social judgment: Theory and research.* New York: Wiley, 1975.
Juliano, D. B. Conceptual tempo, activity, and concept learning in hyperactive and normal children. *Journal of Abnormal Psychology,* 1974, *83,* 629–634.
Kagan, J. Reflection–impulsivity and reading ability in primary grade children. *Child Development,* 1965, *36,* 609–628.
Kagan, J. Reflection–impulsivity: The generality and dynamics of conceptual tempo. *Journal of Abnormal Psychology,* 1966, *71,* 17–24.
Kagan, J., & Kogan, N. Individual variations in cognitive processes. In P. Mussen (Ed.), *Carmichael's manual of child psychology* (Vol. 1). New York: Wiley, 1970.
Kagan, J., & Moss, H. A. *Birth to maturity: A study in psychological development.* New York: Wiley, 1962.
Kagan, J., Pearson, L., & Welch, L. Conceptual impulsivity and inductive reasoning. *Child Development,* 1966, *37,* 593–594.
Kagan, J., Rosman, B. L., Day, D., Albert, J., & Phillips, W. Information processing in the child: Significance of analytic and reflective attitudes. *Psychological Monographs, 1964, 78* (1, Whole No. 578).
Kanouse, D. E. *Language, labeling, and attribution.* New York: General Learning Press, 1971.
Kaspar, J. C., & Lowenstein, R. The effect of social interaction on activity levels in six- to eight-year-old boys. *Child Development,* 1971, *42,* 1294–1298.
Katona, P. G., & Jih, F. Respiratory sinus arrhythmia: Noninvasive measure of parasympathetic cardiac control. *Journal of Applied Physiology,* 1975, *39,* 801–805.
Katz, S., Saraf, K., Gittelman-Klein, R., & Klein, D. F. Clinical pharmacological management of hyperkinetic children. *International Journal of Mental Health,* 1975, *4,* 157–181.
Kazdin, A. E., & Wilson, G. T. Criteria for evaluating psychotherapy. *Archives of General Psychiatry,* 1978, *35,* 407–416.
Kent, R. N., & O'Leary, K. D. A controlled evaluation of behavior modification with conduct problem children. *Journal of Consulting and Clinical Psychology,* 1976, *44,* 586–596.
Kent, R. N., O'Leary, K. D., Diament, C., & Dietz, A. Expectation biases in observational evaluation of therapeutic change. *Journal of Consulting and Clinical Psychology,* 1974, *42,* 774–780.
Keogh, B. K. Hyperactivity and learning disorders: Review and speculation. *Exceptional Children,* 1971, *38,* 101–110.
Keogh, B. K. *Problems of generalization and replication: The need for marker variables in*

learning disability research. Paper presented at the meeting of the International Academy for Research in Learning Disabilities, Kansas City, Missouri, March 1978; The Netherlands, May 1978.

Keogh, B. K., & Barkett, C. J. Children's rights in assessment and school placement. *Journal of Social Issues,* 1978, *34,* 87–100.

Keogh, B. K., & Donlon, G. M. Field dependence, impulsivity, and learning disabilities. *Journal of Learning Disabilities,* 1972, *5,* 331–336.

Keogh, B. K., Hall, R. J., & Becker, L. D. *Early identification of exceptional children for educational programming* (Technical Report SERP 1974-A6). Los Angeles: University of California, Graduate School of Education, 1974.

Keogh, B. K., & Levitt, M. L. Special education in the mainstream: A confrontation of limitations. *Focus on Exceptional Children,* 1976, *8,* 1–11.

Keogh, B. K., Major, S. M., Reid, H. P., Gandara, P., & Omori, H. *Marker variables: A search for comparability and generalizability in the learning disabilities field.* Unpublished manuscript, University of California, Los Angeles, 1979.

Keogh, B. K., & Margolis, J. S. Learn to labor and wait: Attentional problems of children with learning disorders. *Journal of Learning Disabilities,* 1976, *9,* 276–286.

Keogh, B. K., Pullis, M. J., & Cadwell, J. *Studies of temperament, Project REACH.* Work in progress under contract with the Bureau of Education for the Handicapped, 1978.

Keogh, B. K., & Tchir, C. A. *Teachers' perceptions of educationally high-risk children* (Technical Report SERP 1972-A2). Los Angeles: University of California, Graduate School of Education, 1972.

Keogh, B. K., Welles, M. F., & Hall, R. J. *An approach to early identification of high potential and high-risk pupils* (Technical Report 1976-A1). Los Angeles: University of California, Graduate School of Education, 1976.

Keogh, B. K., & Windeguth, A. S. *Teachers' perceptions of educationally high-risk pupils from low socio-economic backgrounds* (Technical Report SERP 1973-A5). Los Angeles: University of California, Graduate School of Education, 1973.

Kinsbourne, M. Minimal brain dysfunction as a neurodevelopmental lag. *Annals of the New York Academy of Sciences,* 1973, *205,* 268–273.

Kirp, D. L., Kuriloff, P. J., & Buss, W. G. Legal mandates and organizational change. In N. Hobbs (Ed.), *Issues in the classification of children* (Vol. 2). San Francisco: Jossey-Bass, 1975.

Klein, D. F., & Gittelman-Klein, R. Problems in the diagnosis of minimal brain dysfunction and the hyperkinetic syndrome. *International Journal of Mental Health,* 1975, *4,* 45–60.

Knights, R. M. Psychometric assessment of stimulant-induced behavior change. In C. K. Conners (Ed.), *Clinical use of stimulant drugs in children.* New York: American Elsevier, 1974.

Knights, R. M., & Hinton, G. G. The effects of methylphenidate (Ritalin) on the motor skills and behavior of children with learning problems. *Journal of Nervous and Mental Disease,* 1969, *148,* 643–653.

Koester, L., & Farley, F. *Arousal and hyperactivity in open and traditional education.* Paper presented at the 85th Convention of the American Psychological Association, San Francisco, August 1977.

Kohlberg, L., La Crosse, J., & Ricks, D. The predictability of adult mental health from childhood behavior. In B. B. Wolman (Ed.), *Manual of child psychopathology.* New York: McGraw-Hill, 1972.

Kohn, M., & Rosman, B. Relationship of preschool social–emotional functioning to later intellectual achievement. *Developmental Psychology,* 1972, *6,* 445–452. (a)

Kohn, M., & Rosman, B. A social competence scale and symptom checklist for the preschool child: Factor dimensions, their cross-instrument generality, and longitudinal persistence. *Developmental Psychology,* 1972, *6,* 430–444. (b)

Koocher, G. P. (Ed.). *Children's rights and the mental health professions.* New York: Wiley, 1976.

Kornetsky, C. *Pharmacology: Drugs affecting behavior.* New York: Wiley, 1976.

Krager, J. M., & Safer, D. J. Type and prevalence of medication used in the treatment of hyperactive children. *New England Journal of Medicine,* 1974, *291,* 1118–1120.

Krager, J. M., Safer, D., & Earhart, J. Follow-up survey results of medication used to treat hyperactive school children. *Journal of School Health,* 1979, *49,* 317–321.

Krischer, K. N. Copper and zinc in childhood behavior. *Psychopharmacology Bulletin,* 1978, *14,* 58–59.

Kupietz, S. S., & Balka, E. B. Alterations in the vigilance performance of children receiving amitriptyline and methylphenidate pharmacotherapy. *Psychopharmacology,* 1976, *50,* 29–33.

Kupietz, S. S., & Richardson, E. Children's vigilance performance and inattentiveness in the classroom. *Journal of Child Psychology and Psychiatry,* 1978, *19,* 155–160.

Lacey, J. I. Somatic response patterning and stress: Some revisions of activation theory. In M. H. Appley & R. Trumball (Eds.), *Psychological stress: Issues in research.* New York: Appleton-Century-Crofts, 1967.

Lacey, J. I., Kagan, J., Lacey, B. C., & Moss, H. A. The visceral level: Situational determinants and behavioral correlates of autonomic response patterns. In P. Knapp (Ed.), *Expression of the emotions in man.* New York: International University Press, 1963.

Ladd, E. T. Pills for classroom peace. *Saturday Review,* November 21, 1970, pp. 47–48.

Lahey, B. B. (Ed.). *Behavior therapy with hyperactive and learning disabled children.* New York: Oxford University Press, 1978.

Lahey, B. B., Stempniak, M., Robinson, E. J., & Tyroler, M. J. Hyperactivity and learning disabilities as independent dimensions of child behavior problems. *Journal of Abnormal Psychology,* 1978, *87,* 333–340.

Lambert, N. M., Sandoval, J., & Sassone, D. Prevalence of hyperactivity in elementary school children as a function of social system definers. *American Journal of Orthopsychiatry,* 1978, *48,* 446–463.

Lambert, N. M., Windmiller, M., Sandoval, J., & Moore, B. Hyperactive children and the efficacy of psychoactive drugs as a treatment intervention. *American Journal of Orthopsychiatry,* 1976, *46,* 335–352.

Langhorne, J. E., Jr., & Loney, J. *One (I), two (II), three (III), four (IV), five (V): Is hyperactivity still alive?* Paper presented at the annual convention of the Midwestern Psychological Association, Chicago, May 1975.

Langhorne, J. E., Jr., Loney, J., & Hacker, M. A transformation program for normalizing data. *Behavior Research Methods and Instrumentation,* 1978, *10,* 745.

Langhorne, J. E., Jr., Loney, J., Paternite, C. E., & Bechtoldt, H. P. Childhood hyperkinesis: A return to the source. *Journal of Abnormal Psychology,* 1976, *85,* 201–209.

Lapouse, R., & Monk, M. A. An epidemiological study of behavior characteristics in children. *American Journal of Public Health,* 1958, *48,* 1134–1144.

Larry P. v. *Riles,* 343 F. Supp. 1306 (N. D. Cal. 1972).

Lasswell, H. D. Communication and the mind. In S. M. Farber & R. H. R. Wilson (Eds.), *Control of the mind.* New York: McGraw-Hill, 1961.

Laufer, M. W. Long-term management and some follow-up findings on the use of drugs with minimal cerebral syndromes. *Journal of Learning Disabilities,* 1971, *4,* 519–522.

Laufer, M. W. Hyperkinetic syndrome and minimal brain dysfunction. *Pediatric Annals,* 1973, *2,* 11–14.

Laufer, M. W. In Osler's day it was Syphilis. In E. J. Anthony (Ed.), *Explorations in child psychiatry.* New York: Plenum, 1975.

Laufer, M. W., & Denhoff, E. Hyperkinetic behavior syndrome in children. *Journal of Pediatrics,* 1957, *50,* 463–474.

Laufer, M. W., Denhoff, E., & Solomons, G. Hyperkinetic impulse disorder in children's behavior problems. *Psychosomatic Medicine,* 1957, *19,* 38–49.

Lefkowitz, M. M., Eron, L. D., Walder, L. O., & Huesman, L. R. *Growing up to be violent.* New York: Pergamon Press, 1977.

Leichner, P. P., Janowsky, D. S., & Reid, A. E. Intravenous methylphenidate as a diagnostic and psychotherapeutic instrument in adult psychiatry. *Canadian Psychiatric Association Journal,* 1976, *21,* 489–496.

Lennard, H. L., & Bernstein, A. Perspectives on the new psychoactive drug technology. In R. Cooperstock & S. L. Lambert (Eds.), *Social aspects of the medical use of psychotropic drugs.* Toronto, Canada: House of Lind, 1974.

Lennard, H. L., Epstein, L. J., Bernstein, A., & Ransom, D. C. *Mystification and drug misuse.* San Francisco: Jossey-Bass, 1971.

Lentz, R. J., Paul, G. L., & Calhoun, J. F. Reliability and validity of three measures of functioning with "hard core" chronic mental patients. *Journal of Abnormal Psychology,* 1971, *78,* 69–76.

Lerer, R. J., & Lerer, M. P. Response of adolescents with minimal brain dysfunction to methylphenidate. *Journal of Learning Disabilities,* 1977, *10,* 223–228.

Lesser, G., Fifer, G., & Clark, D. Mental abilities of children from different social-class and cultural groups. *Monographs of the Society for Research in Child Development,* 1965, *30* (Serial No. 102).

Levy, F., Dumbrell, S., Hobbes, G., Ryan, M., Wilton, N., & Woodhill, J. M. Hyperkinesis and diet: A double-blind crossover trial with a tartrazine challenge. *Medical Journal of Australia,* 1978, *1,* 61–64.

Lewis, J. A., & Lewis, B. S. Deanol in minimal brain dysfunction. *Diseases of the Nervous System,* 1977, *38,* 21–24.

Lewis, J. A., & Young, R. Deanol and methylphenidate in minimal brain dysfunction. *Clinical Pharmacology,* 1975, *17,* 534–540.

Lockhart, J. D. Pediatric drug testing: Is it at risk? *Hastings Center Report,* 1977, *7,* 8–10.

Loney, J. The intellectual functioning of hyperactive elementary school boys: A cross-sectional investigation. *American Journal of Orthopsychiatry,* 1974, *44,* 754–762.

Loney, J., Comly, H. H., & Simon, B. Parental management, self-concept, and drug response in minimal brain dysfunction. *Journal of Learning Disabilities,* 1975, *8,* 187–190.

Loney, J., Kramer, J., & Milich, R. The hyperkinetic child grows up: Predictors of symptoms, delinquency, and achievement at follow-up. In K. D. Gadow & J. Loney (Eds.), *Psychosocial aspects of drug treatment for hyperactivity.* Boulder, CO: Westview Press, in press.

Loney, J., Langhorne, J. E., Jr., & Paternite, C. E. An empirical basis for subgrouping the hyperkinetic/minimal brain dysfunction syndrome. *Journal of Abnormal Psychology,* 1978, *87,* 431–441.

Loney, J., Langhorne, J. E., Jr., Paternite, C. E., Whaley-Klahn, M. A., Broeker, C. T., & Hacker, M. *The Iowa HABIT: Hyperactive/aggressive boys in treatment.* Paper presented at the meeting of the Society for Life History Research in Psychopathology, Fort Worth, Texas, October 1976.

Loney, J., Langhorne, J. E., Jr., Paternite, C. E., Whaley-Klahn, M. A., Broeker, C. T., & Hacker, M. The Iowa HABIT: Hyperkinetic/aggressive boys in treatment. In S. Sells (Ed.), *Life history research in psychopathology* (Vol. 6). Baltimore: Williams & Wilkins, in press.

Loney, J., & Ordoña, T. Using cerebral stimulants to treat minimal brain dysfunction. *American Journal of Orthopsychiatry* 1975, *45*, 564–572.

Lovitt, T. C., & Curtiss, K. A. Academic response rate as a function of teacher and self-imposed contingencies. *Journal of Applied Behavior Analysis*, 1969, *2*, 49–53.

Lucas, A. R., & Weiss, M. Methylphenidate hallucinosis. *Journal of the American Medical Association*, 1971, *217*, 1079–1081.

Lynn, R. *Attention, arousal and the orienting reaction.* Oxford: Pergamon Press, 1966.

Maccoby, E. E., & Hagen, J. W. Effects of distraction upon central versus incidental recall: Developmental trends. *Journal of Experimental Child Psychology*, 1965, *2*, 280–289.

MacDonald, M. L., & Tobias, L. L. Withdrawal causes relapse? Our response. *Psychological Bulletin*, 1976, *83*, 448–451.

Mackay, M. C., Beck, L., & Taylor, R. Methylphenidate for adolescents with minimal brain dysfunction. *New York State Journal of Medicine*, 1973, *73*, 550–554.

Magnusson, D., & Endler, N. S. Interactional psychology: Present status and future prospects. In D. Magnusson & N. S. Endler (Eds.), *Personality at the crossroads: Current issues in interactional psychology.* Hillsdale, NJ: Erlbaum, 1977.

Malamuth, Z. *Self-management training for children with reading problems: Effects on reading performance and sustained attention.* Unpublished doctoral dissertation, University of California, Los Angeles, 1977.

Maletzky, B. M. d-Amphetamine and delinquency: Hyperkinesis persisting? *Diseases of the Nervous System*, 1974, *35*, 543–547.

Mann, H. B., & Greenspan, S. I. The identification and treatment of adult brain dysfunction. *American Journal of Psychiatry*, 1976, *133*, 1013–1017.

Margolin, D. I. The hyperkinetic child syndrome and brain monoamines: Pharmacology and therapeutic implications. *Journal of Clinical Psychiatry*, 1978, *39*, 120–130.

Margolis, J. Academic correlates of sustained attention. *Dissertation Abstracts International*, 1973, *33*, 5555–5556.

Marker, G. Phenothiazines and the mentally retarded: Institutional drug-abuse? *The Mental Health Law Project*, March 1975, pp. 1; 14–15.

Martin, G., & Zaug, P. Electrocardiographic monitoring of enuretic children receiving therapeutic doses of imipramine. *American Journal of Psychiatry*, 1975, *132*, 540–542.

Marwitt, S. J., & Stenner, A. J. Hyperkinesis: Delineations of two patterns. *Exceptional Children*, 1972, *38*, 401–406.

Mash, E. J., & Dalby, J. T. Behavioral interventions for hyperactivity. In R. L. Trites (Ed.), *Hyperactivity in children: Etiology, measurement, and treatment implications.* Baltimore: University Park Press, 1979.

Masters, J. C., & Mokros, J. R. Self-reinforcement processes in children. In H. Reese (Ed.), *Advances in child development and behavior* (Vol. 9). New York: Academic Press, 1974.

Mayron, L. W. Hyperactivity from fluorescent lighting—fact or fancy: A commentary on the report by O'Leary, Rosenbaum, and Hughes. *Journal of Abnormal Child Psychology*, 1978, *6*, 291–294.

Mayron, L. W., Ott, J., Nations, R., & Mayron, E. L. Light, radiation, and academic behavior. Initial studies on the effects of full-spectrum lighting and radiation shielding on behavior and academic performance of school children. *Academic Therapy*, 1974, *10*, 33–47.

McDermott, J. F., Jr., Harrison, S. I., Schrager, J., Wilson, P., Killins, E., Lindy, J., & Waggoner, R. W. Social class and mental illness in children: The diagnosis of organicity and mental retardation. *Journal of the American Academy of Child Psychiatry*, 1967, *6*, 309–320.

McNutt, B. A., Ballard, J. E., Boileau, R., Sprague, R. L., & von Neumann, A. The effects of long-term stimulant medication on growth and body composition of hyperactive children. *Psychopharmacology Bulletin,* 1976, *12,* 13–15.

McNutt, B. A., Boileau, R. A., & Cohen, M. The effects of long-term stimulant medication on the growth and body composition of hyperactive children. *Psychopharmacology Bulletin,* 1977, *13,* 36–38.

Medley, D. M., & Mitzel, H. E. Application of analysis of variance to the estimation of the reliability of observations of teachers' classroom behavior. *Journal of Experimental Education,* 1958, *27,* 23–25. (a)

Medley, D. M., & Mitzel, H. E. A technique for measuring classroom behavior. *Journal of Educational Psychology,* 1958, *49,* 86–92. (b)

Megargee, E. I. The role of inhibition in the assessment and understanding of violence. In J. L. Singer (Ed.), *The control of aggression and violence.* New York: Academic Press, 1971.

Meichenbaum, D. Theoretical and treatment implications of developmental research on verbal control of behavior. *Psychologie Canadienne/Canadian Psychological Review,* 1975, *16,* 22–27.

Meichenbaum, D. H. *Cognitive behavior modification.* New York: Plenum Press, 1977.

Meichenbaum, D. H. Teaching children self-control. In B. Lahey & A. Kazdin (Eds.), *Advances in child clinical psychology* (Vol. 2). New York: Plenum Press, 1978.

Meichenbaum, D. H., & Goodman, J. Reflection–impulsivity and verbal control of motor behavior. *Child Development,* 1969, *40,* 785–797.

Meichenbaum, D. H., & Goodman, J. Training impulsive children to talk to themselves: A means of developing self-control. *Journal of Abnormal Psychology,* 1971, *77,* 115–126.

Mendelson, W., Johnson, N., & Stewart, M. A. Hyperactive children as teenagers: A follow-up study. *Journal of Nervous and Mental Disease,* 1971, *153,* 273–279.

Messer, S. B. Reflection-impulsivity: A review. *Psychological Bulletin,* 1976, *83,* 1026–1052.

Messinger, E. Ritalin and MBD: A cure in search of a disease. *Health/Pac Bulletin,* 1975, *67,* 1–9; 18–21.

Miller, L. B., & Dyer, J. L. Four preschool programs: Their dimensions and effects. *Monographs of the Society for Research in Child Development,* 1975, *40* (Serial No. 161).

Miller, L. C. School behavior check list: An inventory of deviant behavior for elementary school children. *Journal of Consulting and Clinical Psychology,* 1972, *38,* 134–144.

Miller, R. G., Palkes, H. S., & Stewart, M. A. Hyperactive children in suburban elementary schools. *Child Psychiatry and Human Development,* 1973, *4,* 121–127.

Millichap, J. G. Drugs in management of minimal brain dysfunction. *Annals of the New York Academy of Sciences,* 1973, *205,* 321–334.

Millichap, J. G. *The hyperactive child with minimal brain dysfunction: Questions and answers.* Chicago: Yearbook Medical Publishers, 1975. (a)

Millichap, J. G. The paradoxical effects of CNS stimulants on hyperkinetic behavior. *International Journal of Neurology,* 1975, *10,* 241–251. (b)

Millichap, J. G., & Boldrey, E. E. Studies in hyperkinetic behavior II. Laboratory and clinical evaluations of drug treatments. *Neurology,* 1967, *17,* 467–471.

Minde, K., Lewin, D., Weiss, G., Lavigueur, H., Douglas, V., & Sykes, E. The hyperactive child in elementary school: A 5-year, controlled, follow-up. *Exceptional Children,* 1971, *38,* 215–221.

Minde, K., Weiss, G., & Mendelson, N. A 5-year follow-up study of 91 hyperactive school children. *Journal of the American Academy of Child Psychiatry,* 1972, *11,* 595–610.

Minuchin, S., Baker, L., Rosman, B. L., Liebman, R., Milman, L., & Todd, T. C. A conceptual model of psychosomatic illness in children. *Archives of General Psychiatry,* 1975, *32,* 1031–1038.

Mischel, W. On the future of personality measurement. *American Psychologist,* 1977, *32,* 246–254.

Mnookin, R. Children's rights: Beyond kiddie libbers and child savers. *Journal of Clinical Child Psychology,* 1978, *7,* 163–167.
Montagu, J. D. The hyperkinetic child: A behavioural, electrodermal, and EEG investigation. *Developmental Medicine and Child Neurology,* 1975, *17,* 299–305.
Montagu, J. D., & Swarbrick, L. Effective amphetamines in hyperkinetic children: Stimulant or sedative? A pilot study. *Developmental Medicine and Child Neurology,* 1975, *17,* 293–298.
Moos, R. Conceptualizations of human environments. *American Psychologist,* 1973, *28,* 652–665.
Moray, N. *Attention: Selective processes in vision and hearing.* London: Hutchison Educational Ltd., 1969.
Morrison, J. R. Parental divorce as a factor in childhood psychiatric illness. *Comprehensive Psychiatry,* 1974, *15,* 95–102.
Morrison, J. R., & Stewart, M. A. A family study of the hyperactive child syndrome. *Biological Psychiatry,* 1971, *3,* 189–195.
Morrison, J. R., & Stewart, M. A. The psychiatric status of the legal families of adopted hyperactive children. *Archives of General Psychiatry,* 1973, *130,* 791–792.
Murrell, S. A. Relationships of ordinal position and family size to psychological measures of delinquents. *Journal of Abnormal Child Psychology,* 1974, *2,* 39–46.
Needleman, H. L. Lead poisoning in children: Neurologic implications of widespread subclinical intoxication. In S. Walzer & P. H. Wolff (Eds.), *Minimal cerebral dysfunction in children.* New York: Grune & Stratton, 1973.
Needleman, H. L., Gunnoe, C., Leviton, A., Reed, R., Peresie, H., Maher, C., & Barrett P. Deficits in psychologic and classroom performance of children with elevated dentine levels. *New England Journal of Medicine,* 1979, *300,* 689–695.
Neisser, U. *Cognition and reality: Principles and implications of cognitive psychology.* San Francisco: Freeman, 1976.
Newitt, J., Singer, M., & Kahn, H. Some speculations on U. S. drug use. *Journal of Social Issues,* 1971, *3,* 107–122.
Ney, P. G. Four types of hyperkinesis. *Canadian Psychiatric Association Journal,* 1974, *19,* 543–550.
Nie, N. H., Hull, C. H., Jenkins, J. G., Stenbrenner, K., & Bent, D. H. (Eds.), *Statistical package for the social sciences.* New York: McGraw-Hill, 1975.
Obrist, P. A., Lawler, J. E., Howard, J. L., Smithson, K. W., Martin, P. L., & Manning, J. Sympathetic influences on cardiac rate and contractility during acute stress in humans. *Psychophysiology,* 1974, *11,* 405–427.
Obrist, P. A., Webb, R. A., & Sutterer, J. R. Heart rate and somatic changes during aversive conditioning and a simple reaction time task. *Psychophysiology,* 1969, *5,* 696–723.
Obrist, P. A., Webb, R. A., Sutterer, J. R., & Howard, J. L. The cardiac-somatic relationship: Some reformulations. *Psychophysiology,* 1970, *6,* 569–587.
Oettinger, L., Jr. Pediatric psychopharmacology. A review with special reference to deanol. *Diseases of the Nervous System,* 1977, *38,* 25–31.
O'Leary, K. D., Becker, W. C., Evans, M. B., & Saudargas, R. Z. A token reinforcement program in a public school: A replication and systematic analysis. *Journal of Applied Behavior Analysis,* 1969, *2,* 3–13.
O'Leary, K. D., & Drabman, R. Token reinforcement programs in the classroom: A review. *Psychological Bulletin,* 1971, *75,* 379–398.
O'Leary, K. D., & O'Leary, S. G. *Classroom management in the successful use of behavior modification.* New York: Pergamon Press, 1972.
O'Leary, K. D., O'Leary, S. G., & Becker, W. C. Modification of a deviant sibling interaction pattern in the home. *Behavioral Research and Therapy,* 1967, *5,* 113–120.

O'Leary, K. D., Pelham, W. E., Rosenbaum, A., & Price, G. H. Behavioral treatment of hyperkinetic children: An experimental evaluation of its usefulness. *Clinical Pediatrics,* 1976, *15,* 510–515.

O'Leary, K. D., Rosenbaum, A. & Hughes, P. C. Direct and systematic replication: A rejoinder. *Journal of Abnormal Child Psychology,* 1978, *6,* 295–297. (a)

O'Leary, K. D., Rosenbaum, A., & Hughes, P. C. Fluorescent lighting: A purported source of hyperactive behavior. *Journal of Abnormal Child Psychology,* 1978, *6,* 285–289. (b)

O'Malley, J. E., & Eisenberg, L. The hyperkinetic syndrome. *Seminars in Psychiatry,* 1973, *5,* 95–103.

Omenn, G. S. Genetic approaches to the syndrome of minimal brain dysfunction. *Annals of the New York Academy of Sciences,* 1973, *205,* 212–223.

Osborne, J. G. Free-time as a reinforcer in the management of classroom behavior. *Journal of Applied Behavior Analysis,* 1969, *2,* 113–118.

Ott, J. Responses of psychological and physiological functions to environmental light—Part I. *Journal of Learning Disabilities,* 1968, *1,* 298–300.

Ott, J. N. Influence of fluorescent lights on hyperactivity and learning disabilities. *Journal of Learning Disabilities,* 1976, *9,* 417–422.

O'Tuama, L. A., Swisher, C. N., Riechler, R. J., & Routh, D. K. Lack of effect of TRH in minimal brain dysfunction. *Pediatrics,* 1977, *59,* 955–956.

Packard, R. G. The control of "classroom attention:" A group contingency for complex behavior. *Journal of Applied Behavior Analysis,* 1970, *3,* 13–28.

Padway, L. Federal regulation of Ritalin in the treatment of hyperactive children. *Ecology Law Quarterly,* 1978, *7,* 457–495.

Page, J. G., Bernstein, J. E., Janicki, R. S., & Michelli, F. A. A multiclinic trial of pemoline in childhood hyperkinesis. In C. K. Conners (Ed.), *Clinical use of stimulant drugs in children.* New York: American Elsevier, 1974.

Paine, R. S., Werry, J. S., & Quay, H. C. A study of "minimal cerebral dysfunciton." *Developmental Medicine and Child Neurology,* 1968, *10,* 505–520.

Palfrey, J. S., Mervis, R. C., & Butler, J. A. New directions in the evaluation and education of handicapped children. *New England Journal of Medicine,* 1978, *298,* 819–824.

Palkes, H., & Stewart, M. A. Intellectual ability and performance of hyperactive children. *American Journal of Orthopsychiatry,* 1972, *42,* 35–39.

Palkes, H., Stewart, M., & Freedman, J. Improvement in maze performance of hyperactive boys as a function of verbal-training procedures. *Journal of Special Education,* 1971, *5,* 337–342.

Palkes, H., Stewart, M., & Kahana, B. Porteus Maze performance of hyperactive boys after training in self-directed verbal commands. *Child Development,* 1968, *39,* 817–826.

Parks, A. L. *Applied behavior analysis and hyperactivity: Focus on self-management.* Paper presented at the 83rd Annual American Psychological Association Convention, Chicago, September 1975.

Parry, H. J. Use of psychotropic drugs by U.S. adults. *Public Health Reports,* 1968, *83,* 799–810.

Parry, H. J., Balter, M. B., Mellinger, G. D., Cisin, I. H., & Manheimer, D. I. National patterns of psychotherapeutic drug use. *Archives of General Psychiatry,* 1973, *28,* 769–783.

Parry, P. *The effect of reward on the performance of hyperactive children.* Unpublished doctoral dissertation, McGill University, Montreal, 1973.

Paternite, C. E., & Loney, J. *Parenting styles and symptom severity in MBD and hyperactive boys of high and low socioeconomic status.* Paper presented at the annual convention of the Midwestern Psychological Association, Chicago, 1975.

Paternite, C. E., Loney, J., & Langhorne, J. E., Jr. Relationships between symptomatology and

SES-related factors in hyperkinetic/MBD boys. *American Journal of Orthopsychiatry,* 1976, *46,* 291–301.

Patterson, G. R. An application of conditioning techniques to the control of hyperactive children. In L. Ullman & L. Krasner (Eds.), *Case studies in behavior modification.* New York: Holt, Rinehart & Winston, 1965.

Patterson, G. R. *Families: Applications of social learning to family life.* Champaign, IL: Research Press, 1975.

Patterson, G. R., & Guillion, M. E. *Living with children: New methods for parents and teachers.* Champaign, IL: Research Press, 1971.

Patterson, G. R., Jones, R., Whittier, J., & Wright, M. A. A behavior modification technique for the hyperactive child. *Behavior Research and Therapy,* 1965, *2,* 217–226.

Paul, G. L., Tobias, L. L., & Holly, B. L. Maintenance psychotropic drugs in the presence of active treatment programs. A "triple-blind" withdrawal study. *Archives of General Psychiatry,* 1972, *27,* 106–115.

Pelham, W. E. Behavior therapy with hyperactive children. *Psychiatric Clinics of North America,* 1978, *1,* 240–243.

Pelham, W. E., & Ross, A. O. Selective attention in children with reading problems: A developmental study of incidental learning. *Journal of Abnormal Child Psychology,* 1977, *5,* 1–8.

Peters, K. G. *Selective attention and distractibility in hyperactive and normal children.* Unpublished doctoral dissertation, McGill University, 1977.

Peterson, D. R., & Quay, H. C. *Factor-analyzed problem checklist.* Urbana, IL: University of Illinois, Children's Research Center, 1967.

Petti, T., & Campbell, M. Imipramine and seizures. *American Journal of Psychiatry,* 1975, *32,* 538–540.

Pihl, R. O. Conditioning procedures with hyperactive children. *Neurology,* 1967, *17,* 921–923.

Pitkanen, L. The effect of simulation exercises on the control of aggressive behavior in children. *Scandinavian Journal of Psychology,* 1974, *15,* 169–177.

Platt, J. Social traps. *American Psychologist,* 1973, *28,* 641–651.

Pope, L. Motor activity in brain-injured children. *American Journal of Orthopsychiatry,* 1970, *40,* 783–794.

Porges, S. W. Heart rate variability and deceleration as indexes of reaction time. *Journal of Experimental Psychology,* 1972, *92,* 103–110.

Porges, S. W. Heart rate variability: An autonomic correlate of reaction time performance. *Bulletin of the Psychonomic Society,* 1973, *1,* 270–272.

Porges, S. W. Heart rate indices of newborn attentional responsivity. *Merrill-Palmer Quarterly,* 1974, *20,* 231–254.

Porges, S. W. Peripheral and neurochemical parallels of psychopathology: A psychophysiological model relating autonomic imbalance to hyperactivity, psychopathy and autism. In H. W. Reese (Ed.), *Advances in child development and behavior* (Vol. 11). New York: Academic Press, 1976.

Porges, S. W., Bohrer, R. E., Keren, G., Cheung, M. N., Franks, G. J., & Drasgow, F. *Autonomic dysfunction: A physiological manifestation of behavioral hyperactivity.* Unpublished manuscript, University of Illinois, 1977.

Porges, S. W., & Raskin, D. C. Respiratory and heart rate components of attention. *Journal of Experimental Psychology,* 1969, *81,* 497–503.

Porges, S. W., Walter, G. F., Korb, R. J., & Sprague, R. L. The influences of methylphenidate on heart rate and behavioral measures of attention in hyperactive children. *Child Development,* 1975, *46,* 727–733.

Powers, E., & Witmer, H. *An experiment in the prevention of delinquency: The Cambridge-Somerville youth study.* New York: Columbia University Press, 1951.

Prechtl, H., & Stemmer, C. The choreiform syndrome in children. *Developmental Medicine and Childhood Neurology,* 1962, *8,* 149–159.

Preis, K., & Huessy, H. R. Hyperactive children at risk. In M. J. Cohen (Ed.), *Drugs and the special child.* New York: Gardner Press, 1979.

Prentice, N., & Kelly, F. J. Intelligence and delinquency: A reconsideration. *Journal of Social Psychology,* 1963, *60,* 327–337.

Prichep, L. S., Sutton, S., & Hakarem, G. Evoked potentials in hyperkinetic and normal children under certainty and uncertainty. *Psychophysiology,* 1976, *5,* 419–428.

Prinz, R., & Loney, J. Teacher-rated hyperactive elementary school girls: An exploratory developmental study. *Child Psychiatry and Human Development,* 1974, *4,* 246–257.

Prout, H. T. Behavioral intervention with hyperactive children: A review. *Journal of Learning Disabilities,* 1977, *10,* 141–146.

Public Law 93–112, Section 504 (The Vocational Rehabilitation Act Amendments of 1973).

Public Law 93–380 (The Education Amendments of 1974).

Public Law 94–142. The Education for all Handicapped Children Act of 1975. *Congressional Record,* 1975, *14,* H11213, et seq.

Quay, H. C. Classification. In H. C. Quay & J. S. Werry (Eds.), *Psychopathological disorders of childhood* (2nd ed.). New York: Wiley, 1979.

Quay, H. C., Sprague, R. L., Werry, J. S., & McQueen, M. M. Conditioning visual orientation of conduct problem children in the classroom. *Journal of Experimental Child Psychology,* 1967, *5,* 512–517.

Quinn, P. O., & Rapoport, J. L. A one-year follow-up of hyperactive boys treated with imipramine or methylphenidate. *American Journal of Psychiatry,* 1975, *132,* 241–245.

Rapoport, J. L., & Benoit, M. The relation of direct home observations to the clinic evaluation of hyperactive school age boys. *Journal of Child Psychology and Psychiatry,* 1975, *16,* 141–147.

Rapoport, J. L., Buchsbaum, M. S., Zahn, T., Weingartner, H., Ludlow, C., Mikkelsen, E. Dextroamphetamine: Cognitive and behavioral effects in normal and hyperactive boys and normal adult males. *Archives of General Psychiatry,* in press.

Rapoport, J. L., Buchsbaum, M. S., Zahn, T. P., Weingartner, H., Ludlow, C., & Mikkelsen, E. J. Dextroamphetamine: Cognitive and behavioral effects in normal prepubertal boys. *Science,* 1978, *199,* 560–563.

Rapoport, J. L., Quinn, P. O., Bradbard, G., Riddle, K. D., & Brooks, E. Imipramine and methylphenidate treatments of hyperactive boys. *Archives of General Psychiatry,* 1974, *30,* 789–793.

Rappaport, M. M., & Rappaport, H. The other half of the expectancy equation: Pygmalion. *Journal of Educational Psychology,* 1975, *67,* 531–536.

Raskind, M., & Bradford, T. Methylphenidate (Ritalin) abuse and methadone maintenance. *Diseases of the Nervous System,* 1975, *36,* 9–12.

Raven, J. C. *Standard progressive matrices.* London: Lewis, 1958.

Ray, O. S., & Wilson, J. T. Drug-taking behavior. In N. Hobbs (Ed.), *Issues in the classification of children* (Vol. 1). San Francisco: Jossey-Bass, 1975.

Razran, G. The observable unconscious and the inferable conscious in current Soviet psychophysiology: Interoceptive conditioning, semantic conditioning and the orienting reflex. *Psychological Review,* 1961, *68,* 81–147.

Reichard, C. C., & Elder, S. T. The effects of caffeine on reaction time in hyperkinetic and normal children. *American Journal of Psychiatry,* 1977, *134,* 144–148.

Renshaw, D. C. *The hyperactive child.* Chicago: Nelson-Hall, 1974.
Renshaw, D. C. Psychopharmacotherapy in children. In F. J. Ayd, Jr. (Ed.), *Rational psychopharmacotherapy and the right to treatment.* Baltimore: Waverly Press, 1975.
Renstrom, R. The teacher and the social worker in stimulant drug treatment of hyperactive children. *School Review,* 1976, *85,* 97–108.
Report of the conference on the use of stimulant drugs in the treatment of behaviorally disturbed young school children. *Journal of Learning Disabilities,* 1971, *4,* 523–530.
Ridberg, E. H., Parke, R. D., & Hetherington, E. M. Modification of impulsive and reflective cognitive styles through observation of film-mediated models. *Developmental Psychology,* 1971, *5,* 369–377.
Riddle, K. D., & Rapoport, J. L. A 2-year follow-up of 72 hyperactive boys. Classroom behavior and peer acceptance. *Journal of Nervous and Mental Disease,* 1976, *162,* 126–134.
Rie, E. D., & Rie, H. E. Recall, retention, and Ritalin. *Journal of Consulting and Clinical Psychology,* 1977, *45,* 967–972.
Rie, H. E. Hyperactivity in children. *American Journal of Diseases of Children,* 1975, *129,* 783–789.
Rie, H. E., Rie, E. D., Stewart, S., & Ambuel, J. P. Effects of methylphenidate on underachieving children. *Journal of Consulting and Clinical Psychology,* 1976, *44,* 250–260. (a)
Rie, H. E., Rie, E. D., Stewart, S., & Ambuel, J. P. Effects of Ritalin on underachieving children: A replication. *American Journal of Orthopsychiatry,* 1976, *46,* 313–322. (b)
Robin, S. S. A procedure for securing returns to mailed questionnaires. *Sociology and Social Research,* 1965, *50,* 24–35.
Robin, S. S., & Bosco, J. J. Ritalin for school children: The teacher's perspective. *Journal of School Health,* 1973, *43,* 624–628.
Robin, S. S., & Bosco, J. J. The social context of stimulant drug treatment for hyperkinetic children. *School Review,* 1976, *85,* 141–154.
Robins, L. *Deviant children grown up.* Baltimore: Williams & Wilkins, 1966.
Roche, A. F., Lipman, R. S., Overall, J. E., & Hung, W. The effects of stimulant medication on the growth of hyperkinetic children. *Pediatrics,* in press.
Rodin, E., Lucas, A., & Simson, C. A study of behavior disorders in children by means of general purpose computers. In K. Enslein (Ed.), *Proceedings of the 1963 Rochester Conference on data acquisition and processing in biology and medicine* (Vol. 3). New York: Pergamon Press, 1963.
Rogers, J. M. Drug abuse—Just what the doctor ordered. *Psychology Today,* 1971, *5,* 16–24.
Rosenbaum, A., O'Leary, K. D., & Jacob, R. G. Behavioral intervention with hyperactive children: Group consequences as a supplement to individual contingencies. *Behavior Therapy,* 1975, *6,* 315–323.
Rosenbaum, M. S., & Drabman, R. S. Self-control training in the classroom: A review and critique. *Journal of Applied Behavior Analysis,* 1979, *12,* 467–485.
Rosenthal, R. Estimating effective reliabilities in studies that employ judges' ratings. *Journal of Clinical Psychology,* 1973, *29,* 342–345.
Rosenthal, R. H., & Allen, T. W. An examination of attention, arousal, and learning dysfunctions of hyperkinetic children. *Psychological Bulletin,* 1978, *85,* 689–715.
Ross, A. O. *Psychological aspects of learning disabilities and reading disorders.* New York: McGraw-Hill, 1976.
Ross, D. M., & Ross, S. A. *Hyperactivity: Research, theory, action.* New York: Wiley, 1976.
Routh, D. K. The clinical significance of open field activity in children. *Pediatric Psychology,* 1975, *3,* 3–8.

Routh, D. K., & Roberts, R. D. Minimal brain dysfunction in children: Failure to find evidence for a behavioral syndrome. *Psychological Reports,* 1972, *31,* 307–314.

Routh, D. K., & Schroeder, C. S. Standardized playroom measures as indices of hyperactivity. *Journal of Abnormal Child Psychology,* 1976, *4,* 199–207.

Routh, D. K., Schroeder, C. S., & O'Tuama, L. A. Development of activity level in children. *Developmental Psychology,* 1974, *10,* 163–168.

Routh, D. K., Walton, M. D., & Padan-Belkin, E. Development of activity level in children revisited: Effects of mother presence. *Developmental Psychology,* 1978, *14,* 571–581.

Rutter, M. *Children of sick parents.* London: Oxford University Press, 1966.

Rutter, M. Isle of Wight studies, 1964–1974. *Psychological Medicine,* 1976, *6,* 313–332.

Rutter, M., & Graham, P. The reliability and validity of the psychiatric assessment of the child: 1. Interview with the child. *British Journal of Psychiatry,* 1968, *114,* 563–579.

Rutter, M., Graham, P., & Yule, W. *A neuropsychiatric study in childhood.* Philadelphia: Lippincott, 1970.

Rutter, M., Tizard, P., & Whitmore, K. *Education, health and behavior.* New York: Wiley, 1970.

Ryor, J. 94–142—The perspective of regular education. *Learning Disability Quarterly,* 1978, *1,* 6–14.

Sachar, E. J. Growth hormone responses in hyperactive children. *Psychopharmacology Bulletin,* 1977, *13,* 55.

Safer, D. J., & Allen, R. P. Factors influencing the suppressant effects of two stimulant drugs on the growth of hyperactive children. *Pediatrics,* 1973, *51,* 660–667.

Safer, D. J., & Allen, R. P. Side effects from long-term use of stimulants in children. *International Journal of Mental Health,* 1975, *4,* 105–118. (a)

Safer, D. J., & Allen, R. P. Stimulant drug treatment of hyperactive adolescents. *Diseases of the Nervous System,* 1975, *36,* 454–457. (b)

Safer, D. J., & Allen, R. P. *Hyperactive children: Diagnosis and management.* Baltimore: University Park Press, 1976.

Safer, D. J., Allen, R. P., & Barr, E. Depression of growth in hyperactive children on stimulant drugs. *New England Journal of Medicine,* 1972, *287,* 217–220.

Safer, D. J., Allen, R. P., & Barr, E. Growth rebound after termination of stimulant drugs. *Journal of Pediatrics,* 1975, *86,* 113–116.

Sahakian, B. J., & Robbins, T. W. Are the effects of psychomotor stimulant drugs on hyperactive children really paradoxical? *Medical Hypotheses,* 1977, *3,* 154–158.

Saletu, B., Saletu, M., Simeon, J., Viamontes, G., & Itil, T. M. Comparative symptomatological and evoked potential studies with d-amphetamine, thioridazine and placebo in hyperkinetic children. *Biological Psychiatry,* 1975, *10,* 253–275.

Salkind, N. J., & Poggio, J. P. The measurement of hyperactivity: Trends and issues. In M. J. Fine (Ed.), *Principles and techniques of intervention with hyperactive children.* Springfield, IL: Charles C Thomas, 1977.

Salzinger, K., Feldman, R. S., & Portnoy, S. Training parents of brain-injured children in the use of operant conditioning procedures. *Behavior Therapy,* 1970, *1,* 4–32.

Sandberg, S. T., Rutter, M., & Taylor, E. Hyperkinetic disorder in psychiatric clinic attenders. *Developmental Medicine and Child Neurology,* 1978, *20,* 279–299.

Sandoval, J. The measurement of the hyperactive syndrome in children. *Review of Educational Research,* 1977, *47,* 293–318.

Sandoval, J., Lambert, N. M., & Yandell, W. Current medical practice and hyperactive children. *American Journal of Orthopsychiatry,* 1976, *46,* 323–334.

Sandoval, J., & Sassone, D. *Teachers' management strategies with hyperactive children.* Unpublished manuscript, 1977.

Saraf, K. R., Klein, D. F., Gittelman-Klein, R., Gootman, N., & Greenhill, P. EKG effects of imipramine treatment in children. *Journal of the American Academy of Child Psychiatry,* 1978, *17,* 60–69.
Saraf, K. R., Klein, D. F., Gittelman-Klein, R., & Groff, S. Imipramine side effects in children. *Psychopharmacologia,* 1974, *37,* 265–274.
Sarason, I. G. Verbal learning, modeling and juvenile delinquency. *American Psychologist,* 1968, *23,* 254–266.
Satterfield, J. H., & Cantwell, D. Psychopharmacology in the prevention of antisocial and delinquent behavior. *International Journal of Mental Health,* 1975, *4,* 227–237.
Satterfield, J. H., Cantwell, D. P., Lesser, L. I., & Podosin, R. L. Physiological studies of the hyperkinetic child: I. *American Journal of Psychiatry,* 1972, *128,* 1418–1424.
Satterfield, J. H., Cantwell, D. P., & Satterfield, B. T. Pathophysiology of the hyperactive child syndrome. *Archives of General Psychiatry,* 1974, *31,* 839–844.
Satterfield, J. H., Cantwell, D. P., Saul, R. E., Lesser, L. I., & Podosin, R. L. Response to stimulant drug treatment in hyperactive children: Prediction from EEG and neurological findings. *Journal of Autism and Childhood Schizophrenia,* 1973, *3,* 36–48.
Satterfield, J. H., & Dawson, M. E. Electrodermal correlates of hyperactivity in children. *Psychophysiology,* 1971, *8,* 191–197.
Sbordone, M. *Early identification of educationally high-risk and high potential children from kindergarten through first grade.* Unpublished doctoral dissertation, University of California, Los Angeles, 1976.
Schachter, S., & Singer, J. E. Cognitive, social, and physiological determinants of emotional state. *Psychological Review,* 1962, *69,* 379–399.
Schaefer, E. S. Children's reports of parental behavior: An inventory. *Child Development,* 1965, *36,* 413–424.
Schaefer, E. S., & Aaronson, M. R. *Classroom Behavior Inventory: Preschool to primary.* Bethesda, MD: National Institute of Mental Health, 1966.
Schain, R. J. Minimal brain dysfunction in children: A neurological viewpoint. *Bulletin of the Los Angeles Neurological Societies,* 1968, *33,* 145–155.
Schain, R. J. The neurological evaluation of children with learning disorders. *California Medicine,* 1973, *118,* 24-32.
Schain, R. J., & Reynard, C. L. Observations on effects of a central stimulant drug (methylphenidate) in children with hyperactive behavior. *Pediatrics,* 1975, *55,* 709–716.
Schleifer, M., Weiss, G., Cohen, N., Elman, M., Cvejic, H., & Kruger, E. Hyperactivity in preschoolers and the effect of methylphenidate. *American Journal of Orthopsychiatry,* 1975, *45,* 38–50.
Schnackenburg, R. C. Caffeine as a substitute for Schedule II stimulants in hyperkinetic children. *American Journal of Psychiatry,* 1973, *130,* 796.
Schnackenburg, R. C. Caffeine therapy for hyperkinetic children. *Current Psychiatric Therapies,* 1975, *15,* 39–44.
Schopler, E. Parents of psychotic children as scapegoats. *Journal of Contemporary Psychotherapy,* 1971, *4,* 17–22.
Schopler, E. Toward reducing behavior problems in autistic children. *Journal of Autism and Childhood Schizophrenia,* 1976, *6,* 1–13.
Schrag, P., & Divoky, D. *The myth of the hyperactive child and other means of child control.* New York: Pantheon, 1975.
Schrager, J., Lindy, J., Harrison, S., McDermott, J., & Killins, E. The hyperkinetic child: Some consensually validated behavioral correlates. *Exceptional Children,* 1966, *32,* 635–637.
Schweiker, R. F. Factor scores aren't sacred: Comments on "abuses of factor scores." *American Educational Research Journal,* 1967, *4,* 168–170.

Scott, T. J. The use of music to reduce hyperactivity in children. *American Journal of Orthopsychiatry*, 1970, *40*, 677–680.

Scoville, B. *Symposium: Stimulant drugs and the schools: Dimensions in the remediation of social toxicity. III. Government perspectives in the evaluation and regulation of stimulant drugs for hyperkinetic children.* Paper presented at the annual meeting of the Council for Exceptional Children, New York, April 1974.

Sells, S. B. An interactionist looks at the environment. *American Psychologist*, 1963, *18*, 696–702.

Shaffer, D., McNamara, N., & Pincus, J. H. Controlled observations on patterns of activity, attention, and impulsivity in brain-damaged and psychiatrically disturbed boys. *Psychological Medicine*, 1974, *4*, 4–18.

Sheppard, C., Beyel, V., Fracchia, J., & Merlis, S. Polypharmacy in psychiatry: A multi-state comparison of psychotropic drug combinations. *Diseases of the Nervous System*, 1974, *35*, 183–189.

Shih, T. M., Khachaturian, Z. S., Barry, H., III, & Hanin, I. Cholinergic mediation of the inhibitory effect of methylphenidate on neuronal activity in the reticular formation. *Neuropharmacology*, 1976, *15*, 55–60.

Shih, T. M., Khachaturian, Z. S., Barry, H., III, & Reisler, K. L. Differential effects of methylphenidate on reticular formation and thalamic neural activity. *Psychopharmacology*, 1975, *44*, 11–15.

Shure, M. B., & Spivack, G. *A mental health program for kindergarten children: A cognitive approach to solving interpersonal problems.* Philadelphia: Hahnemann Medical College and Hospital, 1974.

Shure, M. B., & Spivack, G. *The PIPS test manual: A cognitive measure of interpersonal problem-solving ability.* Philadelphia: Hahnemann Medical College and Hospital, 1975.

Silbergeld, E. K. Neuropharmacology of hyperkinesis. In W. B. Essmann & L. Valzelli (Eds), *Current developments in psychopharmacology* (Vol. 4). New York: Spectrum, 1977.

Silbergeld, E., & Goldberg, A. Hyperactivity: A lead-induced behavior disorder. *Environmental Health Perspectives*, 1974, 227–232.

Silverman, M., & Lee, P. R. *Pills, profits, and politics.* Berkeley: University of California Press, 1974.

Sleator, E. K., & Sprague, R. L. Pediatric psychopharmacotherapy. In W. G. Clark & J. del Giudice (Eds.), *Principles of psychopharmacology* (2nd ed.). New York: Academic Press, 1978.

Sleator, E. K., & von Neumann, A. W. Methylphenidate in the treatment of hyperkinetic children. *Clinical Pediatrics*, 1974, *13*, 19–24.

Sleator, E. K., von Neumann, A., & Sprague, R. L. Hyperactive children: A continuous long-term placebo-controlled follow-up. *Journal of the American Medical Association*, 1974, *229*, 316–317.

Smith, A. Social dangers of treating the hyperactive child. *Urban League Review*, 1975, *1*, 30–34.

Sokolov, E. N. *Perception and the conditioned reflex.* New York: Macmillan, 1963.

Solomons, G. Drug therapy: Initiation and follow-up. *Annals of the New York Academy of Sciences*, 1973, *205*, 335–344.

Sprague, R. L. Psychopharmacotherapy in children. In M. F. McMillan & S. Henao (Eds.), *Child psychiatry: Treatment and research.* New York: Brunner/Mazel, 1977.

Sprague, R. L. Principles of clinical drug trials and social, ethical and legal issues of drug use in children. In J. S. Werry (Ed.), *Pediatric psychopharmacology: The use of behavior modifying drugs in children.* New York: Brunner/Mazel, 1978.

Sprague, R. L., Barnes, K. R., & Werry, J. S. Methylphenidate and thioridazine: Learning,

reaction time, activity, and classroom behavior in disturbed children. *American Journal of Orthopsychiatry,* 1970, *40,* 615–628.
Sprague, R. L., & Baxley, G. B. Drugs for behavior management, with comment on some legal aspects. In J. Wortis (Ed.), *Mental retardation and developmental disabilities* (Vol. 10). New York: Grune & Stratton, 1978.
Sprague, R. L., & Berger, B. D. Drug effects on learning performance: Relevance of animal research to pediatric psychopharmacology. In R. M. Knights & D. J. Bakker (Eds.), *Rehabilitation, treatment and management of learning disorders.* Baltimore: University Park Press, in press.
Sprague, R. L., Christensen, D. E., & Werry, J. S. Experimental psychology and stimulant drugs. In C. K. Conners (Ed.), *Clinical use of stimulant drugs in children.* New York: American Elsevier, 1974.
Sprague, R. L., Cohen, M. H., & Eichiseder, W. *Are there hyperactive children in Europe and the South Pacific?* Paper presented at the meeting of the American Psychological Association, San Francisco, August 1977.
Sprague, R. L., Cohen, M., & Werry, J. S. *Normative data on the Conners Teacher Rating Scale and Abbreviated Scale* (Technical Report). Urbana, IL: University of Illinois, Children's Research Center, November 1974.
Sprague, R. L., & Gadow, K. D. The role of the teacher in drug treatment. *School Review,* 1976, *85,* 109–140.
Sprague, R. L., & Sleator, E. K. Effects of psychopharmacological agents on learning disabilities. *Pediatric Clinics of North America,* 1973, *20,* 719–735.
Sprague, R. L., & Sleator, E. K. What is the proper dose of stimulant drugs in children? *International Journal of Mental Health,* 1975, *4,* 75–104.
Sprague, R. L., & Sleator, E. K. Drugs and dosages: Implications for learning disabilities. In R. M. Knights & D. J. Bakker (Eds.), *Neuropsychology of learning disorders: Theoretical approaches.* Baltimore: University Park Press, 1976.
Sprague, R. L., & Sleator, E. K. Methylphenidate in hyperkinetic children: Differences in dose effects on learning and social behavior. *Science,* 1977, *198,* 1274–1276.
Sprague, R. L., & Werry, J. S. Methodology of psychopharmacological studies with the retarded. In N. R. Ellis (Ed.), *International review of research in mental retardation* (Vol. 5). New York: Academic Press, 1971.
Spring, C., Blunden, D., Greenberg, L. M., & Yellin, A. M. Validity and norms of a hyperactivity rating scale. *Journal of Special Education,* 1977, *11,* 313–321.
Spring, C., Greenberg, L. M., & Yellin, A. M. Agreement of mothers' and teachers' hyperactivity ratings with scores on drug-sensitive psychological tests. *Journal of Abnormal Child Psychology,* 1977, *5,* 199–204.
Spring, C., & Sandoval, J. Food additives and hyperkinesis: A critical evaluation of the evidence. *Journal of Learning Disabilities,* 1976, *9,* 560–569.
Spring, C., Yellin, A. M., & Greenberg, L. Effects of imipramine and methylphenidate on perceptual–motor performance of hyperactive children. *Perceptual and Motor Skills,* 1976, *43,* 459–470.
Sroufe, L. A. Drug treatment of children with behavior problems. In F. D. Horowitz (Ed.), *Review of child development research* (Vol. 4). Chicago: University of Chicago Press, 1975.
Sroufe, L. A., & Stewart, M. A. Treating problem children with stimulant drugs. *New England Journal of Medicine,* 1973, *289,* 407–413.
Staats, A. W., & Butterfield, W. H. Treatment of nonreading in a culturally deprived juvenile delinquent: An application of reinforcement principles. *Child Development,* 1965, *36,* 925–942.
Stableford, W., Butz, R., Hasazi, J., Leitenberg, H., & Peyser, J. Sequential withdrawal of

stimulant drugs and use of behavior therapy with two hyperactive boys. *American Journal of Orthopsychiatry,* 1976, *46,* 302–312.
Staff Report. *Hyperkinesis control in elementary schools.* Education Committee of the California State Senate, 1974.
Staub, E. The learning and unlearning of aggression. In J. L. Singer (Ed.), *The control of aggression and violence.* New York: Academic Press, 1971.
Steinkamp, M. W. *Relationships between task-irrelevant distractions and task performance of normal, retarded hyperactive, and minimal brain dysfunction children.* Unpublished doctoral dissertation, University of Illinois, 1974.
Stevens, T. M., Kupst, M. J., Suran, B. G., & Schulman, J. L. Activity level: A comparison between actometer scores and observer ratings. *Journal of Abnormal Child Psychology,* 1978, *6,* 163–173.
Stevens-Long, J. The effect of behavioral context on some aspects of adult disciplinary practice and affect. *Child Development,* 1973, *44,* 476–484.
Stewart, M. A. Hyperactive children. *Scientific American,* 1970, *222,* 94–98.
Stewart, M. A. Is hyperactivity abnormal? And other unanswered questions. *School Review,* 1976, *85,* 31–42. (a)
Stewart, M. A. Treating problem children with drugs: Ethical issues. In G. P. Koocher (Ed.), *Children's rights and the mental health professions.* New York: Wiley, 1976. (b)
Stewart, M. A., Mendelson, W. B., & Johnson, N. E. Hyperactive children as adolescents: How they describe themselves. *Child Psychiatry and Human Development,* 1973, *4,* 3–11.
Stewart, M. A., & Morrison, J. R. Affective disorder among the relatives of hyperactive children. *Journal of Child Psychology and Psychiatry,* 1973, *14,* 209–212.
Stewart, M. A., & Olds, S. W. *Raising a hyperactive child.* New York: Harper & Row, 1973.
Stewart, M. A., Pitts, F., Craig, A., & Dieruf, W. The hyperactive child syndrome. *American Journal of Orthopsychiatry,* 1966, *36,* 861–867.
Still, G. F. The Coulstonian Lectures on some abnormal physical conditions in children. *Lancet,* 1902, *1,* 1008–1012; 1077–1082; 1163–1168.
Stollak, G. E., Messé, L. A., Michaels, G. Y., & Catlin, R. T. *Child adjustment and parental interpersonal style.* Paper presented at the meeting of the American Pychological Association, San Francisco, September 1977.
Strauss, A. A., & Lehtinen, L. E. *Psychopathology and education in the brain-injured child.* New York: Grune & Stratton, 1947.
Sulzbacher, S. I. Psychotropic medication with children: An evaluation of procedural biases in results of reported studies. *Pediatrics,* 1973, *51,* 513–517.
Swanson, J. M., & Kinsbourne, M. Stimulant-related state-dependent learning in hyperactive children. *Science,* 1976, *192,* 1354–1357.
Swanson, J. M., & Kinsbourne, M. Should you use stimulants to treat the hyperactive child? *Modern Medicine,* 1978, *46,* 71–80.
Swanson, J. M., & Kinsbourne, M. Artificial color and hyperactive behavior. In R. M. Knights & D. J. Bakker (Eds.), *Rehabilitation, treatment and management of learning disorders.* Baltimore: University Park Press, in press.
Swanson, J. M., Kinsbourne, M., Roberts, W., & Zucker, K. Time-response analysis of the effect of stimulant medication on the learning ability of children referred for hyperactivity. *Pediatrics,* 1978, *61,* 21–29.
Sykes, D. H., Douglas, V. I., & Morgenstern, G. The effect of methylphenidate on sustained attention in hyperactive children. *Psychopharmacologia,* 1972, *25,* 262–274.
Sykes, D. H., Douglas, V. I., & Morgenstern, G. Sustained attention in hyperactive children. *Journal of Child Psychology and Psychiatry,* 1973, *14,* 213–220.
Sykes, D. H., Douglas, V. I., Weiss, G., & Minde, K. K. Attention in hyperactive children and

the effect of methylphenidate (Ritalin). *Journal of Child Psychology and Psychiatry,* 1971, *12,* 129–139.

Tait, C. D., Jr., & Hodges, E. F., Jr. *Delinquents, their families, and the community.* Springfield, IL: Charles C Thomas, 1962.

Tant, J. L. *Problem solving in hyperactive and reading disabled boys.* Unpublished doctoral dissertation, McGill University, 1978.

Tarver, S. G., Hallahan, D. P., Kauffman, J. M., & Ball, D. W. Verbal rehearsal and selective attention in children with learning disabilities: A developmental lag. *Journal of Experimental Child Psychology,* 1976, *22,* 375–385.

Thomas, A., & Chess, S. *Temperament and development.* New York: Brunner/Mazel, 1977.

Thomas, A., Chess, S., & Birch, H. *Temperament and behavior disorders in children.* New York: New York University Press, 1968.

Tiwary, C. M., Rosenbloom, A. L., Robertson, M. F., & Parker, J. C. Effects of thyrotropin-releasing hormone in minimal brain dysfunction. *Pediatrics,* 1975, *56,* 119–121.

Tobias, L. R., & MacDonald, M. L. Withdrawal of maintenance drugs with long-term hospitalized mental patients: A critical review. *Psychological Bulletin,* 1974, *81,* 107–125.

Tonick, I., Friehling, J., & Warhit, J. *Classroom observational code.* Unpublished manuscript of the Point of Woods Laboratory School, State University of New York at Stony Brook, 1973.

Treisman, A. Strategies and models of selective attention. *Psychological Review,* 1969, *76,* 282–299.

Twardosz, S., & Sajwaj, T. Multiple effects of a procedure to increase sitting in a hyperactive retarded boy. *Journal of Applied Behavior Analysis,* 1972, *5,* 73–78.

Ullman, D. G., Barkley, R. A., & Brown, H. W. The behavioral symptoms of hyperkinetic children who successfully responded to stimulant drug treatment. *American Journal of Orthopsychiatry,* 1978, *48,* 425–437.

Ullman, L. P., & Krasner, L. (Eds.). *Case studies in behavior modification.* New York: Holt, Rinehart, & Winston, 1965.

Valins, S., & Nisbett, R. E. *Attribution processes in the development and treatment of emotional disorders.* Morristown, NJ: General Learning Press, 1971.

Varni, J. W. *A cognitive–behavior self-regulation approach to the treatment of the hyperactive child.* Unpublished doctoral dissertation, University of California, Los Angeles, 1976.

Varni, J. W., & Henker, B. A self-regulation approach to the treatment of three hyperactive boys. *Child Behavior Therapy, 1979, 1,* 171–191.

Vygotsky, L. S. *Thought and language.* Cambridge, MA: M.I.T. Press, 1962.

Wade, M. G., & Newell, K. M. Performance criteria for stabilometer learning. *Journal of Motor Behavior,* 1972, *4,* 231–239.

Wahler, R. G., Winkel, G. H., Peterson, R. F., & Morrison, D. C. Mothers as behavior therapists for their own children. *Behavioral Research and Therapy,* 1965, *3,* 113–124.

Waizer, J., Hoffman, S. P., Polizos, P., & Engelhardt, D. M. Outpatient treatment of hyperactive school children with imipramine. *American Journal of Psychiatry,* 1974, *131,* 587–591.

Walberg, H. J., & Marjoribanks, K. Differential mental abilities and home environment: A canonical analysis. *Developmental Psychology,* 1973, *9,* 363–368.

Waldron, I. Increased prescribing of Valium, Librium, and other drugs—An example of the influence of economic and social factors on the practice of medicine. *International Journal of Health Services,* 1977, *7,* 37–62.

Walker, S. Drugging the American child: We're too cavalier about hyperactivity. *Journal of Learning Disabilities,* 1975, *8,* 354–358.

Warren, H. V. Environmental lead: A survey of its possible physiological significance. *Journal of Biosocial Science,* 1974, *6,* 223–238.

Watkins, D. B., Routh, D. K., & Arendshorst, D. S. Effects of teacher presence on compliance and resistance to distress in four- and five-year-old children. *JSAS Catalog of Selected Documents in Psychology,* 1975, *5,* 339 (Ms. No. 1121).

Wechsler, D. *Measurement of adult intelligence.* Baltimore: Williams & Wilkins, 1944.

Weiner, B., & Sierad, J. Misattribution for failure and enhancement of achievement strivings. *Journal of Personality and Social Psychology,* 1975, *31,* 409–414.

Weinrott, M. R. Improving the validity of global ratings. *Journal of Abnormal Child Psychology,* 1977, *5,* 187–197.

Weiss, G. The natural history of hyperactivity in childhood and treatment with stimulant medication at different ages. *International Journal of Mental Health,* 1975, *4,* 213–226.

Weiss, G., Hechtman, L., & Perlman, T. Hyperactives as young adults: School, employer, and self-rating scales obtained during ten-year follow-up evaluation. *American Journal of Orthopsychiatry,* 1978, *48,* 438–445.

Weiss, G., Kruger, E., Danielson, V., & Elman, M. Effects of long-term treatment of hyperactive children with methylphenidate. *Canadian Medical Association Journal,* 1975, *112,* 159–165.

Weiss, G., & Minde, K. K. Follow-up studies of children who present with symptoms of hyperactivity. In C. K. Conners (Ed.), *Clinical use of stimulant drugs in children.* New York: American Elsevier, 1974.

Weiss, G., Minde, K., Douglas, V., Werry J., & Sykes, D. Comparison of the effect of chlorpromazine, dextroamphetamine and methylphenidate on the behavior and intellectual functioning of hyperactive children. *Canadian Medical Association Journal,* 1971, *104,* 20–25.

Weiss, G., Minde, K., Werry, J. S., Douglas, V. I., & Nemeth, E. Studies on the hyperactive child, VIII. Five-year follow-up. *Archives of General Psychiatry,* 1971, *24,* 409–414.

Weissenburger, F. E., & Loney, J. Hyperkinesis in the classroom: If cerebral stimulants are the last resort, what is the first resort? *Journal of Learning Disabilities,* 1977, *10,* 339–348.

Weithorn, C. J., & Ross, R. Who monitors medication? *Journal of Learning Disabilities,* 1975, *8,* 458–461.

Weithorn, C. J., & Ross, R. Stimulant drugs for hyperactivity: Some additional disturbing questions. *American Journal of Orthopsychiatry,* 1976, *46,* 168–173.

Weithorn, L. Drug therapy—Children's rights. In M. J. Cohen (Ed.), *Drugs and the special child.* New York: Gardner Press, 1979.

Wells, W. W. Drug control of school children: The child's right to choose. *Southern California Law Review,* 1973, *46,* 585–616.

Wender, E. H. Food additives and hyperkinesis. *American Journal of Diseases of Children,* 1977, *131,* 1204–1206.

Wender, P. H. *Minimal brain dysfunction in children.* New York: Wiley, 1971.

Wender, P. H. The minimal brain dysfunction syndrome in children. *Journal of Nervous and Mental Diseases,* 1972, *155,* 55–71.

Werner, E., Bierman, J. M., French, F., Simonian, P. K., Connor, A., Smith, R. S., & Campbell, M. Reproductive and environmental casualties: A report on the 10-year follow-up of the children of the Kauai pregnancy study. *Pediatrics,* 1968, *42,* 112–127.

Werry, J. S. Developmental hyperactivity. *Pediatric Clinics of North America,* 1968, *15,* 581–599. (a)

Werry, J. S. Studies on the hyperactive child, IV. An empirical analysis of the minimal brain dysfunction syndrome. *Archives of General Psychiatry,* 1968, *19,* 9–16. (b)

Werry, J. S. Organic factors in childhood psychopathology. In H. C. Quay & J. S. Werry (Eds.), *Psychopathological disorders of childhood.* New York: Wiley, 1972.

Werry, J. S. Medication for hyperkinetic children. *Drugs,* 1976, *11,* 81–89.
Werry, J. S. The use of psychotropic drugs in children. *Journal of the American Academy of Child Psychiatry,* 1977, *16,* 446–468.
Werry, J. S. Measures in pediatric psychopharmacology. In J. S. Werry (Ed.), *Pediatric psychopharmacology: The use of behavior modifying drugs in children.* New York: Brunner/Mazel, 1978. (a)
Werry, J. S. (Ed.). *Pediatric psychopharmacology: The use of behavior modifying drugs in children.* New York: Brunner/Mazel, 1978. (b)
Werry, J. S., & Aman, M. G. Methylphenidate and haloperidol in children: Effects on attention, memory, and activity. *Archives of General Psychiatry,* 1975, *32,* 790–795.
Werry, J. S., Dowrick, P. W., Lampen, E. L., & Vamos, M. J. Imipramine in enuresis—psychological and physiological effects. *Journal of Child Psychology and Psychiatry,* 1975, *16,* 289–299.
Werry, J. S., & Quay, H. C. Observing the classroom behavior of elementary school children. *Exceptional Children,* 1969, *35,* 461–470.
Werry, J. S., & Sprague, R. L. Hyperactivity. In C. G. Costello (Ed.), *Symptoms of psychopathology.* New York: Wiley, 1970.
Werry, J. S., & Sprague, R. L. Psychopharmacology. In J. Wortis (Ed.), *Mental retardation* (Vol. 4). New York: Grune & Stratton, 1972.
Werry, J. S., & Sprague, R. L. Methylphenidate in children: Effect of dosage. *Australian and New Zealand Journal of Psychiatry,* 1974, *8,* 9–19.
Werry, J. S., Sprague, R. L., & Cohen, M. N. Conners Teacher Rating Scale for use in drug studies with children—An empirical study. *Journal of Abnormal Child Psychology,* 1975, *3,* 217–230.
Werry, J. S., Sprague, R. L., Weiss, G., & Minde, K. Some clinical and laboratory studies of psychotropic drugs in children. In W. L. Smith (Ed.), *Drugs and cortical function.* Springfield, IL: Charles C Thomas, 1970.
Whalen, C. K. Hyperactivity and psychostimulant treatment. In J. R. Lachenmeyer & M. S. Gibbs (Eds.), *Psychology of the abnormal child.* New York: Gardner Press, in press.
Whalen, C. K., Collins, B. E., Henker, B., Alkus, S. R., Adams, D., & Stapp, J. Behavior observations of hyperactive children and methylphenidate (Ritalin) effects in systematically structured classroom environments: Now you see them, now you don't. *Journal of Pediatric Psychology,* 1978, *3,* 177–187.
Whalen, C. K., & Henker, B. Psychostimulants and children: A review and analysis. *Psychological Bulletin,* 1976, *83,* 1113–1130.
Whalen, C. K., & Henker, B. The pitfalls of politicization. A response to Conrad's "The discovery of hyperkinesis: Notes on the medicalization of deviant behavior." *Social Problems,* 1977, *24,* 590–595.
Whalen, C. K., Henker, B., Collins, B. E., Finck, D., & Dotemoto, S. A social ecology of hyperactive boys: Medication effects in structured classroom environments. *Journal of Applied Behavior Analysis,* 1979, *12,* 65–81. (a)
Whalen, C. K., Henker, B., Collins, B. E., McAuliffe, S., & Vaux, A. Peer interaction in a structured communication task: Comparisons of normal and hyperactive boys and of methylphenidate (Ritalin) and placebo effects. *Child Development,* 1979, *50,* 388–401. (b)
Whalen, C. K., Henker, B., Dotemoto, S., Vaux, A., & McAuliffe, S. Hyperactivity and methylphenidate: Peer communication patterns. In K. D. Gadow & J. Loney (Eds.), *Psychosocial aspects of drug treatment for hyperactivity.* Boulder, CO: Westview Press, in press.
WhereAre the Children? *Common Sense from Closer Look,* December 1978, pp. 7–9.
White, J. H. The use and misuse of psychotropic drugs in children. *Psychiatry Digest,* 1976, *37,* 13–16.
White, S. H. Evidence for a hierarchical arrangement of learning processes. In L. P. Lipsitt & C.

C. Spiker (Eds.), *Advances in child development and behavior* (Vol. 2). New York: Academic Press, 1965.
White, S. H. Some general outlines of the matrix of developmental changes between five and seven years. *Bulletin of the Orton Society,* 1970, *20,* 41–57.
Whitehead, P., & Clark, L. Effect of lithium carbonate, placebo and thioridazine on hyperactive children. *American Journal of Psychiatry,* 1970, *127,* 124–125.
Wiener, J. (Ed.). *Psychopharmacology in childhood and adolescence.* New York: Basic Books, 1977.
Willey, R. F. Abuse of methylphenidate (Ritalin). *New England Journal of Medicine,* 1971, *285,* 464.
Williams, J. I., & Cram, D. M. Diet in the management of hyperkinesis. A review of the tests of Feingold's hypotheses. *Canadian Psychiatric Association Journal,* 1978, *23,* 241–248.
Williams, J. I., Cram, D. M., Tausig, F. T., & Webster, E. Relative effects of drugs and diet on hyperactive behaviors: An experimental study. *Pediatrics,* 1978, *61,* 811–817.
Winsberg, B. G., Bialer, I., Kupietz, S., & Tobias, J. Effects of imipramine and dextroamphetamine on behavior of neuropsychiatrically impaired children. *American Journal of Psychiatry,* 1972, *128,* 1425–1431.
Winsberg, B. G., Goldstein, S., Yepes, L. E., & Perel, J. M. Imipramine and electrocardiographic abnormalities in hyperactive children. *American Journal of Psychiatry,* 1975, *132,* 542–545.
Winsberg, B. G., Yepes, L. E., & Bialer, I. Pharmacologic management of children with hyperactive/aggressive/inattentive behavior disorders. *Clinical Pediatrics,* 1976, *15,* 471–477.
Witter, C. Drugging and schooling. *Trans-Action,* 1971, *8,* 30–34.
Wolff, S. Behavioral characteristics of primary school children referred to a psychiatric department. *British Journal of Psychiatry,* 1967, *113,* 885–893.
Wood, D. R., Reimherr, F. W., Wender, P. H., & Johnson, G. E. Diagnosis and treatment of minimal brain dysfunction in adults. *Archives of General Psychiatry,* 1976, *33,* 1453–1460.
Wyatt v. *Stickney,* 344 F. Supp. 387 (M.D. Ala. 1972).
Yando, R. M., & Kagan, J. The effects of teacher tempo on the child. *Child Development,* 1968, *39,* 27–34.
Yarrow, M. R., Campbell, J. D., & Burton, R. V. *Child rearing: An inquiry into research and methods.* San Francisco: Jossey-Bass, 1968.
Yepes, L. E., Balka, E. B., Winsberg, B. G., & Bialer, I. Amitriptyline and methylphenidate treatment of behaviorally disordered children. *Journal of Child Psychology and Psychiatry,* 1977, *18,* 39–52.
Zahn, T. P., Abate, F., Little, B., & Wender, P. Minimal brain dysfunction, stimulant drugs, and autonomic nervous system activity. *Archives of General Psychiatry,* 1975, *32,* 381–387.
Zelniker, T., Charles, L., & Schain, R. J. Attentional behavior and drugs in hyperactive children. *Clinical Research* (Abstract, 1977).
Zentall, S. Optimal stimulation as theoretical basis of hyperactivity. *American Journal of Orthopsychiatry,* 1975, *45,* 549–563.
Zentall, S., & Zentall, T. R. Activity and task performance of hyperactive children as a function of environmental stimulation. *Journal of Consulting and Clinical Psychology,* 1976, *44,* 693–697.
Zentall, S., Zentall, T. R., & Booth, M. E. Within-task stimulation: Effects on activity and spelling performance in hyperactive and normal children. *Journal of Educational Research,* 1978, *71,* 223–230.
Zukow, P. G., Zukow, A. H., & Bentler, P. M. Rating scales for the identification and treatment of hyperkinesis. *Journal of Consulting and Clinical Psychology,* 1978, *46,* 213–222.

Index

Q

R